SUBSURFACE DISPOSAL IN GEOLOGIC BASINS—A STUDY OF RESERVOIR STRATA

Published with the aid of a fund established by the New York Committee for the mid-year meeting of the Association, November 1926.

Memoir 10

S U B S U R F A C E DISPOSAL IN GEOLOGIC BASINS —A STUDY OF RESERVOIR STRATA

edited by

John E. Galley

Published by The American Association of Petroleum Geologists,
Tulsa, Oklahoma, U.S.A., 1968

Published August 1968
Library of Congress Catalog Card No. 68–31404

Composed, printed, and bound by The Collegiate Press
GEORGE BANTA COMPANY, INC.
Menasha, Wisconsin 54952

CONTENTS

FOREWORD

The publication of this book by The American Association of Petroleum Geologists is a direct outgrowth of a request in 1958 by an agency of the United States Atomic Energy Commission for help in certain geologic studies. It demonstrates the Association's awareness of its civic responsibilities, as well as its ability to provide valuable geological information in a rather unusual field of interest.

The request was for the studies of geologic basins in which safe underground disposal of radioactive waste might be attempted on an experimental basis. The investigation was to employ modern methods of subsurface analysis which have been developed by petroleum geologists.

Because the techniques proposed for disposal of radioactive waste are generally applicable to many other industrial wastes, the emphasis in this collection of papers is on the subsurface disposal of industrial wastes in general.

The editor and authors recognize the fact that space for fluids that are introduced into subsurface reservoirs is limited and is made available only by artificially increasing reservoir rock pressures, and that natural formation fluids are displaced in the process of making room for injected fluids. Therefore, only limited quantities of waste fluids can be disposed of in reservoirs from which natural fluids have not been withdrawn.

However, we believe that by careful selection of disposal sites and reservoir strata, based on thorough geological investigations, subsurface disposal of especially toxic or obnoxious wastes may help to lessen industry's vexing problem of pollution of the surface environment. It follows that subsurface studies will be indispensable in the selection of sites for the plants which produce the wastes if onsite disposals into the subsurface are either intended or likely.

Publication of this book was made possible by financial support from the U.S. Atomic Energy Commission. The AEC also gave permission to publish the six basin papers beginning on page 43.

The editor and authors hope that the papers in this book will lead to wider appreciation of the value of subsurface strata as disposal reservoirs, and to more advanced studies which may answer some of the many questions that still perplex geologists and engineers who are faced with industrial-waste disposal problems.

JOHN E. GALLEY
Editor

Kerrville, Texas
August 7, 1967

ECONOMIC AND INDUSTRIAL POTENTIAL OF GEOLOGIC BASINS AND RESERVOIR STRATA[1]

JOHN E. GALLEY[2]
Kerrville, Texas 78028

ABSTRACT

One potential value of subsurface strata in geologic basins is the available space for storage or disposal of industrial waste liquids and solids. Disposal methods which are being developed include the injection of liquids into deep permeable formations, the storage of solids in caverns constructed in salt beds, and the incorporation of liquids in cement slurries which are injected into artificially produced fractures in shale and allowed to harden. Six of the papers in this volume describe geologic basins where such disposal methods might be used successfully.

Physical limitations on the use of these methods include restricted space capacities in reservoir strata, pressure limits, possibilities of escape through pressure-induced fractures, adverse hydrodynamic conditions, and possible plugging of rock pores by precipitates or other materials. These limitations, and the principles governing subsurface-disposal techniques, are discussed in the three papers following this introductory paper.

INTRODUCTION

In 1958 the AAPG acceded to a request from the atomic-energy industry to assist in the evaluation of geologic basins as possible sites for the safe subsurface disposal of radioactive wastes. Two broad findings that are of concern to subsurface geologists resulted from the AAPG studies: (1) geological literature does not contain comprehensive descriptions of all geologic basins, not even all of those in the United States, and (2) the economic value of a geologic basin is not limited to its potential production of oil or other minerals; its physical properties themselves may have unappreciated value.

Detailed descriptions of the subsurface geology of several basins have been published. However, the reports concern principally the tectonics, stratigraphy, lithology, and geologic history of the basins. Information about the petrophysics, *i.e.*, the physical characteristics of the rocks—porosity, permeability, density, pressure responses, *etc.*—is either sketchy or absent. The chemical and physical characteristics of the subsurface fluids in the basins also generally are disregarded. Moreover, subsurface descriptions are widely scattered in the literature, having appeared in AAPG publications and other geological journals, in field-trip guidebooks published by local geological societies, in oil and gas trade journals, and in state and federal survey reports.

The private files of oil and gas producers contain confidential reports of subsurface studies of most of the geologic basins in the United States. Most, however, concern only the same four geologic parameters—tectonics, stratigraphy, lithology, and geologic history. Some petrophysical and fluid data have been obtained for all of the major oil-producing basins and for several "barren" provinces, but such data generally are buried in routine engineering files; only rarely have they been combined with geologic data to produce a complete description of a basin.

Because of the inadequacy of these subsurface interpretations, there is no basin whose full economic and industrial potential has been realized.

SPACE RESOURCES IN GEOLOGIC BASINS

In their preoccupation with the search for petroleum, subsurface geologists tend to overlook one of the potential values of subsurface strata in

[1] Manuscript received, August 7, 1967.

[2] Geological consultant.

The assistance of advisors who critically read the manuscript is acknowledged with appreciation: C. W. Brown, W. de Laguna, M. King Hubbert, J. C. Maxwell, R. P. McNeal, A. F. van Everdingen, Don L. Warner, and Karl F. Zeisler. The writer is indebted to many other geologists and engineers for his liberal education in waste-disposal problems and the hydrology of groundwaters, and for sound advice in the application of this knowledge. Special recognition is due W. G. Belter, J. A. Lieberman, and C. V. Theis. The writer alone is responsible for the views expressed in this paper.

geologic basins—the storage space that is available for injected fluids. A few industries, particularly those concerned with natural gas and liquefied petroleum gas, have developed subterranean storage reservoirs. A few others have exploited locally the potentials of permeable subsurface reservoirs for the disposal of toxic or obnoxious waste fluids (Donaldson, 1964; Warner, 1965, and this volume). The oil industry disposes of large quantities of oil-field brines (17 million bbl/day in 1963: La Moreaux, p. 12) by injection into permeable subsurface strata.

Because deep subsurface strata are saturated by natural fluids, storage space in rock pores is limited; however, by artificially increasing the pressures in the strata it is possible to develop additional storage capacity for substantial quantities of selected waste liquids.

The disposal of toxic or obnoxious substances in deep strata is potentially a valuable use of subsurface space. The practice has limitations, however, which must be understood and carefully observed; they are discussed in the following paragraphs and in more detail in the other papers in this volume.

DISPOSAL CONCEPTS

The ultimate in waste-disposal technology would be a system which would accept an unlimited volume of waste and contain it forever outside of man's sphere of life. In the first century of the industrial revolution, volumes of waste were small and a concept of "dilute and disperse" was adequate. Factory sites were selected at riverside locations for simple reasons: easy transport of materials and goods by riverboat, ample supplies of water for processing and cooling, and easy disposal of wastes—into the rivers. Factories were few and population was sparse. The streams swept the waste away and, because of dilution, seemed to eliminate it completely from the environment.

As industrial areas expanded and installations were crowded together, and as population became dense, the concept of "dilute and disperse" seemed inadequate. In many places the degree of dispersion between the point of waste entry and the next point of stream use was slight.

A similar history developed with respect to disposal into surface trenches or "evaporation" ponds, from which contaminants seep into freshwater aquifers and eventually reach a producing water well or a surface stream. Examples of contamination by oil-field brine disposed into pits are familiar to most petroleum engineers.

The discharge of waste effluents into streams or pits is a cheap and easy disposal method that has an obvious appeal to operators. Today, however, new concepts of disposal are needed. One already applied to hazardous waters is that of "concentrate and contain"—but containment is not always achieved. Containers are subject to leakage or to leaching by circulating waters, depending on the type of construction (metal tanks, lined pits, *etc.*), and escape of the wastes nullifies the concept.

Another aspect of the concept of containment is the developing technology for converting fluid or soluble wastes to unleachable solids. In the disposal of such solids the main problem is to provide space, although radioactive solids need also to be shielded. The economics of such a method would determine its acceptability.

A further step might be conversion of the waste into a usable product, in which case it no longer would be waste. Today, however, there are large volumes of wastes which either cannot be converted economically or are "indestructible" as wastes, and it is these which are considered here.

Industrial wastes consist of a variety of materials—solid, liquid, and gaseous. If liquid, they may be organic or inorganic, alkaline or acidic, dilute or concentrated, clear or turbid, viscous or fluid, stable or unstable; the range of chemical and physical properties is broad. However, those properties can be altered by chemical, physical, or biological processes. Organic chemicals can be decomposed, acids and bases can be neutralized, solids in suspension can be removed, viscosity can be reduced, *etc.* Even though technology may not make possible the economical conversion of all waste material into either usable or innocuous products, processes can be engineered to adapt the waste to a selected disposal method.

The need for protection of man's environment is more compelling today than ever, and plant operators are facing increasingly difficult problems.

The solutions may involve methods which increase the overall cost of operations and thus require economic reappraisals. The premise that public health and safety are secondary considerations is unacceptable; thus the alternative must be public acceptance of these higher costs as the inescapable price of an increasingly complex society.

ROLE OF THE GEOLOGIST

QUALIFICATIONS AND OPPORTUNITIES

Well-informed subsurface geologists are uniquely qualified to serve as advisors in problems of subsurface waste disposal; they thus can aid in efforts to eliminate pollution from surface environments.

They have the opportunity to develop their own special abilities as guides and interpreters in the analysis and evaluation of subsurface storage potentials. In making their services available, they can fulfill a public responsibility in the urgent national cause of pollution control. Their opportunity was emphasized by Emrich (1966), who cited the needs for geologists in public-health activities.

INITIAL STEPS

Petroleum geologists already are committed to a public responsibility in the search for safe and efficient disposal methods for wastes other than oil-field brines. Their participation began more than 10 years ago when, in April 1957, petroleum geologists took part in a conference at Princeton University which considered problems of underground disposal of radioactive wastes (Hess, 1957). The meeting had been called by a committee of the Division of Earth Sciences of the National Academy of Sciences–National Research Council. The group was asked to provide assistance to the U.S. Atomic Energy Commission in its expanding search for safe disposal methods for hazardous wastes. Subsequently a report of a subcommittee of the American Petroleum Institute recommended, in part, that the AAPG be asked to provide advice and assistance in compiling significant information on geologic basins having potential disposal reservoirs (Moore, 1958).

In October 1958, Wallace de Laguna, of Oak Ridge National Laboratory, made a request to the Executive Committee of the AAPG that the Association assist ORNL in a long-range geological study of areas in which waste liquids might be injected experimentally into deep permeable reservoirs. At the request of the Executive Committee, such a study was undertaken, beginning in December of 1958, by a subcommittee of the AAPG Research Committee. Six of the papers in this volume are the results of these studies.

AAPG STUDY PROGRAM

Selection of the areas to be studied was the subcommittee's first concern. The Princeton conference already had suggested to the AEC that permanent containment of liquid radioactive wastes might be achieved by first processing them so as to make them heavier than formation waters and then injecting them into permeable subsurface formations in low areas in structural basins. Accordingly, the selections were limited to basin areas. Further, only basins in relatively stable regions were considered, in order to avoid uncertainties that might accompany operations in faulted areas.

An effort was made to select basins in which a substantial thickness of salt lies at shallow depths, and in which thick shale sequences could be expected at intermediate depths. The reasons for these qualifications are discussed in the succeeding paragraphs. The basins that were selected, and the subcommittee members to whom the studies were assigned, are as follows.

Appalachian basin	T. P. McCann
Denver basin	G. S. Garbarini
Dunning Cove syncline	J. C. Maxwell
Michigan basin	L. I. Briggs, Jr.
Salina basin	R. W. Edmund
San Juan basin	J. A. Peterson

The studies of the five larger basins were performed by local committees of petroleum geologists, to whom credit is given in the individual papers. The investigation of the Dunning Cove syncline was the basis for a Master's thesis at Princeton University by John E. Hardaway under the direction of J. C. Maxwell

The stimulation and challenge of a new objective in geological investigations must be recognized as motives in attracting geologists to participate in the local study programs. The AEC provided funds for travel expenses and for some of the drafting, typing, and reproductions. Nevertheless, it was clear from the start that much tedious and time-consuming work would be involved, most or all of it to be done outside of regular work hours, and that the only compensation would be the satisfaction of having performed a civic duty. The geologists who accepted the responsibilities for doing the work were, in effect, consultants to an agency of the American people, serving without pay because they believed that the objectives were worthy.

The AAPG basin studies began as geological analyses of selected basins in which test injections might prove the feasibility of subsurface disposal for waste liquids. Porous and permeable sandstone formations were the preferred disposal reservoirs. Meanwhile, environmental technologists in the nuclear-energy industry were attempting to develop other methods of disposal, including the emplacement of solids in solution cavities in salt beds and the incorporation of liquids in cement slurries which could be injected into artificial fractures in shale where they would solidify into permanently buried seams. In order to provide sites where all three suggested disposal methods could be tested, the local committees were requested to describe salt beds and thick shale sequences at suitable depths, as well as the deeper permeable sandstone bodies.

During the investigations and discussions, it became evident that disposal by deep-well injection, by burial in salt, and by grouting in fractured shale might be suitable not only for radioactive waste but also for various types of industrial wastes, both liquid and solid. This realization opened wide vistas of possible applications of subsurface geology to solving some of industry's growing pollution problems. Studies in the selected basin areas were reconnaissance rather than detailed. They included not only the geology and hydrology of the subsurface, but also geographic factors on the basis of which industrial sites might be chosen. The geographic investigations were not exhaustive in scope or in depth, but the authors have produced outlines of the principal characteristics of physiography, climate, culture, and other pertinent aspects of the geography of the basin areas.

PROPOSED SUBSURFACE-DISPOSAL METHODS

The principal features of the three proposed disposal methods for which the geological studies were made are described here in order to provide background for understanding the nature of the six basin papers.

DEEP-WELL INJECTION INTO PERMEABLE RESERVOIRS

Early in the history of the petroleum industry, when surface drainage was becoming contaminated by oil-field brines, operators developed the now-common practice of injecting salt-water wastes into permeable subsurface sandstones—commonly the reservoirs from which the oil and salt water originally were produced, but also in shallower or deeper formations. Where it became obvious that the brines were contaminating fresh-water sands that were being used for domestic supplies, deeper sandstones had to be selected. This disposal practice matured and, under the control of state laws, has become standard.

More recently other industries have turned to deep-well injections as a possible solution for disposal problems (Donaldson, 1964; Warner, 1965, 1967, and this volume), and a decade ago the AEC began to focus attention on the method as a possible means for disposing of certain types of radioactive-waste liquids.

Superficially, the injection of liquids into deep permeable reservoirs appears to be a "made-to-order" disposal method for toxic or obnoxious fluids. In practice, it has some fundamental limitations which will prevent its widespread use for disposal of unlimited quantities of all kinds of waste fluids. However, such injection methods undoubtedly will be used increasingly in waste disposal and, if properly managed, will be a factor in controlling the pollution of man's environment.

Before the subject is discussed more fully, definitions are needed in order to avoid misunderstanding between geologists and the specialists in sanitary and environmental engineering, whose technical vocabularies differ in some respects. The differences arise largely from differences in perspective. Whereas sanitary engineers are accustomed to working with the shallowest thin veneer of earth constituents, involving mainly unconsolidated materials, petroleum geologists tend to ignore these surficial materials and to be interested only in hard rock, such as sandstone or limestone, which underlies the unconsolidated materials.

In other words, the petroleum geologist becomes interested only after surface casing has been set in a borehole. He largely ignores the fresh-water aquifers and thus overlooks an opportunity to acquaint himself with a facet of subsurface geology on which someday his life literally may depend. Geologists who have worked in arid or semiarid regions, and who perhaps have participated in a search for additional water resources, will appreciate the truth in this assertion more readily than those to whom copious quantities of fresh, clean surface or near-surface waters always have been available.

In the practice of waste disposal by deep-well injection, the term "deep" refers to rock formations, not soil, which are below and so isolated from fresh-water aquifers that injected liquids will not enter potential water supplies either by natural means or by any process that is induced by the injection. This usage calls for permeable rock layers several thousand feet deep (generally at least 3,000 ft, more than 900 m) in geologic basins, confined above by thick, relatively impermeable and fracture-resistant strata such as shale or salt deposits.

To a geologist, "rock" is ordinarily ". . . any consolidated or coherent and relatively hard, naturally formed mass of mineral matter" (Howell, 1957, p. 249), although, strictly speaking, he may include also noncoherent mineral matter "constituting an essential and appreciable part of the earth's crust" (Howell, 1957). To a geologist, "soil" is the surficial zone of unconsolidated earth materials consisting of disintegrated or decomposed rock particles, usually mixed with organic matter. ". . . This complex assemblage of rock debris that covers the bedrock is the *mantle*.[3] . . . The term *soil* is sometimes applied erroneously to mantle of any kind, but properly it refers only to the part of the mantle which has been so decom-

posed and otherwise modified that it supports rooted plants" (Longwell, Knopf, and Flint, 1948, p. 28, 46). "In the strict sense of the word, *soil* is the relatively porous, fine-grained, upper portion of the mantle rock containing an admixture of vegetable matter and capable of supporting plant life. The term is, however, often used rather loosely" (Miller, 1949, p. 174).

In the technology of waste disposal, the term "soil" includes sediments and sedimentary rocks, and is used by some workers to include all rocks above the crystalline basement. In the same vocabulary of waste disposal, the generally igneous or metamorphic rocks with complex structure, called "basement" by geologists, usually are referred to simply as "rock" or "bedrock" by engineers.

The differences in usage were explained by Legget (1939, p. 539): "Surface material, generally containing organic matter, is of little consequence to the civil engineer. His use of the word soil applies to all unconsolidated material in the earth's crust, extending possibly to depths of several thousand feet below the surface. This wide use of the word is not strictly in accord with geological terminology, in which its use is sometimes restricted to products of rock weathering that have not been transported from their original position." In a later statement (1962, p. 68), Legget explained further: "The records of geology show that the early geologists used the term [soil] in exactly the same way as engineers of today to denote all loose fragmented material in the earth's crust no matter how far below the surface it might be. . . . With the mutual understanding that exists within the scientific world, the joint use of the word is gradually being accepted without much question; the context usually shows in which sense the word is used."

As used in subsurface geology, a "basin" is a "depressed area with the strata dipping inwards" (Howell, 1957, p. 26). It may or may not have a topographic expression. If caused by tectonic events which created a downwarp of the strata, it is called a "structural basin." If it is a catchment area filled or being filled with sediments, it is referred to as a "sedimentary basin." The hydrologic system within a basin is usually an integrated system which is controlled by the shape of the

---

[3] The use of the word "mantle" in this sense is different from and unrelated to its use in reference to the layer of earth materials lying between the earth's crust and its core, bounded above by the Mohorovičić discontinuity.

basin as well as by the character of the rocks in it. A sedimentary basin may be affected by post-depositional tectonics, in which case the original hydrologic system will be altered or destroyed and eventually replaced by a new system.

In waste-disposal terminology, a basin may be a topographic basin or, more commonly, strictly a drainage basin. Locally it may be a pond in which waste liquids are collected.

All of the aforementioned distinctions should be kept in mind, inasmuch as most papers in this volume were written from the geologist's point of view. The reader's understanding also will be aided by appreciation of the quantitative hydrologic differences between shallow aquifers and deep "salaquifers" or brine-bearing aquifers. In a shallow aquifer the rate of flow is measured in feet per day, and the distances from points of input of fluids ("discharge" of waste effluents *into* the aquifer) to points of output (springs or wells; "points of use") are measurable in miles or tens of miles.

On the other hand, in a tectonically stable basin at depths of several thousand feet, where there is indurated rock instead of loose soil or unconsolidated sand, the textures tend to be "tight" and permeability values are relatively low. In such environments the natural rate of flow is rarely more than about 3 ft (0.9 m) per year (M. King Hubbert, Washington, personal commun.). In 1,000 years, therefore, under natural conditions a fluid would not move as far as 1 mi (1.6 km). Most of the geologic basins that might be considered for deep-well disposal of waste liquids range from tens to hundreds of miles in width. The natural flow therefore is insignificant and may be disregarded in considering the fluid mechanics of deep-well disposal.

Ideally, reservoir space that is suitable for deep-well disposal should be restricted vertically and unrestricted laterally (A. F. van Everdingen, Dallas, personal commun.). Thus, an ideal disposal reservoir would be a thick, porous and permeable blanket sandstone underlying essentially the entire basin area, and confined above and below by impermeable beds. If the area of a permeable formation which is sealed by confining impermeable strata is greatly restricted, the injection pressures may increase and eventually exceed the pressure required to fracture the reservoir

sandstone. To avoid the risk of fracture in such circumstances, input volumes would have to be reduced gradually until the operation is halted.

Fracturing of the reservoir rock may not be harmful in itself. In fact, under certain conditions the operators may wish to fracture the rock as a means of increasing its ability to receive fluids. The concern that commonly arises in connection with proposed high-pressure injections is that the confining impermeable formations also may be fractured and thus allow the waste liquids to escape from the reservoir formation.

It has been demonstrated that vertical fractures that are induced in petroleum reservoirs do not penetrate adjacent soft formations which have a high Poisson ratio relative to the reservoir rock. Fractures will propagate, however, through adjacent formations that are hard and brittle and have a low Poisson ratio, as exemplified by some dense limestones and quartzites. A requirement for a suitable disposal site, therefore, is a thick layer of soft rock such as shale or salt between the injection reservoir and any permeable aquifer or reservoir which is to be protected from invasion (C. W. Brown, Dallas, personal commun.).

Subsurface geologists will appreciate the importance of lithologic and petrophysical data that can be derived from cores and by modern logging techniques. The value of obtaining such data in all exploratory holes generally is recognized, because it is only by careful study and experienced interpretation of those data that a thorough knowledge of reservoir characteristics can be obtained. The value of good-quality drill-stem-test charts should not be overlooked; the fact that the natural rate of flow in a deep subsurface reservoir may be ignored in computing the movements of injected fluids does not obviate the need for hydrologic and petrophysical data. The receptivity of the reservoir is an expression of all of its characteristics, and the success of the operation will depend largely on the proper understanding and use of these parameters of the hydrologic system. A full set of potentiometric[4] maps of the

[4] "A device that is useful in plotting the regional flow through a given stratum is the *potentiometric surface.* To every point on the upper surface of a given stratum there corresponds a head *h.* If this height from the standard datum is plotted in the vertical line through each point of measurement and a smooth surface passed through each point so plotted, the surface obtained may be known as the potentiometric surface for the stratum considered, because at every point its elevation is a measure of the potential of water in the upper surface of the

reservoirs in a basin area is an important adjunct to a pre-disposal investigation.

Although the natural hydrodynamic system might be thought to be a sufficient deterrent to the escape of waste liquids injected into an area of low potential, consideration also must be given to the effects of pressure buildup as fluids are added to the reservoir. Prolonged injections conceivably might convert a potentiometric low into a potentiometric high.

Another aspect of injection mechanics is made evident by publicity regarding injections in the deep disposal well at Rocky Mountain Arsenal near Denver, Colorado. Here the injection reservoir is fractured Precambrian basement rock at a depth of 12,000 ft (3,657.6 m). The frequency of earth tremors attending periods of injection has indicated that the tremors are caused by slippage along faults, the movements being the result of the release of stress when the pressures produced by injection of fluid overcome the friction on opposing rock surfaces (Evans, 1966). Regardless of the structural dynamics creating the fractures and the rock slippages, it is important to realize that the hydrodynamic system in a rock formation which owes its permeability to open fractures is largely unknown. In light of the present state of knowledge derived from subsurface studies, an undisturbed system of intergranular porosity is more reliable for producing the planned results.

It commonly is pointed out, and should be emphasized, that fluids injected into a permeable subsurface reservoir stratum do not occupy space that formerly was empty, because there is no empty space in the earth. Even where oil-field brines are returned to the original producing formation, they do not move into empty pores. Withdrawal of the oil-field fluids does not completely empty the reservoir pore space; it temporarily reduces the local formation pressure until other fluids can move in to replace the produced fluids. Space is made for injected fluids by the pressure of injection, whether it is only the hydrostatic pressure caused by the weight of the column of fluid or pressure artificially increased by pumping. Space limitations and the possible

resultant pressure excesses are among the restrictions governing the rate of fluid injection and the volume of fluid which can be injected into a reservoir. They are discussed by van Everdingen (this volume).

As pointed out by Warner (1965 and this volume), reservoir space in subsurface strata is limited; therefore, concentration of wastes before injection is desirable. Even with such precautions, as deep-well disposal operations become more common there will be an increasing likelihood of mutual interference by expanding circles of pressure influence from several injection wells in a single reservoir formation (van Everdingen, this volume). The prospect necessitates the keeping of complete and accurate records of pressure data on the injection wells and on observation wells that will need to be drilled for that purpose. Legal restrictions on multiple usage of reservoirs eventually may be necessary.

Both van Everdingen's and Warner's papers in this volume discuss the problems of compatibility between injected liquids and the reservoir rock and formation fluids, particularly with respect to the dangers of pore plugging. This and other problems in deep-well injection, as described in their papers, highlight the importance of collection and analysis of rock and fluid samples from the intended deep reservoir and careful interpretation of the resulting data in conjunction with analysis of the waste materials to be injected. In addition, because it hardly will be possible to explore a basin completely, operating data subsequently should be collected, preserved, and analyzed in an effort to improve understanding of the character of the reservoir, which in most cases will be known from only a limited number of test wells.

DISPOSAL IN SALT

Since 1958 Oak Ridge National Laboratory has been conducting investigations into the feasibility of storage in man-made caverns in salt beds as a disposal method for highly concentrated hazardous wastes. Comprehensive tests have been conducted both in the laboratory and in salt mines in central Kansas. Initial experiments were directed toward the use of caverns for the disposal of liquids, but because of subsequent progress in techniques for solidification of liquid wastes, and also

stratum to which it refers, irrespective of the elevation of the stratum" (Hubbert, 1953, p. 1973–1974).

because of anticipated failures where liquids might be squeezed out of the enclosing salt under pressure of the overburden, the concept evolved into a method for the storage of solids.

The unique physical properties of halite make it especially adaptable for use in burial of obnoxious materials. It is essentially impermeable, plastic, and easy to mine; moreover, it is not associated in the earth with potable water. Because of its plasticity, the salt will flow eventually into mined openings that are not purposely kept open, thus effectively sealing any solids placed there and insulating them permanently from circulating water.

Because its use requires the construction of artificial caverns, the method is not likely to be suitable for the disposal of large quantities of material. However, it is a satisfactory method for safe burial of extremely hazardous or obnoxious solid wastes.

Any contemplated salt-storage program should be preceded by careful investigation of local geologic conditions and by tests of compatibility of the specific waste materials with the salt environment. Final acceptance or rejection of the program would be determined by the economics of the procedures in comparison with that of other equally safe methods.

Papers concerning the methods for disposal in salt include those by Boegly *et al.* (1966), Bradshaw (1966), de Laguna (1962), Empson *et al.* (1966), Pierce and Rich (1962), and Schaffer *et al.* (1966).

DISPOSAL IN ARTIFICIAL FRACTURES

The success of artificial-fracturing techniques that were developed by the oil industry during the last two decades led to consideration of a unique procedure for disposal of harmful or obnoxious wastes. The procedure involves preparation of a slurry of cement containing the liquid wastes that are to be disposed of, and injection of the slurry through a well into artificial fractures which have been prepared in advance for this purpose; hardening of the cement immobilizes the wastes. The disposal reservoir probably would be a shale sequence of suitable thickness and lithology.

Preferably the shale formation would be one in which all of the induced fractures would be horizontal, in order to avoid the possibility of contaminating natural fluids in overlying or underlying strata. Regional tectonic stress patterns, bedding characteristics, and especially depths below the surface presumably would be the principal parameters determining the orientation of the fractures. There is not universal agreement as to the depths at which horizontal fractures might be assured. In general, the consensus seems to be that at shallow depths (*e.g.*, less than 1,000 ft or 300 m) most hydraulically induced fractures are horizontal, whereas at greater depths they are vertical.

Safety precautions would include selection of a shale formation with sufficient thickness to absorb any vertical fractures, and field tests to determine the fracture characteristics.

Field experiments with this disposal technique at Oak Ridge National Laboratory have progressed to the stage of injecting slurries of *bona fide* waste liquids (W. de Laguna, Oak Ridge, personal commun.). Several types of slurry were tried; advances of the slurry fronts in the subsurface were recorded in predrilled observation holes; core holes were drilled later in order to survey the final orientation, extent, outline, and thickness of the grout sheets; and precise spirit leveling at the surface provided "before-and-after" elevation maps of the test areas. Depths of the injections ranged generally from about 900 to 1,000 ft (274.3 to 304.8 m) below the surface.

All evidence indicates that the grout sheets at Oak Ridge are horizontal, and the project is considered to be successful. Readers should be aware, however, that geologic conditions such as depth, structure, and lithology at Oak Ridge might be uniquely favorable for the development of horizontal fractures and hence for this disposal technique. Its application elsewhere should be approached with caution.

As is true of burial in salt beds, the method of disposal in fractured shale is not adaptable to great volumes of waste liquids. It is, however, a possible solution to the problem of disposal of intermediate volumes of liquids which cannot be rendered safe for surface disposal. Quantities ranging upward from perhaps 500,000 or 1 million gal (roughly 2-4 million l) a year can be disposed of economically at a favorable plant site or even at one well site; the ultimate limit is related to such factors as the thickness and depth of the shale "reservoir" and perhaps the degree of disturbance by uplift at the surface.

A useful discussion of the technique of disposal into fractured shale reservoirs is provided by de Laguna (1966).

IMPORTANCE OF STRUCTURAL BASINS

It will have become apparent to the reader that not all of the outlined disposal methods require basin structure. Burial in salt beds and in fractured shale can be accomplished satisfactorily in areas of broad regional uplift as well as in basins. The injection of fluids into deep permeable reservoirs involves several considerations because not only are natural hydrodynamic gradients involved, but also artificial gradients that are established temporarily by the injection pressures.

Under some conditions, broad regional upwarps may be as suitable for deep-well injections as are basins. Generally, however, upwarps are not favored because (1) the incidence of faulting commonly is greater than in basins, (2) unconformities and other stratigraphic discontinuities also are more common, and (3) lateral transitions in lithofacies may be more numerous or more abrupt on uplifts, depending on the sedimentary history relative to times of tectonic development. All of these phenomena may affect the ability of the reservoir rock to contain or to transmit fluids, and their effects must be anticipated.

Of even more concern is the distance from points of injection to outcrops or subcrops of the reservoir strata. Consider, for example, the hypothetical case of a deeply buried blanket sandstone of uniform transmissibility extending across the area of two or more basins and the intervening uplifts, and sandwiched everywhere between impermeable shale formations. If the sandstone does not crop out on one of the uplifts, and if the enclosing shale strata are not removed at an unconformity, the hydrologic environment within the sandstone reservoir is a unit system and fluids injected on an uplift will be no more likely to escape than will those injected in a basin. Although examples of a condition similar to that postulated can be found in the subsurface, it is more common to find reservoir strata truncated at outcrops or subcrops on the rim of a basin. Usually, therefore, the hydrologic system in a

permeable reservoir rock is unique to the basin in which it occurs. That is why the principal attention in this volume is given to reservoirs in structural basins.

VALUE OF SUBSURFACE ANALYSES
IN SITE SELECTION

The story of water pollution is replete with examples of industrial plants whose sites were selected on the basis of careful geographic evaluations, but with no realization of eventual crises that would be imposed on the plant operations when expansions and population congestion overtook the original waste-disposal facilities. Fouling of the environment by excessive disposal into pits and streams inevitably leads to frantic efforts to develop alternate disposal methods, and sometimes the proposed alternatives are either prohibitively expensive or geologically impossible at the site in question.

Take the case, for example, of a hypothetical plant on the bank of a full-flowing river, where a copious water supply is assured and stream flow in the river is sufficient to provide ample dilution and dispersion of plant effluents that are discharged into it. Assume also that the effluents contain toxic elements that cannot be safely or economically removed or converted. When plant enlargement and the construction of other plants on the same river eventually swell the total effluent waste streams to volumes which the river no longer can accommodate safely, it is decided to drill a series of wells into which the effluents will be diverted. Exploratory drilling, however, reveals that a fresh-water aquifer (or a stratified succession of them) underlies the plants to a depth of 1,000 or perhaps even 3,000 ft (not an unrealistic figure), and that a rapidly expanding cluster of communities depends on this groundwater for municipal and domestic needs at several locations down-gradient from the plant sites.

Assume that directly underlying the aquifers is a basement of fractured crystalline rock whose fluid content has not been explored. The hydrology of the basement fluids is unknown, and therefore the outlet for any fluids introduced into the basement rock is unknown. An expensive exploratory program would be required in order to obtain the necessary complete picture of the subsurface environment. Plant operators in such a circumstance are in a dilemma if the foreseen exploratory and development costs are high enough to make the profitability of the whole operation doubtful, or if the proposed disposals appear to be unsafe. The crises could have been avoided had the subsurface geology been investigated prior to site selection.

The example just described may be extreme, but it is not exaggerated. Such circumstances are in fact more common than generally may be realized. The point of the illustration is that disposal methods which once were adequate because of a spacious environment and perhaps relatively simple operations and products now are becoming obsolete because of changed conditions. It will not be possible to wait until the next century to modernize disposal concepts and methods to conform with late-20th-century conditions.

Not only the geographic and the surficial geologic environments, but also the deep subsurface environment in all its many aspects, will have to be examined before a site is accepted for construction of a plant which will produce indestructible toxic wastes.

In such exploratory programs the services of well-informed subsurface geologists will be increasingly in demand. It is essential to national welfare—indeed, to human welfare—that subsurface geologists prepare themselves to meet the demand.

Selected References

Boegly, W. J., Jr., et al., 1966, Project Salt Vault—a demonstration disposal of high-level radioactive solids in Lyons, Kansas, salt mine: Health Physics, v. 12, p. 417–424.

Bradshaw, R. L., 1966, Project Salt Vault—effects of temperature and radiation on plastic flow and mine stability: Proc. Symposium on Solidification and Long-Term Storage of Highly Radioactive Wastes, Conf-660208, Div. Tech. Inf., U.S. Atomic Energy Comm., p. 707–723.

de Laguna (see Laguna).

Donaldson, E. C., 1964, Subsurface disposal of industrial wastes in the United States: U.S. Bur. Mines Inf. Circ. 8212.

Empson, F. M., et al., 1966, Project Salt Vault—design and operation: Proc. Symposium on Solidification and Long-Term Storage of Highly Radioactive Wastes, Conf-660208, Div. Tech. Inf., U.S. Atomic Energy Comm., p. 671–685.

Emrich, G. H., 1966, Careers in public health: Geotimes, v. 11, p.15–16.

Evans, D. M., 1966, The Denver area earthquakes and the Rocky Mountain Arsenal disposal well: Mountain Geologist, v. 3, p. 23–36.

Hess, H. H., chm., 1957, The disposal of radioactive waste on land: Rept. Comm. on Waste Disposal, Div. Earth Sci., Natl. Acad. Sci–Natl. Research Council Pub. 519.

Howell, J. V., 1957, Glossary of geology and related sciences: Washington, Am. Geol. Inst., 325 p.

Hubbert, M. K., 1953, Entrapment of petroleum under hydrodynamic conditions: Am. Assoc. Petroleum Geologists Bull., v. 37, p. 1954–2026.

Laguna, W. de, 1962, Engineering geology of radioactive waste disposal: Geol. Soc. America Eng. Geology Reviews, v. 1, p. 129–160.

——— 1966, Disposal of radioactive wastes by hydraulic fracturing; Pt. 1, General concept and first field experiments; Pt. 2, Mechanics of fracture formation and design of observation and monitoring wells: Nuclear Eng. and Design, v. 3, p. 338–352; 432–438.

La Moreaux, P. E., chm. (no date), Water problems associated with oil production in the United States: Oklahoma City, Subcomm. on Water Problems Associated with Oil Production, Research Comm., Interstate Oil Compact Commission.

Legget, R. F., 1939, Geology and engineering: New York, McGraw-Hill Book Co., Inc.

——— 1962, Geology and engineering: New York, McGraw-Hill Book Co., Inc.

Longwell, C. R., Adolph Knopf, and R. F. Flint, 1948, Physical geology, 3d ed.: New York, John Wiley and Sons.

Miller, W. J., 1949, An introduction to physical geology, 5th ed.: New York, D. Van Nostrand Co., Inc.

Moore, T. V., chm., 1958, Problems in the disposal of radioactive waste in deep wells: Subcomm. on Disposal of Radioactive Waste, Central Comm. on Drilling and Production Practice, Div. Prod., Am. Petroleum Institute, Rept. Oct. 1958.

Parker, F. L., 1963, Ground disposal of radioactive wastes: Proc. Natl. Tech. Task Comm. on Industrial Waste, St. Louis, Dec. 1963.

Pierce, W. G., and E. I. Rich, 1962, Summary of rock salt deposits in the United States as possible storage sites for radioactive waste materials: U.S. Geol. Survey Bull. 1148.

Roedder, Edwin, 1959, Problems in the disposal of acid aluminum nitrate high-level radioactive waste solutions by injection into deep-lying permeable formations: U.S. Geol. Survey Bull. 1088.

Schaffer, W. F., et al., 1966, Project Salt Vault—design and demonstration of equipment: Proc. Symposium on Solidification and Long-Term Storage of Highly Radioactive Wastes, Conf-660208, Div. Tech. Inf., U.S. Atomic Energy Comm., p. 685–707.

Warner, D. L., 1965, Deep-well injection of liquid waste: U.S. Public Health Serv. Pub. 999-WP-21.

——— 1967, Deep wells for industrial waste injection in the United States—summary of data: U.S. Dept. of the Interior, Federal Water Pollution Control Adm., WP-20-10.

Weeren, H. O., 1966, Disposal of radioactive wastes by hydraulic fracturing, Pt. 3, Design of ORNL's shale-fracturing plant: Nuclear Eng. and Design, v. 4, p. 108–117.

SUBSURFACE DISPOSAL OF LIQUID INDUSTRIAL WASTES BY DEEP-WELL INJECTION[1]

DON L. WARNER[2]

Cincinnati, Ohio 45202

ABSTRACT

Disposal of concentrated, unusable, relatively untreatable liquid wastes is an important problem in water-pollution control. Deep-well injection is one means for disposing of such wastes.

The feasibility of deep-well injection depends on site suitability, waste characteristics, economics, and legal considerations. Geologic factors determine site suitability and have an important influence on economics and the suitability of waste for injection. Thus, careful geologic evaluation is a prerequisite for deep-well waste injection.

There are at least 110 deep industrial-waste injection wells in the United States. A wide variety of wastes is injected through these wells under extremely varied conditions of flow rate and pressure. Subsurface reservoirs range in age from Pleistocene to Precambrian and, with a few exceptions, are composed of sandstone, limestone, or dolomite.

INTRODUCTION

Waste disposal and water- and air-pollution control have become increasingly difficult. Weinberger (1965, p. 93) has stated that, ". . . in recent years, unprecedented population and industrial growth and concentration, revolutionary new technologies, and changing land uses and practices have thrust enormous pollution problems on a relatively unprepared science. The research must now deal with new problems caused by the sheer mass of pollutants and by a whole host of new pollutants that are highly complex in composition and which may persist for extremely long periods, even indefinitely, in water."

Engineers and scientists are working on methods for treating and concentrating waste streams from domestic and industrial sources, but some wastes cannot be treated effectively, and waste concentrates must be disposed of. Several processes by which concentrated unusable wastes can be disposed of are: spreading on the surface of the earth, deep-well injection, placement in underground cavities, wet oxidation, and incineration (U.S. Dept. Health, Education and Welfare, 1965, p. 90–112). Another method of disposal, which has been suggested for radioactive wastes,

is injection into artificially fractured shale (de Laguna and Houser, 1960).

Deep-well injection long has been important in water-pollution control, primarily for the disposal of oil-field brine brought to the surface during the production of oil and gas. In recent years, however, injection wells have been used more commonly for the permanent underground storage of various industrial wastes, some of which have created serious pollution problems where discharged into surface and ground waters (Scopel, 1964, and Water Well Jour., 1965). In addition to their use for disposal of the more conventional industrial wastes, deep wells have been considered for the disposal of radioactive wastes (de Laguna, this volume), wastes from saline-water conversion plants (Koenig, 1958), and wastes from advanced waste-treatment plants (Koenig, 1964).

The principles discussed in this paper apply specifically to the disposal of liquid industrial wastes other than oil-field brine or liquid radioactive wastes, although they commonly apply to all of these liquids.

Oil-field brine injection and waterflood injection differ from industrial-waste injection in several ways. 1. Preinjection waste treatment and corrosion prevention can be very difficult with some industrial wastes. 2. Brine and waterflood injection wells are in developed oil fields where abundant subsurface data are available, whereas

[1] Manuscript received, October 24, 1966.

[2] Research geologist-engineer, Engineering Activities, Research and Development, Cincinnati Water Research Laboratory, Federal Water Pollution Control Administration, Department of the Interior.

there may be no data available at sites where industrial-waste injection is contemplated. 3. Brine
and waterflood wells commonly inject into de-
pressured subsurface reservoirs, perhaps even into
the same reservoir from which the fluids were removed, whereas industrial wastes are more likely
to be injected into reservoirs that have virgin
fluid pressures. 4. Industrial-waste injection wells
generally are constructed with elaborate precau-
tion to insure long life and safe operation. 5. The
liquids injected during oil-field operations are
normally natural waters and there is little concern
regarding their subsurface distribution, whereas
industrial wastes can be of such character that it
is important to know how they are distributed
within the injection zones and where they are
likely to migrate.

The feasibility of deep-well injection as a solution to a particular waste-disposal problem depends on (1) the geologic and engineering suitability of available injection-well sites, (2) the volume and physical and chemical characteristics of
the waste, (3) economics, and (4) legal considerations. This paper emphasizes the aspects of the
feasibility of deep-well industrial-waste injection
that are of particular significance to geologists.

Site Suitability

The general geologic characteristics that dictate
the suitability of areas for deep-well injection can
be outlined. More detailed studies, such as the
ones included in this publication, are then necessary to show the distribution, depth, and physical
characteristics of specific potential injection zones
within areas that are deemed generally suitable.
Detailed local geological and engineering studies
of the characteristics of these potential injection
zones are necessary before a recommendation can
be made regarding site suitability.

GENERAL CONSIDERATIONS

Oil-industry experience has shown that nearly
all types of rocks can, under favorable circumstances, have sufficient porosity and permeability
to yield or accept large quantities of fluids. Sedimentary rocks, especially those deposited in a marine environment, are most likely to have the geologic characteristics suitable for waste-injection
wells. These characteristics are (1) an injection

zone with sufficient permeability, porosity, thickness, and areal extent to act as a liquid-storage
reservoir at safe injection pressures, and (2) an
injection zone that is vertically below the level of
fresh-water circulation and is confined vertically
by rocks that are, for practical purposes, impermeable to waste liquids.

Vertical confinement of injected wastes is important not only for the protection of usable
water resources, but also for the protection of developed and undeveloped deposits of hydrocarbons and other minerals. The effect of lateral
movement of waste on such natural resources also
must be considered.

Sandstone, limestone, and dolomite are commonly porous and permeable enough in the unfractured state to be suitable injection zones.
Naturally fractured limestone, dolomite, shale,
and other rocks also may be satisfactory. Rocks
with solution or fracture porosity may be prefera-
ble to rocks with intergranular porosity, because
solution and fracture flow channels are commonly
relatively large in comparison to intergranular
pores and are not, therefore, as likely to be
plugged by suspended solids in the injected liquids. Waste injection into limestone and dolomite
has proved particularly successful in some places
because the permeability of these rocks can be
improved greatly with acid treatment.

Unfractured shale, clay, slate, anhydrite, gypsum, marl, and bentonite have been found to provide good seals against the upward flow of oil and
gas (Russell, 1960). Limestone and dolomite may
be satisfactory confining strata; but these rocks
commonly contain fractures or solution channels,
and their adequacy must be determined carefully
in each case.

The minimum depth of burial, the necessary
thickness of confining strata, and the minimum
salinity of water in the injection zone have not
been established quantitatively, and it may be
possible to specify these constraints only for individual cases, as has been done in the past.

The minimum depth of burial can be considered to be the depth at which a confined saline-
water-bearing zone is present; it may range from
a few hundred to several thousand feet.

The minimum salinity of water in the injection
zone probably will be specified by regulatory

agencies in most states, but will be at least 1,000 mg of dissolved solids per liter of water except under unusual circumstances. Water containing less than 500 mg/l now is considered to be acceptable for potable water used by interstate carriers (U.S. Public Health Service, 1962), and formerly (U.S. Public Health Service, 1946), if such water was not available, water containing 1,000 ppm of dissolved solids was considered acceptable. The minimum salinity may be set at a level higher than 1,000 mg/l of dissolved solids to provide a margin of safety and because water with several times this dissolved-solids content is used in certain areas for domestic, industrial, or agricultural purposes.

Russell (1960) has stated that a confining stratum only 10 to 20 ft thick may provide a good seal to retain oil and gas. Such thin confining beds generally would not be satisfactory for containing injected waste because they would be very susceptible to hydraulic fracturing, and even a small fault could completely offset them vertically. Fortunately, in many places hundreds or thousands of feet of impermeable strata enclose potential injection zones and virtually ensure their segregation.

The thickness and permeability necessary to allow fluid injection at the desired injection rate can be estimated from equations developed by petroleum engineers and groundwater hydrologists (van Everdingen, this volume). The geometry of the injection zone also determines its suitability for waste injection. A thick lens of highly permeable sandstone might not be satisfactory for injection if it is small and surrounded by impermeable beds, because pressure buildup in the lens would be rapid in comparison to that in a "blanket" sandstone.

It may be desirable in some cases to inject wastes into a known geologic structural feature. Under favorable conditions this practice would help to ensure the confinement of the waste within a specified area and also might allow its recovery at a later date if, for example, recovery of the dissolved solids should become economically feasible. Wastes of relatively high specific gravity stored in closed synclines would not tend to leak upward into fresh-water-bearing strata and would not move laterally into hydrocarbon-bearing anticlinal features under hydrostatic conditions.

In addition to stratigraphy, structure, and rock properties, which are factors routinely considered in subsurface studies, aquifer hydrodynamics may be significant in the evaluation of waste-injection well sites. The presence of a natural hydrodynamic gradient in the injection zone will cause the injected waste to be distributed asymmetrically about the well bore (Theis, 1956) and transported through the aquifer even after injection has ceased. The entrapment of fluids is modified under hydrodynamic conditions (Hubbert, 1953). Several aspects of the subsurface movement of natural fluids or injected wastes under a hydrodynamic gradient are discussed by Young and Galley (1965).

Hydrodynamic dispersion—the mixing of displacing and displaced fluids during movement through porous media—may cause much wider distribution of waste in the injection zone than otherwise would be anticipated. Dispersion is known to occur in essentially homogeneous isotropic sandstone (Harleman and Rumer, 1963), and it could lead to particularly rapid lateral distribution of waste in heterogeneous sandstone (Skibitzke and Robinson, 1963) and fractured or cavernous strata. Sorption of waste constituents by aquifer minerals retards the spread of waste from the injection site (Kaufman et al., 1961).

The mathematical models now available are satisfactory for accurately predicting the movement of waste in most natural aquifers only under restrictive, simplified physical circumstances. Even if knowledge of the physics of fluid movement in natural aquifers were considerably more advanced, the determination of the physical parameters that characterize an injection zone still would be a problem if few subsurface data were available. These restrictions do not, however, preclude the quantitative estimation of the rate and direction of movement of injected waste.

The maximum pressure at which liquids can be injected without causing hydraulic fracturing may be the factor limiting the intake rate and operating life of an injection well. The injection pressure at which hydraulic fracturing will occur is related directly to the magnitude of regional rock stress and the natural strength of the injection zone (Hubbert and Willis, 1957). In some areas, the pressure at which hydraulic fracturing will occur can be estimated before drilling on the basis of experience in nearby oil fields.

Other considerations in the determination of site suitability are (1) the presence of abnormally high natural fluid pressure and temperature in the potential injection zone that may make injection difficult or uneconomical; (2) the local incidence of earthquakes that can cause movement along faults and damage to the subsurface well facilities; (3) the presence of abandoned, improperly plugged wells that penetrate the injection zone and provide a means for escape of injected waste to groundwater aquifers or to the surface; and (4) the mineralogy of the injection zone and chemistry of interstitial waters, which may determine the injectability of a specific waste.

It has been suggested that the numerous earthquakes recorded in the area of Denver, Colorado, since 1962 may be related directly to injection into a 12,000-ft-deep waste-disposal well at the Rocky Mountain Arsenal (Evans, 1966). Statistical evidence (Bardwell, 1966) and microseismicity studies (Healy et al., 1966) tend to support this hypothesis; however, a mechanism by which this injection well could have initiated the earth movements that have occurred has not been demonstrated satisfactorily. If further study shows that fluid injection into deep wells can initiate earth movements of significant magnitude, then that aspect of site suitability will be a consideration.

GENERAL EVALUATION OF SUITABLE AREAS

The suitability of an injection-well site must be determined finally from a detailed analysis of local geology, but generalizations based on regional geologic considerations can be made concerning the suitability of certain areas for waste-injection wells.

Synclinal basins (Fig. 1), including those described in this volume, and the Atlantic and Gulf Coastal Plains are particularly favorable sites for deep waste-injection wells because they contain relatively thick sequences of salt-water-bearing sedimentary rocks and because the subsurface geology of these basins commonly is relatively well known. Galley (1962) discussed general aspects of geologic basin studies as related to deep-well disposal of radioactive waste.

Reports on basins other than those considered in this volume have been written by Repenning (1961) on the Central Valley of California, Sandberg (1962) on the Williston basin, Beikman (1962) on the Powder River basin, MacLachlan (1964) on the Anadarko basin, and LeGrand (1962) on the Atlantic and Gulf Coastal Plains; Love and Hoover (1960) briefly summarized the geology of many sedimentary basins in the United States. The geologic data in these reports can be used directly for evaluation of the areas for industrial-waste disposal; however, because the reports are oriented primarily toward radioactive-waste disposal, the conclusions may require modification for application to the injection of other wastes.

Not all of the generally acknowledged synclinal basins are shown on Figure 1, nor was it possible to consider each basin and its size and configuration in detail. A more accurate concept of the size and configuration of the basins can be obtained from the Tectonic Map of the United States (Longwell et al., 1944; Cohee et al., 1962), from Ball et al. (1951), and from published articles concerning the geology of the individual basins.

Just as major synclinal basins are geologically favorable sites for deep-well injection, other areas may be generally unfavorable because the sedimentary-rock cover is thin or absent. Extensive areas where relatively impermeable igneous-intrusive and metamorphic rocks are exposed at the surface are shown in Figure 1. With the possible exception of small parts, these areas can be eliminated from consideration for waste injection. The exposure of igneous and metamorphic rocks in the Arbuckle Mountains, Wichita Mountains, Llano and Ozark uplifts, the exposures just south of the Canadian Shield, and other such exposures are perhaps not extensive, but they are significant because the sedimentary sequence thins toward them and the salinity of the formation waters decreases toward the outcrops around the exposures.

Regions shown on Figure 1 where a thick volcanic sequence lies at the surface generally are not suitable for waste-injection wells. Although volcanic rocks have fissures, fractures, and interbedded gravel that will accept injected fluids,

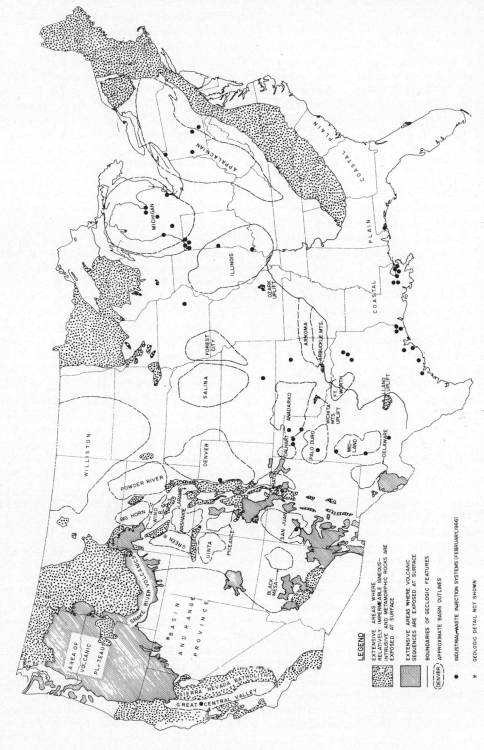

Fig. 1.—Geologic features significant in deep waste-injection well-site evaluation, and locations of industrial-waste injection systems. Geologic data from Tectonic Map of the United States (Longwell et al., 1944; revised, Cohee et al., 1962), and basin outlines from Oil and Gas Field Map of the United States (Vliisides and Quirin, 1964).

they contain fresh water.

The immense and geologically complex Basin and Range province (Fig. 1) is a series of narrow basins and intervening, structurally positive ranges. Some of the basins might provide waste-injection sites, but their geology is mostly unknown and the cost of obtaining sufficient information to insure safe construction of injection wells would be very great.

The geology of the West Coast is complex and not well known. Relatively small Tertiary sedimentary basins in southern California yield large quantities of oil and gas, and probably are geologically satisfactory sites for waste-injection wells. There are similar basins along the coast of northern California, Oregon, and Washington, but little is known about their geology.

Areas not underlain by major basins or prominent geologic features may be generally satisfactory for waste injection if they are underlain by a sufficient thickness of sedimentary rocks that contain saline water, and if potential injection zones are sealed from fresh-water-bearing strata by impermeable confining beds.

OTHER FACTORS

Site suitability has been given primary emphasis, but the suitability of waste for injection, the economics of the project, and legal considerations may be equally important factors in determining the feasibility of deep-well injection.

SUITABILITY OF WASTE FOR INJECTION

The suitability of waste for subsurface injection depends on its volume and physical and chemical characteristics, and on the physical and chemical properties of the potential injection zones and their interstitial fluids.

Waste disposal into subsurface aquifers constitutes the use of limited storage space, and only concentrated, very objectionable, relatively untreatable wastes should be considered for injection. The fluids injected into deep aquifers do not occupy empty pores, and each gallon of waste will displace a gallon of the fluid which saturates the storage zone. Optimal use of underground storage space will be realized (1) by use of deep-well injection only where more satisfactory alternative methods of waste treatment and disposal

are not available and (2) by minimization of the injected-waste volumes through good waste management.

The intake rate of an injection well is limited, and its operating life may depend on the total quantity of fluid injected. The variable limiting the injection rate or well life can be the injection pressure required to dispose of the produced waste. Injection pressure is a limiting factor because excessive pressure causes hydraulic fracturing and possible consequent damage to confining strata (Hubbert and Willis, 1957, p. 165); the pressure capacity of injection-well pumps, tubing, and casing is limited; in some states maximum injection pressures are specified by regulatory agencies. The initial pressure required to inject waste at a specified rate and the rate at which injection pressure increases with time can be calculated if the physical properties of the aquifer and the waste are known (van Everdingen, this volume). The intake rate of waste-injection wells now in use has been found to range most commonly from 100 to 400 gpm, but intake rates can be higher or lower than this range.

The operating life of an injection well may be related to the volume of injected waste, because the distance injected waste can be allowed to spread laterally may be restricted by law or by other considerations. The storage volume or effective porosity in the vicinity of an injection well can be computed very simply, but dispersion, adsorption, and chemical reaction complicate the calculation of the distribution of injected waste.

The injectability of a particular waste depends on the physical and chemical characteristics of the waste, the aquifer, and the aquifer fluids, because physical or chemical interactions between the waste and the aquifer minerals or fluids can cause plugging of the aquifer pores and consequent loss of intake capacity. Plugging can be caused by suspended solids or entrained gas in the injected waste, reactions between injected fluids and aquifer minerals, reactions between injected and interstitial fluids, and autoreactivity of the waste at aquifer temperature and pressure. Plugging at or near the well bore also can be caused by bacteria and mold.

Wastes that are not initially injectable commonly can be treated to make them so. To prevent plugging and corrosion problems, suspended solids, dissolved iron and manganese, and entrained air are removed routinely from water to be injected during oil-field operations (Ostroff, 1965).

Knowledge of the mineralogy of the aquifer and the chemistry of interstitial fluids and waste should indicate the reactions to be anticipated during injection. Laboratory tests can be performed with rock cores and formation and waste-water samples to confirm anticipated reactions.

Selm and Hulse (1959) listed the reactions between injected and interstitial fluids that can cause the formation of plugging precipitates—(1) precipitation of alkaline earth metals such as calcium, barium, strontium, and magnesium as relatively insoluble carbonates, sulfates, orthophosphates, fluorides, and hydroxides; (2) precipitation of metals such as iron, aluminum, cadmium, zinc, manganese, and chromium as insoluble carbonates, bicarbonates, hydroxides, orthophosphates, and sulfides; and (3) precipitation of oxidation-reduction reaction products.

The plugging effect of such precipitates is not certain (Stahl, 1962), but if plugging is considered to be a possibility, the waste can be treated to make it nonreactive, or nonreactive water can be injected ahead of the waste to form a buffer between the waste and the aquifer water (Warner, 1966).

Common minerals that react significantly with wastes are the acid-soluble carbonate minerals and the clay minerals. Acidizing of reservoirs containing carbonate minerals is an effective well-stimulation technique, and reaction of acidic wastes with carbonate minerals thus might be expected to be beneficial. An undesirable effect of the reaction of acid waste with carbonate minerals could be evolution of CO_2 that might increase pressure and cause plugging if present in excess of its solubility. Roedder (1959) reported that the reaction of acid aluminum nitrate waste with calcium carbonate results in a gelatinous precipitate that could cause plugging.

Clay minerals are known to reduce the permeability of sandstone to water in comparison to its permeability to air (Baptist and Sweeney, 1955). The permeability of a clay-bearing sandstone to water decreases with decreasing water salinity, decreasing the valence of the cations in solution and increasing the pH of the water.

Ostroff (1965) and Warner (1965, 1966) give additional references and discussion concerning waste injectability. Factors that bear on waste injectability, such as aquifer mineralogy, temperature and pressure, and chemical quality of aquifer fluids, are a logical part of feasibility reports because the treatment necessary to make a waste injectable can be an important part of total waste-injection cost.

ECONOMICS

Cost can determine the feasibility of deep-well injection as a waste-disposal method, and to a large degree geologic factors determine the cost of constructing and operating injection wells.

Geologic parameters that influence construction costs are well depth, drilling characteristics of the rock sequence, and nature of the injection zone; parameters that influence operation costs are permeability, porosity, and thickness of the injection zones and fluid pressure in the reservoir, all of which determine the intake rate and operating pressure. Other geologic factors that influence costs are the mineralogy and chemistry of the aquifer minerals and fluids, which may determine the preinjection waste treatment that is necessary.

Koenig (1964) analyzed the costs of injection-well construction and operation and concluded that injection capacity of a well has the greatest influence on unit waste-disposal costs, well depth is second in importance, and operating pressure is third.

LEGAL CONSIDERATIONS

Legal aspects of waste injection can be of utmost concern because state and federal laws and the policies of regulatory agencies commonly determine where and how waste injection may be undertaken.

Texas and Ohio have passed laws that pertain specifically to deep-well industrial-waste disposal. Other states regulate deep-well disposal under general pollution-control laws or laws written to control oil and gas operations. No state has laws specifically prohibiting deep-well waste injection;

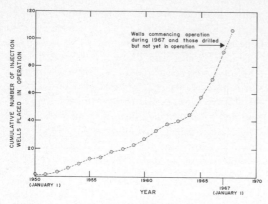

FIG. 2.—Number of injection wells placed in operation each year during period January 1950 to January 1967.

however, the present policies of some state regulatory agencies appear to prevent its use where it might be feasible otherwise.

The responsibility of passing judgment on the feasibility of deep-well injection is important because a single unfortunate experience with subsurface waste storage could affect greatly the attitude of a state regulatory agency toward that waste-disposal method. Also, frequent failure in attempts to utilize an injection system influences the attitude of investors toward deep-well waste injection as a means of waste disposal.

INJECTION SYSTEMS IN USE

Publications concerning individual industrial-waste injection systems provide the best available review of experience to date. Some references are: Adinoff (1955), Arlin (1962), Barraclough (1966), Batz (1964), Cecil (1950), Dean (1965), Graves (1961), Henkel (1953, 1955), Holland and Clark (1965), Hundley and Matulis (1962), Lansing and Hewett (1955), Lee (1950), MacLeod (1961), Mechem and Garrett (1963), Moffett (1960), Paradiso (1956), and Sadow (1963). Donaldson's (1964) publication describes several such systems.

Information from the states and review of the literature show that as of November 1967 there were at least 110 industrial-waste injection wells in use in 16 states (Warner, 1967). Thirty-two of these wells are in Texas. Louisiana has reported 24 wells; Michigan, 21; Indiana, 9; Pennsylvania, 5; California, 4; Illinois, 3; Florida, 2; Kansas,

2; and West Virginia, 2. There is one well each in Colorado, Iowa, New Mexico, Ohio, Oklahoma, and Tennessee. The locations of many of the injection-well systems are shown on Figure 1. Some of the locations shown represent more than one well at a single site.

Figure 2 shows the number of injection wells placed in operation during each year from January 1950 to January 1967. More wells (46) were put into operation during the 3-year period 1964–1967 than during the previous 14-year period, 1950–1963 (45 wells). This increase in the rate of construction can be attributed to increased emphasis on water-pollution control and the more widespread acceptance of this disposal method because of its successful use.

A wide variety of wastes is being injected through deep wells. Refineries and natural-gas purification plants; chemical, petrochemical, and pharmaceutical plants; and metal-product plants utilize about 80 percent of the injection systems. Some of the systems are operated by a paper mill, a uranium mill, an airline maintenance facility, a nylon plant, a coking plant, an aerospace facility, and a photo-processing facility. It is not feasible to discuss the wastes from each plant. The papers of the authors listed above describe the types of wastes being injected, show the system designs used in a variety of circumstances, and discuss the problems that have arisen during operation.

Existing wells range from a few hundred to more than 12,000 ft in total depth. Injection is into reservoirs that range in age from Pleistocene to Precambrian. Reservoirs consist of unconsolidated sands, sandstones, and limestones or dolomites, with the exception of a few wells. The most notable exception is the Rocky Mountain Arsenal injection well near Denver, Colorado, which was completed in fractured Precambrian gneiss at a depth of about 12,000 ft.

Available injection-rate and pressure data are not considered satisfactory, but they do indicate the ranges within which the systems are operating. Injection rates for a single well range from a few gallons per minute to more than 900 gpm; the most usual rate is between 100 and 400 gpm. Well-head injection pressures range from negative to 4,000 psi, but most systems are injecting at a well-head pressure of less than 1,000 psi.

SUMMARY

Deep-well injection appears to be a promising method for emplacing and permanently storing certain liquid wastes in subsurface reservoirs. Injection wells have had only limited use for disposal of wastes other than oil-field brine, but their use for disposal of industrial wastes is expected to increase as pollution control is emphasized and as the production of industrial wastes increases.

The feasibility of subsurface storage as a solution to a particular waste-disposal problem depends on (1) the geologic and engineering suitability of available injection-well sites, (2) the volume and physical and chemical characteristics of the waste, (3) economics, and (4) legal considerations.

The geologic and engineering suitability of available injection-well sites is of immediate concern to geologists and petroleum engineers, but geologic and engineering factors have an important influence on other aspects of feasibility. For example, the economics of drilling, completing, and operating an injection system may depend mainly on such variables as the depth, thickness, and permeability of the injection zone. The volume and physical and chemical character of the wastes that can be injected also depend on reservoir properties.

It is expected that geologists and petroleum engineers will be called on more frequently in the future to assist in evaluating the feasibility of subsurface waste storage. The determination of geologic and engineering feasibility is straightforward in some cases, but in others it is not, and great care should be used in the preparation of final recommendations.

REFERENCES

Adinoff, J., 1955, Disposal of organic chemical wastes to underground formations, in 9th indus. waste conf. proc., Purdue, 1954: Purdue Univ. Ext. Ser. No. 87, p. 32–38.

Arlin, Z. E., 1962, Deep-well disposal of uranium tailing water, in Proc. 2d conf. on ground disposal of radioactive wastes, Chalk River, Canada, Sept. 26–29, 1961: U.S. Atomic Energy Comm. TID-7628, book 2, p. 356–360.

Ball, M. W., et al., eds., 1951, Possible future petroleum provinces of North America: Am. Assoc. Petroleum Geologists Bull., v. 35, no. 2, p. 141–498; reprinted as a special volume, 1951, 358 p.

Baptist, O. C., and S. A. Sweeney, 1955, Effect of clays on the permeability of reservoir sands to various saline waters, Wyoming: U.S. Bur. Mines Rept. Inv. 5180, 23 p.

Bardwell, G. E., 1966, Some statistical features of the relationship between Rocky Mountain Arsenal waste disposal and frequency of earthquakes: Mountain Geologist, v. 3, no. 1, p. 37–42.

Barraclough, J. T., 1966, Waste injection into a deep limestone in northwestern Florida: Ground Water, v. 4, no. 1, p. 22–25.

Batz, M. E., 1964, Deep-well disposal of nylon waste water: Chem. Eng. Progress, v. 60, no. 10, p. 85–88.

Beikman, H. M., 1962, Geology of the Powder River basin, Wyoming and Montana, with reference to subsurface disposal of radioactive wastes: U.S. Geol. Survey Trace Elements Inv. Rept. 823 (open file), 85 p.

Cecil, L. K., 1950, Underground disposal of process waste water: Indus. Eng. Chemistry, v. 42, no. 4, p. 594–599.

Cohee, G. V., et al., 1962, Tectonic map of the United States: U.S. Geol. Survey and Am. Assoc. Petroleum Geologists, scale 1 : 2,500,000.

Dean, B. T., 1965, The design and operation of a deep-well disposal system: Water Pollution Control Federation Jour., v. 37, no. 2, p. 245–254.

de Laguna (see Laguna).

Donaldson, E. C., 1964, Subsurface disposal of industrial wastes in the United States: U.S. Bur. Mines Inf. Circ. 8212, 34 p.

Evans, D. M., 1966, The Denver area earthquakes and the Rocky Mountain Arsenal disposal well: Mountain Geologist, v. 3, no. 1, p. 23–26.

Galley, J. E., 1962, Geologic basin studies as related to deep-well disposal, in Proc. 2d conf. on ground disposal of radioactive wastes, Chalk River, Canada, Sept. 26–29, 1961: U.S. Atomic Energy Comm. TID-7628, book 2, p. 347–355.

Graves, B. S., 1961, Underground disposal of sour water, in 24th ann. short course for water and sewerage plant superintendents and operators proc.: Louisiana State Univ. Eng. Expt. Sta. Bull. No. 67, p. 74–80.

Harleman, D. R. F., and R. R. Rumer, Jr., 1963, Longitudinal and lateral dispersion in an isotropic porous medium: Jour. Fluid Mechanics, v. 16, pt. 3, p. 385–394.

Healy, J. H., W. H. Jackson, and J. R. Van Schaack, 1966, Microseismicity studies at the site of the Denver earthquakes, in Geophysical and geological investigations relating to earthquakes in the Denver area, Colorado: U.S. Geol. Survey Open-File Rept., March.

Henkel, H. O., 1953, Surface and underground disposal of chemical wastes at Victoria, Texas: Sewage and Indus. Wastes, v. 52, no. 9, p. 1044–1049.

——— 1955, Deep-well disposal of chemical wastes: Chem. Eng. Progress, v. 51, no. 12, p. 551–554.

Holland, H. R., and F. R. Clark, 1965, A disposal well for spent sulphuric acid from aklylating isobutane and butylenes, in 19th indus. waste conf. proc.: Purdue Univ. Eng. Ext. Ser. No. 117, pt. 1, p. 195–199.

Hubbert, M. K., 1953, Entrapment of petroleum under hydrodynamic conditions: Am. Assoc. Petroleum Geologists Bull., v. 37, p. 1954–2026.

——— and D. G. Willis, 1957, Mechanics of hydraulic fracturing: Am. Inst. Mining Metall. Engineers

Petroleum Div. Trans., T.P. 4597; Jour. Petroleum Technology, June, p. 153–168.

Hundley, C. L., and J. T. Matulis, 1962, Deep-well disposal, *in* 17th indus. waste conf. proc., Purdue, May 1961: Purdue Univ. Eng. Ext. Ser. No. 112, p. 176–180.

Kaufman, W. J., *et al.*, 1961, Disposal of radioactive wastes into deep geologic formation: Water Pollution Control Federation Jour., v. 33, no. 1, p. 73–84.

Koenig, L., 1958, Disposal of saline water conversion brines—an orientation study: U.S. Dept. Interior Office of Saline Water, Research and Develop. Prog. Rept. No. 20.

——— 1964, Ultimate disposal of advanced-treatment waste, Part 1, Injection: U.S. Public Health Service Pub. No. 999-W-10, AWTR-8, p. 3–83.

Laguna, W. D. de, and B. L. Houser, 1960, Disposal of radioactive waste by hydraulic fracturing: U.S. Atomic Energy Comm. Ornl-2994, p. 128–136.

Lansing, A. C., and P. S. Hewett, 1955, Disposal of phenolic waste to underground formations, *in* 9th indus. waste conf. proc.: Purdue Univ. Eng. Ext. Ser. No. 87, p. 184–194.

Lee, J. A., 1950, Throw your wastes down a well: Chem. Eng., v. 9, Sept., p. 137–139.

LeGrand, H. E., 1962, Geology and ground-water hydrology of the Atlantic and Gulf Coastal Plain as related to disposal of radioactive wastes: U.S. Geol. Survey Trace Elements Inv. Rept. 805, 169 p.

Longwell, C. R., *et al.*, 1944, Tectonic map of the United States: Tulsa, Oklahoma, Am. Assoc. Petroleum Geologists.

Love, J. D., and Linn Hoover, 1960, A summary of the geology of sedimentary basins of the United States, with reference to the disposal of radioactive wastes: U.S. Geol. Survey Trace Elements Inv. Rept. 768 (open file), 92 p.

MacLachlan, M. E., 1964, The Anadarko basin (of parts of Oklahoma, Texas, Kansas, and Colorado): U.S. Geol. Survey Trace Elements Inv. Rept. 831, 75 p.

MacLeod, I. C., 1961, Disposal of spent caustic and phenolic water in deep wells: 8th Ontario Indus. Waste Conf. Proc., p. 49–60.

Mechem, O. E., and J. H. Garrett, 1963, Deep injection disposal well for liquid toxic waste: Am. Soc. Civil Engineers Proc., Jour. Construction Div., p. 111–121.

Moffett, J. G., Jr., 1960, Underground disposal of industrial wastes, *in* 23rd ann. short course for water and sewage plant superintendents and operators proc.: Louisiana State Univ. Eng. Expt. Sta. Bull. No. 65, p. 155–162.

Ostroff, A. G., 1965, Introduction to oilfield water technology: Englewood Cliffs, New Jersey, Prentice Hall, Inc., 412 p.

Paradiso, S. J., 1956, Disposal of fine chemical wastes, *in* 10th indus. waste conf. proc.: Purdue Univ. Eng. Ext. Ser. No. 89, p. 49–60.

Repenning, C. A., 1961, Geologic summary of the Central Valley of California, with reference to disposal of liquid radioactive waste: U.S. Geol. Survey Trace Elements Inv. Rept. 769 (open file), 69 p.

Roedder, E., 1959, Problems in the disposal of acid aluminum nitrate high-level radioactive waste solutions by injection into deep-lying permeable forma-

tions: U.S. Geol. Survey Bull. 1088, 65 p.

Russell, W. L., 1960, Principles of petroleum geology: New York, McGraw-Hill Book Co., 490 p.

Sadow, R. D., 1963, How Monsanto handles its petrochemical wastes: Wastes Eng., Dec., p. 640–644.

Sandberg, C. A., 1962, Geology of the Williston basin, North Dakota, Montana, and South Dakota, with reference to subsurface disposal of radioactive wastes: U.S. Geol. Survey Trace Elements Inv. Rept. 809 (open file), 148 p.

Scopel, L. J., 1964, Pressure injection disposal well, Rocky Mountain Arsenal, Denver, Colorado: Mountain Geologist, v. 1, no. 1, p. 35–42.

Selm, R. P., and B. T. Hulse, 1959, Deep-well disposal of industrial wastes, *in* 14th indus. waste conf. proc.: Purdue Univ. Eng. Ext. Ser. No. 104, p. 566–586.

Skibitzke, H. E., and G. M. Robinson, 1963, Dispersion in ground water flowing through heterogeneous materials: U.S. Geol. Survey Prof. Paper 386-B, p. B1-B3.

Stahl, C. D., 1962, Compatibility of interstitial and injection waters: Producers Monthly, v. 26, no. 11, p. 14–15.

Theis, C. V., 1956, Problems of ground disposal of nuclear wastes, *in* 1955 internat. conf. on peaceful uses of atomic energy proc., v. 9, Reactor technology and chemical processing: United Nations, p. 679–683.

U.S. Department of Health, Education and Welfare, 1965, Summary Report, Jan. 1962–June 1964, Advanced waste treatment research: U.S. Public Health Service Pub. No. 999-WP-24, AWTR-14, 142 p.

U.S. Public Health Service, 1946, Drinking water standards: Public Health Repts., v. 61, no. 11, p. 371–384.

——— 1962, Public Health Service drinking water standards: U.S. Public Health Service Pub. No. 956, 61 p.

Vlissides, S. D., and B. A. Quirin, 1964, Oil and gas fields of the United States (map): U.S. Geol. Survey, scale 1:2,500,000.

Warner, D. L., 1965, Deep-well injection of liquid waste: U.S. Public Health Service Environmental Health Ser. Pub. No. 999-WP-21, 55 p.

——— 1966, Deep-well waste injection—reaction with aquifer water: Am. Soc. Civil Engineers Proc., v. 92, no. SA4, p. 45–69.

——— 1967, Deep wells for industrial waste injection in the United States—summary of data: U.S. Dept. Interior, Fed. Water Pollution Control Adm., Water Pollution Control Research Ser., Pub. No. WP-20-10, 45 p.

Water Well Journal, 1965, Operation deep well: v. 19, no. 1, May, p. 28–29.

Weinberger, L. W., 1965, Statement, *in* Special Subcommittee on Air and Water Pollution of the Committee on Public Works, United States Senate, 89th Congress, 1st Session, Pt. 1, General hearings held on progress and programs relating to the abatement of water pollution, Washington, D.C., May 19, 20, and 21, 1965: Washington, D.C., U.S. Govt. Printing Office, p. 92–112.

Young, Addison, and J. E. Galley, eds., 1965, Fluids in subsurface environments: Tulsa, Oklahoma, Am. Assoc. Petroleum Geologists Mem. 4, 414 p.

IMPORTANCE OF DEEP PERMEABLE DISPOSAL FORMATIONS IN LOCATION OF A LARGE NUCLEAR-FUEL REPROCESSING PLANT[1]

WALLACE DE LAGUNA[2]

Oak Ridge, Tennessee 37830

ABSTRACT

The most important disposal problem in location of a large nuclear-fuel reprocessing plant is that of low-level waste. Disposal into large bodies of surface water has been common; however, underground disposal into deep permeable formations seems to offer the best possibilities for disposal of low-level waste. The most favorable method for disposal of medium-level waste is disposal into hydraulically fractured shale. Shale with the necessary requirements generally is found in basin areas suitable for low-level waste disposal. A favored method for disposal of high-level waste is storage in solid form in mined cavities in salt. Thus the selection of a site that also has salt beds is advantageous, but not required, because alternate means for disposal of high-level waste can be found.

Maximum permissible concentrations of radioactive nuclides in air and water have been derived. As more information is gained, the values may be increased or decreased, and thus may alter the requirements for a plant site.

Disposal of radioactive wastes into deep permeable formations is now practicable only for low-level waste, but it holds potential for disposal of certain medium- and high-level wastes, and also of such gaseous wastes as krypton-85.

LOW-LEVEL WASTE

BASIC PROBLEMS OF DISPOSAL

The five major and one minor structural and sedimentary basins described in this book were chosen because they contain deeply buried permeable formations into which, at selected locations, it should be possible to pump substantial volumes of fluid wastes with considerable assurance that they would not return to the surface for many hundreds of years, or would not travel far enough underground to create an unexpected hazard. The basins, or the sections of them recommended for consideration for waste disposal, are far, either laterally or vertically, from important oil or gas reservoirs, and there has been little drilling in the areas of greatest interest. Consequently, few qualitative and virtually no quantitative data are directly available. There are almost no data on the permeability and pressure distribution in the disposal formations, and though the petroleum geologist is skilled at estimating the probable underground conditions by extrapolation from known areas, precise prediction of the directions and rates of movement of fluid in the proposed dis

posal formations, either under natural conditions or after waste injection, is impossible.

Thus, the nuclear engineer may question the value of the basin reports herein, because any radioactive-waste disposal operation would have to be conducted with a maximum assurance that no hazard would be created even at a time far in the future. Certain industrial wastes are as dangerous as the radioactive wastes, and equal care is required in their disposal. Therefore, what is the value of these basin reports, now that they are available?

The answer must be speculative because it depends in part on the controversial question of the possible long-range hazards of even small increases in the radioactivity of our environment, and in part on how the nuclear-power industry of the future will develop, both geographically and technically. The future production of other industrial wastes, which are creating equally important disposal problems, is also uncertain.

Any attempt to evaluate the basic problems of the nuclear-power industry and their possible solutions must be based on the probable waste-disposal requirements of the nuclear-fuel reprocessing plants of the future. The power reactors must return their fuel periodically to these plants for removal of the so-called "fission products." These

[1] Manuscript received, July 14, 1965.

[2] Health Physics Division, Oak Ridge National Laboratory (operated by Union Carbide Corporation for the U.S. Atomic Energy Commission).

21

fission products are the source of the radioactive wastes. There is a strong economic incentive to make the fuel-reprocessing plants large—the larger the plant, the lower the unit cost of operation. Counterbalancing this is the shipping cost of the fuel. As the industry grows, more reprocessing plants will be built, each to serve the reactors in the area adjacent to it. However, plant size is a far more important factor than shipping cost, and for several years only a small number of reprocessing plants probably will be built, each growing in size as the industry expands; not for many years should there be a trend to increase the number of new plants to cut shipping charges. What the most economical pattern will be cannot be predicted, but probably the number of reprocessing plants in a fully developed future nuclear-power economy will be relatively small, perhaps 10 or 20, in comparison to the number of nuclear-power generating stations, which well may be in the hundreds.

At present a 6-ton-a-day reprocessing plant is believed to be the minimum size that could be economical. The 1-ton-a-day plant now under construction in New York would be larger if more fuel were available for it; and if it is to be converted from an experimental or pilot plant to an economically competitive unit, it will have to be expanded considerably, as is no doubt the intention. In the attempt to evaluate the waste-disposal problems of a future fuel-reprocessing plant, the anticipated requirements of a 6-ton-a-day plant provide a starting point, but it must be emphasized that these requirements are minimal and that the plant site should be chosen so that considerable expansion will be possible.

The writer will not attempt to describe the wastes or the waste-disposal problems of other industries, such as petroleum refining, steel, or paper, because each involves special considerations. Much of the following discussion would be applicable to such waste-disposal problems if the proper changes were made in volume and composition. Harrington (1962), in his analysis of the water required for a 6-ton-a-day nuclear-fuel reprocessing plant, predicts a minimum rate of production of low-level waste of 85,000 gal per day (gpd), but he indicates that this volume might reach 250,000–500,000 gpd, depending on the

waste-management techniques adopted within the plant. In practice, the volume will depend partly on the processes used and partly on the care exercised in keeping the volume of low-level wastes to a minimum.

The low-level waste comes from three general sources. One is the condensate from the evaporator used to reduce the volume of high-level waste that must be aged in tanks before final treatment and disposal. This condensate is estimated to be about 60,000 gpd; after recovery of the acid there will be water very low in dissolved solids, but containing small but significant quantities of the fission products and a large proportion of the tritium from the fuel. The second source of low-level waste is contaminated water, similar in gross chemical composition to the water supply of the plant, but containing widely varied quantities of fission products. This type of waste comes from many sources, including contaminated cooling and process water. The third type of low-level waste may be called "chemical," for these solutions contain significant quantities of acids, bases, detergents, complexing agents, or organic compounds; they differ significantly from contaminated water. Typical sources of such wastes are the final stages of the separations process and decontamination operations. Typical present-day low-level wastes are shown in Table I, but Bruce (1960), Kenny (1960), and Campbell et al. (1963) provide more complete discussions of the volumes and compositions of the several types of low-, medium-, and high-level wastes.

TREATMENT

In theory, it might be possible to treat all of the low-level wastes and recirculate them into the plant. To some extent this will be done, depending partly on whether the plant has an abundant supply of water of good quality, and partly on the ease of waste disposal. In practice, complete recycling is impractical and some low-level waste will have to be treated and discharged to the environment. Whatever the volume, it certainly will be too large for more than very brief storage.

Three methods of treatment are available to reduce the level of activity in the waste before discharge. The first is *chemical precipitation*, in which a flocculent rather than a granular precipitate is formed. The possible advantage is that the floc, particularly if aided by proper additives, will carry down active material which otherwise might remain in solution or in suspension. The disadvantage is that the floc is hard to separate from the supernatant, and is consequently bulky. Decontamination factors vary greatly with the circumstances, but may range from 2 to 100. Several small installations are using such relatively simple treatment to reduce the activity of the waste to a low enough level that it may be discharged safely into a river or a sewer; however, for a large reprocessing plant, further treatment almost certainly would be required.

Chemical treatment, particularly if it removed virtually all suspended solids, could rather easily be followed by a second method of treatment, *ion exchange,* resulting in additional decontamination factors of up to 1,000 or more, depending greatly on the circumstances. The activity in the final effluent after careful multistage treatment can be brought down to almost any desired level, but to achieve high factors of decontamination is expensive, and in this regard the problem is one of economics. In practice, very substantial but still incomplete decontamination is feasible, and the low-level waste discharged from the plant will carry a small proportion of the radioactive materials separated from the fuel.

The third method of treatment, *evaporation,* can be used to accomplish in one operation, but generally at greater expense, what chemical treatment and ion exchange accomplish in two. At present, evaporation of high-, medium-, or low-level waste is used more commonly for reducing the volumes of liquid waste that must be stored or further treated for disposal than as a method of converting the waste into a form suitable for ultimate disposal.

A 6-ton-a-day plant processing fuel with a burn-up of 10,000 megawatt days per ton (Mwd/ton) would produce daily 750 curies of tritium, which could not be removed economically from the low-level waste and would have to be discharged into the environment. Blomeke (1964) suggests several possible methods for disposing of the tritium, but points out that all of these methods have potentially serious drawbacks.

In summary, in normal operation the reprocess-

TABLE I. STABLE CHEMICAL AND RADIOACTIVE COMPOSITION OF SELECTED PRESENT-DAY LOW-LEVEL WASTE STREAMS

Constituent	Concentration (mg/l)		
	ORNL[1]	NRTS[2]	HAPO[3]
Calcium	30	100	
Sodium	30	150	2
Magnesium	10	30	
Bicarbonate	80	170	
Nitrate	26	10	2
Sulfate	12	550	
Ammonia	—	—	150
Organic	—	—	150

Nuclide	Concentration (µc/ml)			
	ORNL[1]	NRTS ICPP[2]	NRTS MTR[4]	HAPO[3]
3-H	—	8×10^{-4}	4×10^{-4}	—
89–90Sr	4×10^{-5}	3×10^{-6}	8×10^{-6}	4×10^{-3}
137Cs	2×10^{-5}	—	9×10^{-6}	2×10^{-2}
131I	—	3×10^{-5}	1×10^{-4}	3×10^{-4}
106Ru–Rh	4×10^{-6}	4×10^{-6}	2×10^{-5}	8×10^{-3}
144Ce	—	6×10^{-6}	1×10^{-4}	8×10^{-3}
6Co	6×10^{-5}	—	3×10^{-5}	—
51Cr	—	—	2×10^{-4}	—
115Cd	—	—	8×10^{-5}	—
95Zr–Nb	1×10^{-6}	—	5×10^{-5}	3×10^{-2}

[1] ORNL, large laboratory complex.
[2] NRTS–ICPP, fuel-reprocessing plant.
[3] HAPO, condensate from high-level waste-storage tanks.
[4] NRTS–MTR, test reactor.

ing plant will discharge into the environment on the order of 100,000–500,000 gpd of low-level waste from which most, but never all, of the fission-product contaminants have been removed, and which contains hundreds or perhaps thousands of curies of tritium.

During the last few years there has been a variety of accidents in chemical-reprocessing plants as a result of criticality incidents, chemical explosions, broken pipes, leaking tanks, and other mechanical or human failures. None of these accidents directly overcontaminated the low-level waste stream, although this is possible, but the cleanup after several of them added considerable activity to the low-level waste in a chemical form not easily removed because of the cleaning compounds used. The low-level waste commonly is held briefly in an equalization basin before treatment, and several of the plants have emergency retention basins for potentially difficult batches of waste. However, even a minor accident can disrupt temporarily the normal operation of the low-level treatment plant and result in the discharge of waste which has not been decontaminated to the usual standard. A major accident could seriously overload the low-level-waste disposal system.

PRESENT PRACTICES FOR DISPOSAL

Oak Ridge National Laboratory now is producing about 500,000 gpd of low-level waste which is treated by a lime-soda process for the removal of strontium, and with clay which absorbs much of the cesium and is carried down with the carbonate floc. About 80 percent of the strontium, the critical nuclide, is removed. The total cost is about 40 cents per 1,000 gal. The effluent from the plant is discharged into the Clinch River, where within a few miles it is diluted to levels which approximate those caused by fallout and the natural radioactive materials in the water. Tests have been made of a different method of chemical treatment followed by ion exchange, which in a pilot plant removed more than 99 percent of the strontium and in operation would cost about 1 dollar per 1,000 gal.

At Hanford, Washington, low-level wastes from chemical reprocessing have been discharged for years into the gravel, sand, and sandy clay of glacial and lacustrine origin several miles from the Columbia River. Despite the complex geology and hydrology of the site, detailed investigations have shown that it takes the water in these wastes several years to reach the river, and that all the fission products except the tritium take an even longer time because of adsorption. In effect, this shallow ground disposal provides long enough detention for significant decay of nearly all the fission products except tritium, and thus can be considered an additional treatment for decontamination of the waste. Shallow disposal under very different geologic conditions is practiced at the National Reactor Testing Station, Idaho, and at the Savannah River Plant, South Carolina.

Valuable as this method may be, particularly for reducing peak discharges after an accident, it is limited geologically to areas underlain by deep, extensive deposits of relatively permeable materials which normally are of considerable value as sources of groundwater. The slow travel underground over considerable distances which is required to provide significant retention time is far more likely to be possible in arid or semi-arid areas, and is uncommon in the United States east of the 100th meridian (Richardson, 1962) except locally, as in the deep sedimentary deposits of the Atlantic Coastal Plain. Particularly because of the large quantities of tritium which would be released by a major fuel-reprocessing plant, shallow ground disposal of the low-level waste is likely to be advantageous in only a few unusual, isolated areas, for in most localities it would seriously contaminate valuable groundwater resources.

At the Windscale works in England, low-level waste is discharged into the sea through a pipeline which extends a considerable distance offshore. Extensive studies of the fish, ocean bottom, beach sand, and edible seaweed in the area have shown that the persons liable to the greatest exposure as the result of the discharges are those who eat a special type of bread made from the seaweed. Thus, a critical pathway to a critical group has been defined, and subsequent work has established the relation between the number of curies of each of the more important nuclides discharged into the sea and the resulting exposure to individuals in the critical group. This relation has been used to establish the total number of curies of each nuclide that may be discharged. Such an approach has the advantage of concentrating attention on a small segment of the environment and of the population, thus eliminating the need for extensive studies. The method must be supplemented, however, by sufficient additional data to give some measure of the average exposure to the general public living in the area and to the population at large, because for these groups smaller permissible maximum exposures may be required.

MAXIMUM PERMISSIBLE EXPOSURES AS RELATED TO LOW-LEVEL-WASTE DISPOSAL

The problem of determining maximum permissible exposures to radiation is complex and controversial, but unavoidable. All of the national and international bodies which have been charged with establishing safe limits have agreed that exposure to radiation should be kept to a minimum. This admonition is not sufficient, however, to govern the activities of persons working in branches of the nuclear industry where some exposure is unavoidable; therefore, maximum permissible occupational exposures have been worked out and almost universally adopted for persons who are exposed to radiation in the course of their employment. These limits, insofar as possible, do not allow appreciable risk to the individual or permit hazards more severe than those commonly accepted in other industries. On the basis of these maximum permissible occupational exposures, maximum permissible concentrations (MPC's) of the radioactive nuclides in air and water have been derived for people employed in the nuclear industry.

The values adopted for the individual radionuclides are not final, but are revised periodically as more data become available. The revisions may increase or decrease the maximum permissible concentrations. More importantly, the MPC values are set by consideration of the danger of somatic damage to the individual, not on the basis of the potential genetic hazard to future generations. Although the possibility of genetic damage may be exaggerated greatly in the public mind, the MPC's of some radionuclides, including tritium, may have to be reduced greatly when more is learned about the problem of genetic damage. Any increase in MPC's will ease the problem of waste disposal, particularly low-level-waste disposal, and any decrease will make the disposal problem more difficult. Although it is hoped that the trend will be to increase the MPC values, provision must be made in planning and plant location for the more stringent requirements which would result from decreases in the MPC values.

There is general agreement that limits lower than the occupational MPC's should be applied to special groups living near or affected by nuclear industry, but not employed in it, and for the general public. The groups, if any, into which the public should be divided and the amount of reduction of the maximum permissible occupational exposures have not been agreed upon, and involve questions beyond the scope of this review. The question of nonoccupational exposure, however, is related definitely to the problem of low-level-waste disposal. For example, in fixing the maximum permissible exposure to the critical group affected by the contamination of seaweed by the releases from Windscale, maximum permissible occupational exposures were reduced by a factor

of 10, as had been recommended for small nonoccupational groups at the time the study was carried out (Dunster, *et al.*, 1964). Since then the suggestion has been made, but not adopted universally, that these small groups should be treated like the public at large, and that for all of them the maximum permissible occupational exposure should be reduced by a factor of 30 or 100, depending on the critical body organ involved. The low-level waste discharged from the Windscale works—at the time of the study (1953–1962)—was well within the calculated and observed capacity of the sea to dilute and disperse the activity. However, if plans to expand the plant substantially are carried through, and if the maximum permissible exposures to the critical group are reduced, it is possible that the low-level waste will have to be decontaminated more thoroughly prior to discharge. Any fuel-reprocessing plant which is discharging low-level waste into the environment must be able to adjust to a reduction in the concentrations or total amounts of activity which it may discharge coupled with a need to increase the size and hence the rate of waste production of the plant.

One curie of tritium need be diluted in only 9,000 gal of water to reduce the concentration to the present occupational MPC (Internat. Comm. on Radiological Protection, 1959). However, if it is decided that the exposure to the public at large should be no more than 1 percent of the occupational maximum permissible exposure, then each curie of tritium discharged would have to be diluted in 900,000 gal, and the 750 curies discharged daily by a 6-ton-a-day plant would require 675 million gal of water for dilution. A 30-ton-a-day plant processing fuel with 20,000 Mwd/ton burn-up would produce tritium requiring more than 6 billion gpd of water for dilution. Some additional dilution also would be required for the other radioactive contaminants in the low-level waste, but these requirements are so speculative that no quantitative evaluation is possible. In general, however, if the low-level wastes are not diluted greatly, very thorough decontamination will be required before discharge. Such decontamination may be difficult and expensive to achieve even in routine operation, and very difficult in the event of even a relatively minor accident at the plant.

Moreover, the maximum permissible exposures for small critical groups of people or for the general public never were intended to be used as indicators of safe levels for deliberate routine exposure, a point made repeatedly by all of the regulatory and advisory groups which established these limits. Consequently, no major nuclear installation today is deliberately contaminating its environment up to the permissible limit, and all apply self-imposed limitations which restrict still further the total quantities or concentrations of activity discharged. Also, no one source, such as the low-level liquid waste, should deliberately be allowed to contribute all of the exposure permitted to the general public, because some allowance must be made for other sources of exposure.

Brookhaven National Laboratory, Long Island, New York, is in an area of rapidly expanding population. The laboratory has formal permission to discharge a total of 1.5 curies a year of gross activity to its sewage-plant filter beds, which drain into the Peconic River. However, it has limited the discharge to the filters to 20 percent of this amount, and has set an informal limit of about 0.1 curie for the total annual discharge to the river proper. The Oak Ridge National Laboratory, during the late 1950's, was contaminating the Clinch River locally up to an average of about 30 percent of the MPC then applicable. Although this contamination was mainly the result of temporary conditions carried over from wartime operations, and the level was decreasing gradually, the laboratory went to considerable expense, including the construction of the Process Waste Treatment Plant, to reduce the contamination as rapidly as possible. Numerous similar examples could be cited. The basic reason for this universally conservative attitude is the recommendation made by all advisory and regulatory bodies that exposure to radiation be kept to a minimum, and that the maximum permissible exposures are limits which it would be unwise to exceed, not working levels for routine operation. Carlbom (1963) stated:

The difficulties in applying the ICRP[3] recommendations to waste-disposal problems lie partly in the

[3] International Commission on Radiological Protection.

calculation of doses received from active waste products in the environment, and partly in deciding which is the acceptable margin between the maximum permissible exposure and the maximum acceptable risk. This second problem always comes up because the ICRP has given a general recommendation to keep all exposures as low as possible in addition to the recommended maximum permissible exposures. What is badly needed is a strict set of rules for active waste disposal stating maximum *permitted,* rather than permissive exposures and standardized calculation rules for doses from environmental activity.

A commercial fuel-reprocessing plant, therefore, will not operate under conditions such that its low-level waste is diluted only to 1 percent of the occupational MPC, but will require some additional factor of safety. The 6-ton-a-day plant would require more, and perhaps substantially more, than 675 million gpd of water to dilute the released tritium, and the 30-ton-a-day plant, processing fuel with a higher burn-up, would require more than 6 billion gpd.

The flow of the Clinch River at Oak Ridge averages about 3 billion gpd; the Connecticut River at its mouth has an average flow of 12 billion gpd; and the Ohio River below Pittsburgh has an average flow of 20 billion gpd. It is obvious that only the larger rivers of the United States could serve to dilute routinely, on a continuing basis, the low-level waste from a major fuel-reprocessing plant, and then only if the plant were the only installation contributing radioactive contaminants to the environment.

If the reprocessing plant is to discharge waste into the river, there is a strong implication, but no requirement, that the plant will be near the river. The possibility that the river will be contaminated directly in the event of a major accident at the plant or the tanks used for temporary storage of the high-level waste will depend on the local circumstances, but it is a potential hazard.

The discharge of the low-level wastes from a major fuel-reprocessing plant, whether into a river, a lake, or an ocean, or into shallow permeable formations, involves an element of risk, both in the routine operation of the plant and in the event of a major accident.

DISPOSAL INTO DEEP PERMEABLE FORMATIONS

Disposal into deep permeable formations has been suggested (Moore, 1959) for medium- and high-level wastes. However, the underground disposal of large quantities of highly concentrated radioactive fluids would require sufficiently detailed knowledge of subsurface conditions to make possible demonstrably reliable, very long-range predictions of the waste movement. The required information could be obtained only by a prohibitively expensive program of test drilling, and even then it might not be possible to secure approval. However, in the case of low-level wastes it is necessary only to show that deep underground disposal would provide a factor of safety measurably greater than dilution in a large body of surface water, which in general would be the only alternative.

The great value of the basin reports in this book is that they outline and describe specific parts of six structural or sedimentary basins in the United States where conditions appear to be particularly favorable for the deep underground disposal of liquid waste, as well as for other types of disposal operations. Because the basins have been chosen partly for their simplicity of structure and hydrology, and for the obvious high degree of containment that would be provided, a minimum of exploratory work would be required to prove that these areas could be used safely for the disposal of low-level waste. The principal additional work required would be the drilling of wells in the basins to determine the rate at which liquid could be injected into the proposed disposal formation, because quantitative information on the porosity of the disposal formation is almost nonexistent. The same wells, although much less expensive than true test wells, generally would provide the additional required information about the overlying formations, and the total cost of site exploration and selection would be negligible in comparison to that required for high-level waste. Deep underground disposal would require very small additional operating cost, because the treatment used to decontaminate the low-level waste includes the removal of suspended solids, and the plant effluent in most cases could be pumped directly down the disposal well or wells. The wells would require maintenance and occasional replacement, but these costs probably would not be significant. Such simple installation and operation of a deep underground liquid-waste disposal system will be possible only in areas

which, like those described in this volume, have been selected carefully by experienced professional geologists familiar with the areas. The elimination of unfavorable areas required far more effort than is evident from reading the reports.

The advantages to be gained by the disposal of low-level waste into deep permeable formations, where conditions are favorable, are fairly obvious. First, the widespread low-level contamination of a major body of surface water can be avoided. This advantage cannot be measured quantitatively because the possible hazards of such contamination are still controversial, but some advantage would be gained. Second, the potential consequences of a major accident at the processing plant probably would be less serious, or, phrased differently, provision for the containment of a major accident could be provided at less expense. This possible advantage, however, is also dependent on other factors, but the basic problem would be simplified insofar as underground disposal would permit locating the plant at a distance from, rather than adjacent to, a major body of water.

DISPOSAL OF MEDIUM-LEVEL WASTES

A 6-ton-a-day plant will produce about 6,000 gpd of medium-level waste from fuel decladding and some additional medium-level waste from other operations, including the decontamination of the low-level wastes. The medium-level wastes (Table II) are typically high in dissolved solids, but evaporation can be used to reduce the volume of most of them by a factor of 10 or more. The 1,000–2,000 gpd of waste concentrates produced

TABLE II. STABLE AND RADIOACTIVE COMPOSITIONS OF INTERMEDIATE-LEVEL DECLADDING WASTES

Zirflex		Sulfex	
Constituent	Concentration	Constituent	Concentration
$ZrFe^{-2}$, M	0.55	H_2SO_4, M	2.2
NH_4^+, M	1.72	Stainless steel	45 g/l
Sn^{+4}, M	0.01	Uranium	0.03 g/l
F^-, M	0.55	FP, $\mu c/cc$	~3,000
NO_3^-, M	0.07	^{60}Co c/gal	0.5
FP, $\mu c/cc$	~6,000	Gal/ton fuel	1,340
Gal/ton fuel	1,700		

could be stored permanently in tanks, but this generally is not regarded as a desirable method for their ultimate disposal. Chemical treatment could reduce the volume still further and the resulting sludges could be immobilized in concrete or tar and buried on land or disposed of at sea, but in general neither method is believed to be entirely satisfactory.

At Hanford and Oak Ridge, medium-level wastes of this general type have been disposed of directly into the ground through cribs or seepage pits; adsorption on the soil or clay was relied on to retain the radioactive components. Both installations, independently, have become dissatisfied with this type of disposal within the last few years, although in each area groundwater sampling showed that no demonstrable hazard was being created and that all of the more hazardous nuclides were being retained underground near the point of release. The dissatisfaction arose because of the impossibility of proving positively that long-continued disposal will not create a hazard eventually, for very large inventories of such nuclides as strontium-90 were being built up in the ground. The similar conclusions reached at the two installations are more significant because the geologic and hydrologic conditions at the two sites are very dissimilar. Therefore, it appears unlikely that direct disposal of medium-level waste into the soil at shallow depth ever will be used for large-scale routine operations, although the method has great value in emergencies.

Several years of experimentation at Oak Ridge have culminated in the apparently successful disposal of considerable volumes of simulated and some actual medium-level waste by hydraulic fracturing in shale. The Oak Ridge plant could dispose of as much as 10,000 gpd of liquid waste and sludge. The geologic requirements, as now understood, are 300 ft or more of shale at a depth of less than 3,000 ft, overlain by a rock cover sufficiently impermeable to isolate the disposal formation from the surface. Structurally, the shale preferably should be undeformed and horizontal, although successful tests have been made where the dip is 20° or more. The critical requirement is that the horizontal stresses in the shale and cover rock must not be significantly less than the vertical stress, or, in geologic terms, that the

area must not be one of recent normal faulting. Jointing does not appear to be a major factor at Oak Ridge.

What appears to be suitable shale is present as part of the rock cover overlying each of the permeable formations proposed in the basin reports in this book for the disposal of waste fluids. In general, because shale is the most common of all sedimentary deposits, a shale cover would be expected at almost any site that is suitable for the deep disposal of low-level wastes into a permeable formation. The requirements for disposal by fracturing are not as exacting, because the waste is injected into an impermeable rock where it is isolated from the groundwater, and is mixed with cement while it is being injected so that the slurry hardens soon after it is in place; the possibility of future migration is therefore very remote. No shale can be assumed to be suitable for disposal by hydraulic fracturing without having been tested in the field, but relatively simple preliminary tests using water have been developed. With few possible exceptions, any area suitable for the deep disposal of low-level wastes into permeable formations also may be suitable for disposal of medium-level wastes by hydraulic fracturing at rates as high as 20,000 gpd.

DISPOSAL OF HIGH-LEVEL WASTES

A fuel-reprocessing plant will produce high-level waste which can be reduced in volume by evaporation to about 100 gal for each ton of fuel reprocessed. In general the volume will be reduced to the most concentrated solution which can be stored in tanks without making the problem of heat removal too difficult. The condensate

TABLE III. COMPOSITION OF PUREX ACID AND NEUTRALIZED HIGH-LEVEL WASTE[1]

Component	Concentration	
	Acid	Neutralized
H^+, M	3.7	—
Na^+, M	0.4	0.78
Fe^{+3}, M	0.2	0.03
Al^{+3}, M	0.1	0.02
NO_3^- and NO_2, M	5.0	0.83
OH^-, M		0.03
$SO_4^=$, M	0.2	0.03
$SiO_2 \times H_2O$, M	~0.01	~0.002
Total fission products, M	~0.2	~0.03
Total activity	~10^3–10^4 curies/gal	~10^3–10^4 curies/gal
Volume (gal/ton fuel)	100	600

[1] After J. O. Blomeke. unpublished data.

from this volume reduction is the tritium-rich, low-level waste which contributes so significantly to the problem of low-level-waste disposal.

After most of the short-half-lived nuclides have decayed, the concentrated high-level waste will be pumped from the temporary-storage tanks and converted to a solid by one of the several processes now in the late stages of development. The solidified waste will have to be stored under conditions of maximum security. The method now favored is storage in mined cavities in salt, preferably at depths of less than 1,200 ft. Suitable salt beds are present at or near several of the locations suggested as suitable for the disposal of fluid wastes in deep permeable formations. Second best, but still acceptable, would be storage in mined cavities in rock above the water table or, in the absence of suitable rock, in thick-walled structures built on the surface. Because of their relatively small volume, the high-level solid wastes could be shipped from the reprocessing plant for ultimate disposal at some other site, although shipping would be expensive. The siting requirements for high-level-waste disposal therefore are not critical in the selection of a site for a fuel-reprocessing plant.

Conclusions

The basin reports in this book describe several areas in which it probably would be possible to dispose of substantial volumes of clear liquid waste into a deep permeable formation with a high degree of assurance that the hazardous constituents would not migrate far laterally or reach the surface for a very long time. A relatively inexpensive drilling program could determine the potential for such disposal at any one of the sites. The reports, therefore, have considerable potential value as guides for the disposal of industrial wastes, although the special problems of radioactive-waste disposal are emphasized in this paper.

In carefully selected areas, where disposal of waste into deep permeable formations can be proved safe and feasible most easily, it holds great promise for virtually eliminating the complex and controversial problems which otherwise would be raised by the need to discharge even very low-level radioactive waste into the surface environment. Because the sites where the waste

can be disposed of underground do not need to be adjacent to a major river, the hazards from a serious accident at the plant are lessened. These arguments suggest that a major factor in the selection of the sites for the relatively few but very large fuel-reprocessing plants of the future should be the suitability of the sites for underground disposal of the low-level wastes. Consideration will have to be given to the opportunities for disposal of the other types of waste, but if the geology is suitable for deep underground disposal of low-level waste, it probably also will be suitable for the disposal of medium-level wastes into shale by hydraulic fracturing.

Although high-level-waste disposal will be more complex and expensive, the siting requirements for the ultimate disposal of the solidified high-level waste are not particularly critical. The selection of a site for the deep underground disposal of low-level waste which also has the salt beds needed for the most promising method for ultimate disposal of the high-level solids is desirable, but alternative methods for disposal of the high-level solids can be utilized. The alternative methods for disposal of the low-level fluid wastes appear to be appreciably less desirable, and therefore low-level-waste disposal is the critical factor in site selection.

Alternative viewpoints lead to the same conclusion. The preceding argument is that a fuel-reprocessing plant will produce several types of waste, which differ so significantly in volume, composition, and level of activity that no one method of disposal can be used advantageously to dispose of all of them; consequently, the site for a fuel-reprocessing plant should be chosen so that several disposal methods can be used, each for the type of waste for which it is best adapted.

The subject also may be approached by attempting to answer the question, "What are the limitations and the potentials of each of the principal methods of ultimate waste disposal?"

With considerable effort and expense, it probably would be possible to segregate all but insignificant quantities of the radioactive materials from the medium- and low-level wastes and store them either as liquid or as sludge in tanks, or as solids in salt, in mined cavities in rock above the water table, or in vaults built on or near the land surface. Tritium, and the much larger quantities of radioactive krypton-85, probably would have to be discharged into the atmosphere, although perhaps these, too, could be separated and stored. Problems in site selection, under these circumstances, would be less dependent on the local geology, but engineering difficulties and economic considerations make this approach impractical.

Hydraulic fracturing eventually may prove adequate for the disposal of even high-level waste. Fracturing in sandstone of moderate porosity but low permeability also may be a means by which to dispose of much or all of the low-level wastes. The potential of this method, therefore, is not necessarily confined to disposal of the medium-level wastes, although at this early stage of investigation this appears to be the job for which it is best suited.

As far back as 1957, the first report of the Committee on Waste Disposal of the Division of Earth Sciences of the National Academy of Sciences (Hess, 1957) stated:

Disposal of waste in porous beds interstratified with impermeable beds in a synclinal structure is a possibility for the more distant future. This is of particular interest for disposal of the large volumes of waste to be expected in the future.

At that time little distinction was made between high-, medium-, and low-level wastes. The API subcommittee (Moore, 1959) concluded that high-level waste could be disposed of into deep permeable formations. However, both they and the committee of the Division of Earth Sciences emphasized the need for both general studies of such topics as ion exchange and heat dissipation and specific, detailed geologic studies of any proposed disposal site. Enough now is known about heat dissipation and ion exchange to make possible satisfactory working estimates as a guide to deep-well disposal of medium- or high-level radioactive waste.

Although the detailed geologic studies required for high-level-waste disposal into deep permeable formations were described in a preceding section as "prohibitively expensive," this is only part of the problem. The root of the problem is the objections which are certain to be raised by the public and by many hydrologists because of what they will regard as the uncertainty of the safety of the operation. The public will see it mainly as a penny-saving operation likely to poison the groundwater on a grand scale; the average hydrologist, familiar with problems of widespread groundwater contamination by seawater, detergents, and such organic compounds as phenol or leaded gasoline, may question the very large margins of safety resulting from the adsorption on rock surfaces and clay minerals of the radioactive fission products. Further proof of the safety of such disposal will be required before extensive drilling and testing programs are warranted.

However, a start can be made by disposal of low-level wastes at or near MPC values, which after several years well may demonstrate that the method can be both safe and practical. Then the level of activity in the wastes disposed of deep underground could be increased, and substantial reductions in the amount and cost of the pretreatment required would result. Disposal of radioactive wastes into deep permeable formations is now practicable only for low-level wastes, but in geologically favorable areas it holds great potential, not only for disposal of certain medium- and high-level wastes, but perhaps also for disposal of such gaseous wastes as krypton-85, for which no good alternative method of disposal has been suggested.

The writer believes that ample justification for emphasis on the presence of deep permeable formations at the site of any fuel-reprocessing plant can be found in the known unique value of such formations for low-level-waste disposal. Time and experience may show them to be suitable for disposal of higher level wastes, but this possibility, although well worthy of study, is not as yet an argument to present to governmental or industrial administrators who are concerned with the selection of a site for a fuel-reprocessing plant.

In the early months of 1964 it was proved that large nuclear-power plants could be built in most areas to produce electricity at a cost competitive with that of electricity generated from fossil fuels. There is no immediate need for additional fuel-reprocessing plants, but the need may come much sooner than expected; the problem of site selection is so complex and vital that the sites for the future plants should be selected and tested before they are needed, not hurriedly after the need has arisen. Knowledge that reprocessing-plant sites are available where the waste-disposal problem in all its complex aspects can be managed safely would provide additional assurance to companies considering building nuclear-power plants, and to the general public, who are unquestionably concerned over the safety of our expanding nuclear-power economy.

REFERENCES

Blomeke, J. O., 1964, Management of fission product tritium in fuel processing wastes: Oak Ridge Natl. Lab. TM-851.

Bruce, F. R., 1960, The origin and nature of the radioactive wastes in the United States atomic energy program, *in* Disposal of radioactive wastes, Internat. radioactive waste disposal conf., Monaco, 1959: Vienna, Internat. Atomic Energy Agency.

Campbell, B. C., *et al.*, 1963, Current practice in the management of high-level radioactive wastes in the United States of America, *in* Treatment and storage of high-level radioactive wastes, Internat. radioactive waste disposal conf., Vienna, 1962: Vienna, Internat. Atomic Energy Agency, p. 23–40.

Carlbom, L., 1963, Site selection criteria in Swedish practice, *in* Siting of reactors and nuclear research centers, Internat. radioactive waste disposal conf., Bombay, India: Vienna, Internat. Atomic Energy Agency, p. 483.

Dunster, H. J., *et al.*, 1964, Environmental monitoring associated with the discharge of low activity radioactive waste from Windscale Works to the Irish Sea: Health Physics, v. 10, p. 353–362.

Harrington, F. E., 1962, Water requirements for a radiochemical reprocessing plant: Oak Ridge Natl. Lab. TM-244.

Hess, H. H., chm., 1957, The disposal of radioactive waste on land: Rept., Comm. on Waste Disposal, Div. Earth Sci., Natl. Acad. Sci.–Natl. Research Council Pub. 519.

International Commission on Radiological Protection, 1959, Recommendations and report of Committee II: London, Pergamon Press.

Kenny, A. W., 1960, Origin, nature, disposal and control of the radioactive wastes arising from the use of radioisotopes, *in* Disposal of radioactive wastes, Internat. radioactive waste disposal conf., Monaco, 1959: Vienna, Internat. Atomic Energy Agency, p. 64–88.

Moore, T. V., chm., 1959, Problems of the disposal of radioactive wastes into deep wells: Rept., Subcomm. on Disposal of Radioactive Waste of the Am. Petroleum Institute, 86th Congress of U.S., 1st Sess., Joint Comm. on Atomic Energy, v. 3, p. 2028–2045.

Richardson, R. M., 1962, Significance of climate in relation to the disposal of radioactive waste at shallow depth below ground: Saclay, Internat. Colloquium on Retention and Migration of Radioactive Ions in Soils, p. 207–211.

FLUID MECHANICS OF DEEP-WELL DISPOSALS[1]

A. F. VAN EVERDINGEN[2]

Dallas, Texas 75206

ABSTRACT

The fundamental law which governs the flow of slightly compressible fluids in permeable formations has been used to compute three unit functions useful in well or reservoir analysis. These unit functions give quantitative information on (1) the change of pressure in the well or formation as a result of unit rate of injection during a period of time, (2) the amount of fluid which can be disposed of per unit pressure increase in a given time, and (3) the effect of an enlarged borehole on the injection pressure. Numerical data on the first two functions have been published previously (van Everdingen and Hurst, 1949). The data for the function giving the effect of an enlarged borehole are presented for the first time.

Accurate prediction of pressures and pressure changes is now possible provided sufficient information is available on the physical characteristics of the formation, the formation fluids, and the injected fluids. The numerical values of these characteristics can vary considerably. To simplify computations, conversion factors are used so that the solutions given here can be used to solve most of the problems irrespective of the numerical values of the characteristics encountered.

INTRODUCTION

In April of 1965, Don L. Warner, of the U. S. Department of Health, Education and Welfare, published a report entitled, "Deep Well Injection of Liquid Waste, A Review of Existing Knowledge and An Evaluation of Research Needs." The report contains information on practically every facet of liquid-waste injection, collected from a wide variety of sources as shown by a list of 147 references. The writer hopes that this paper will contribute to a better understanding of the pressure increases caused by the injection of fluids into porous strata by (a) presenting in a more usable form information already available in the literature and (b) improving the understanding of the phenomena observed during the operations.

FLUID DISPOSAL—AN OUTLINE

The following discussions and formulations concern fluids of uniform density, commonly referred to as "Newtonian fluids," whose viscosity is a function of temperature and, to a much smaller degree, of pressure. Of chief concern is water in which all kinds of salts can be dissolved as long as they do not alter materially its characteristic properties. Suspensions and solutions whose constituents may react with either the formations or the fluids already present therein are not considered. The relations between rates of disposal and characteristics of the formations which will be given for Newtonian fluids may apply for suspensions for considerable periods of time; however, the fact that a porous formation can act as a sieve and eventually can become clogged will lead to unpredictable deviations from the relations given.

The porosity and thickness of formations determine the quantity of fluid which can be stored per unit volume. Permeability and thickness of the formation plus the viscosity of the fluid determine the force required per unit rate of disposal.

Of the other factors which affect the pressure-time relation—namely, size of the reservoir, radius of the well bore, and compressibility of fluids and formations—the influence of the size of the reservoir is probably the most difficult to grasp. Because the fluids to be disposed of are only slightly compressible (compressibilities of 5×10^{-5} to 10^{-4} per atmosphere are normal), it is obvious that only reservoirs of considerable extent can be used successfully.

In the process of underground disposal, the fluids present in the formation are displaced by a nearly equal volume of disposable liquids. Because the volumes are so nearly equal, a knowledge of the fluid content per unit volume

[1] Manuscript received, October 27, 1966; revised, February 1968.

[2] Vice President, DeGolyer and MacNaughton.

of reservoir rock gives a first approximation of the volume which will be occupied by the injected fluid. The efficiency with which the injected fluid displaces the fluid already present increases with homogeneity of the formation and to some extent with the absolute permeability of the formation, just as the saturation of an oil-bearing formation increases with increasing permeability. The presence of small cracks and other variations in permeability will cause the front of the disposal liquids to advance irregularly. Therefore, disposal operations should be undertaken in reservoirs of considerable extent only after their characteristics over a wide area have been averaged to obtain meaningful figures.

The flow of such slightly compressible fluids obeys the same differential equation as, for example, the conduction of heat, which long has been studied. The equation states that the difference in volumes of fluids flowing in and out of an annulus between two hypothetical concentric rings around a well bore is equal to the expansion of fluids in the annulus. Most important is the linearity of the fundamental equation, which allows great freedom in using a solution. Once a solution is obtained it may be multiplied or divided by a constant or shifted in time to fit a variety of operating conditions. In short, the solutions may be superposed. It is not necessary to understand the manner in which the solutions were derived; however, the conditions under which they are valid should be clearly defined and understood, and adhered to strictly.

Standard Solutions
(Unit Functions)

Reservoirs differ in many respects. The permeability may be as low as 1 md or as high as several darcys; the thickness may range from a few feet to several hundred feet; the porosity may range from a few percent, as in Ellenburger Limestone reservoirs, to as much as 30 percent, as in Woodbine Sand reservoirs; and the viscosity of the fluid may be about 1 cp (centipoise) in shallow formations at low reservoir temperature or a few tenths of a centipoise in formations at 10,000 ft (3,048 m) having a temperature of 220°F (104°C).

Clearly, solutions are needed which can be made to fit any of a variety of reservoir conditions and which, in addition, can be used to reflect the variations in rates during disposal operations.

If t is the time, q_t the rate, and Q_t the volume, all in "dimensionless units," then their numerical values can be found by use of the following set of conversion factors, where T is the time in seconds, q_T the production (injection) rate in cubic centimeters per second per centimeter of formation, and Q_T the volume of fluid in cubic centimeters.

In the following formulae the permeability in darcys is denoted by k, the viscosity (at reservoir conditions) in centipoises by μ, the porosity as a fraction by ψ, the compressibility in vol/vol/atm by c, the well radius in centimeters squared by r_w^2, and the thickness of the formation in centimeters by h.

Time conversion: $\quad t = kT/(\mu\psi cr_w^2)$

Rate conversion: $\quad q_t = q_T\mu/(2\pi kh)$

Volume conversion: $\quad Q_t = Q_T/(2\pi\psi chr_w^2)$

Because it is necessary to determine the effect of variations and even interruptions in the rate of fluid disposal, the following unit functions[3] were defined and computed.

1. The P_t *function* gives the cumulative pressure change, at the well's radius, when from time zero onward unit rate of production has been taken from, or unit rate of fluid has been injected into, a formation of unit thickness. The numerical values of this function are given in Table I. The values are shown in Figure 1, where the pressure increase is plotted *versus* the log of the time. The pressure increase is linear for all times greater than 100 at a rate of $1.151 = 1/2 \ln 10$ atm per cycle. This linear increase is due to the fact that for $t > 100$ the P_t function can be represented by $-1/2 \text{ Ei}(-1/4t)$ and also by $(1/2 \ln t + 0.4045)$. For comparison, these two most-used approximations for the P_t function also are given in Table I.

2. The Q_t *function* gives the cumulative volume of fluid produced from or injected into a formation of unit thickness if from time zero onward the pressure against the face of the well bore was decreased (or increased) by 1 atm. The numerical values of this function are given in Table II.

3. The $\overline{P}_t$ *function* gives the pressure decrease in a well produced at unit rate whose radius has been considerably enlarged by remedial work. It is assumed that within the enlarged, effective radius the porosity of the formation is unaffected by the remedial work, the permeability is increased to infinity, and the compressibility of the fluids in-

[3] See Appendix.

TABLE I. P_t, CUMULATIVE PRESSURE CHANGE IN ATMOSPHERES AS A FUNCTION OF THE DIMENSIONLESS TIME, t
(For use of $-1/2$ Ei$(-1/4t)$ and $1/2 \ln t + 0.4045$, see notes.)

Time, t	P_t	$-1/2$ Ei$(-1/4t)$	Time, t	P_t	$-1/2$ Ei$(-1/4t)$	$1/2 \ln t + 0.4045$
0.010	0.1081	—	10.0	1.6554	1.5683	1.5558
0.015	0.1312	—	15.0	1.8323	1.7669	1.7585
0.020	0.1503	—	20.0	1.9615	1.9086	1.9024
0.030	0.1818	—	30.0	2.1481	2.1093	2.1051
0.040	0.2077	—	40.0	2.2831	2.2521	2.2489
0.060	0.2499	—	60.0	2.4762	2.4538	2.4517
0.080	0.2846	—	80.0	2.6148	2.5972	2.5955
0.100	0.3144	0.01246	100.0	2.7231	2.7084	2.7071
0.150	0.3753	0.03917	150.0	2.9204	2.9107	2.9098
0.200	0.4245	0.07321	200.0	3.0626	3.0543	3.0537
0.300	0.5028	0.1463	300.0	3.2627	3.2569	3.2564
0.400	0.5650	0.2161	400.0	3.4051	3.4006	3.4002
0.600	0.6628	0.3376	600.0	3.6064	3.6032	3.6030
0.800	0.7394	0.4378	800.0	3.7495	3.7470	3.7468
1.00	0.8030	0.5221	1,000.0	3.8606	3.8585	3.8584
1.50	0.9278	0.6873				
2.00	1.0235	0.8117				
3.00	1.1678	0.9947				
4.00	1.2765	1.1285				
6.00	1.4377	1.3210				
8.00	1.5573	1.4598				
10.00	1.6554	1.5683				

Note 1: From $t = 1,000$ onward the differences between the P_t values and the values of $-1/2$ Ei$(-1/4t)$ and $1/2 \ln t + 0.4045$ are so small as to be negligible. Hence, from $t = 1,000$ onward, pressure drops can be computed most easily from the last formula, $1/2 \ln t + 0.4045$.

Note 2: For values of t smaller than 0.010, use $P_t = 2\sqrt{t}/\sqrt{\pi} - t/2 + t\sqrt{t}/2\sqrt{\pi}$.

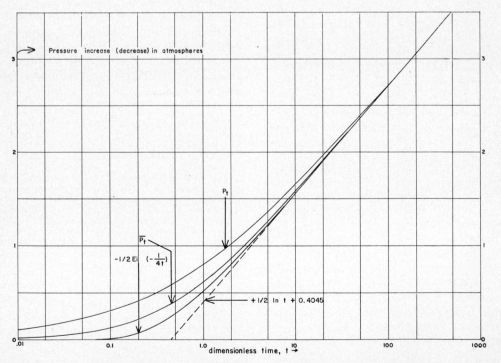

FIG. 1.—P_t curve represents pressure increase in a well when fluid is injected at unit rate from time zero on. $\overline{P}_t$ curve represents pressure increase when effective radius of well bore has been increased considerably by acidization or shooting. The curves for $-1/2$ Ei$(-1/4t)$ and $1/2 \ln t + 0.4045$ represent approximations for P_t valid for large times.

jected is the same as that of fluids present in the formation.

APPLICATIONS OF P_t AND Q_t FUNCTIONS

It is assumed that (1) the formation used for disposal is at a depth of 3,000 ft (914 m); (2) the formation fluids are under a pressure of 1,350 psia; (3) thickness of the permeable zone is 60 ft (18.3 m); (4) the zone used has an average permeability of 250 md and a porosity of 19 percent; (5) the fluid has a viscosity of 0.5 cp at reservoir temperature of 140°F (60°C); and (6) the compressibility of the fluid and of the formation both are estimated as 3×10^{-6}/lb, so that the total effective compressibility is 6×10^{-6}/lb or 0.9×10^{-4}/atm. Each well will be completed as a 6-in. (15.24-cm) hole open throughout the thickness of the permeable formation.

The question is asked whether 100,000 gal (378,540 l) a day can be disposed of, in one or more wells, without excessive pressure increase. If more than one well is required, how far apart should such wells be drilled, and what would be the effect of the distance between the disposal wells on their pressure history?

To solve these and similar problems, the rate of disposal, 100,000 gpd, is expressed in cubic centimeters per second:

$$100,000 \text{ gpd} = 100,000 \times 3,785/86,400$$
$$= 4,380 \text{ cc/sec} = q_T.$$

From the rate conversions shown, the dimensionless rate per unit thickness is derived:

$$q_t = \frac{0.5 \times 4,380}{2\pi \times 0.250 \times 60 \times 30.5} = 0.762$$

To determine the injection pressure to be expected after 1 day, 1 year, 2 years, 3 years, and 4 years, these times are converted into dimensionless units by the conversion factor for time using the formation, fluid, and well characteristics enumerated above. For these conditions, the dimensionless time is related to the time in seconds by the formula,

$$t = \frac{kT}{f\mu cr_w^2} = \frac{0.250\,T}{0.19 \times 0.5 \times 0.9 \times 10^{-4} \times 58} = 504\,T.$$

Thus the following values are obtained.

For 1 day $= 86,400$ sec, $t = 43.6 \times 10^6$.

For 1 yr $= 365.25$ days

$\qquad = 31,560,000$ sec, $t = 15,910 \times 10^6$.

For 2 yr $= 63,120,000$ sec, $t = 31,810 \times 10^6$.

For 3 yr $= 94,680,000$ sec, $t = 47,720 \times 10^6$.

For 4 yr $= 126,240,000$ sec, $t = 63,620 \times 10^6$.

For these large times (even 1 day makes $t > 1,000$), the formula used for the pressure increase is

$$P_t = 1/2 \ln t + 0.4045,$$

which gives $P_{1\text{ day}} = 1/2 \ln 43.6 \times 10^6 + 0.4045$ atm $= 9.20$ atm $= 135$ psi, so that the total pressure increase, ΔP, at the end of the day equals $0.762 \times 135 = 103$ psi. With continuation of the injection of 100,000 gpd, the increase in pressure at the end of 5 successive years was computed and is shown in the following table; at the end of each of 5 successive years, ΔP equals 0.762 times the P_t for that time.

If at the end of the first year the rate of injection were doubled, the superposition theorem states that the pressure-time relation resulting from this increase would be the same as for the first 100,000 gpd; the same figures appear, only shifted. Doubling the rate at the end of the third year to 400,000 gpd adds twice the pressure increase resulting from 100,000 gpd. The total increase (above the original pressure) is the sum of the individual figures.

Pressure Increase (lb) Due to Injection Rate of 100,000 gpd			Effect of Rate Increases On Pressure Increase		
Time (end of)	t	ΔP	Injection Rate	ΔP	
1 year	15.9×10^9	136	100,000	136	$=136$
2 years	31.8×10^9	140	200,000	$140+136$	$=276$
3 years	47.7×10^9	142	200,000	$142+140$	$=282$
4 years	63.6×10^9	144	400,000	$144+142+272$	$=558$
5 years	79.5×10^9	145	400,000	$145+144+280$	$=569$

For one of several reasons it may be desirable to limit the pressure increase caused by injection. If conditions permit, the injection could be interrupted for 1 year, during which time the increase would almost disappear, as shown in the following table. For the computation of the effect of such an interruption, the procedure followed is the same as used before. The interruption is considered to result from continuing the injection and at the same time producing 400,000 gpd, making the injection rate zero—a mathematical "trick" that allows use of the superposition theorem in order to obtain quantitative figures.

$$(200/14.7) \times 2\pi\psi chr_w^2 Q_t$$
$$= (200/14.7) \times 6.28 \times 0.19 \times 0.9 \times 10^{-4} \times 60 \times 30.5 \times 58 Q_t$$
$$= 155 Q_t.$$

Year	t	ΔP^1	Injection Rate	ΔP	
1	15.9×10^9	136	100,000	136	$=136$
2	31.8×10^9	140	200,000	$140+136$	$=276$
3	47.7×10^9	142	200,000	$142+140$	$=282$
4	63.6×10^9	144	400,000	$144+142+272$	$=558$
5	79.5×10^9	145	400,000	$145+144+280$	$=569$
6	95.4×10^9	146	$400,000-400,000$	$146+145+284-4\times136=$	31
7	111.3×10^9	147	$400,000-400,000$	$147+146+288-4\times140=$	21
8	127.2×10^9	148	$400,000-400,000$	$148+147+290-4\times142=$	17
9	143.2×10^9	148	$400,000-400,000$	$148+148+292-4\times144=$	12
10	159.1×10^9	149	$400,000-400,000$	$149+148+294-4\times145=$	11

[1] Pressure increase for 100,000 gpd at dimensionless time, t, indicated.

The table shows that almost 95 percent of the pressure increase has disappeared after a 1-year shutdown. From the foregoing, it is clear that a 1-day interruption after 5 years of injection brings the pressure increase down to $569 - (4 \times 103) = 157$ lb.

The total increase in pressure which can be allowed safely depends mainly on the depth of the formation. Therefore, the important question commonly is phrased differently: Supposing that a pressure increase of 200 lb (maximum 300 lb) can be allowed safely, how much fluid can be disposed of during successive years? To obtain quantitative answers, the Q_t curve is used because this function gives the *cumulative* quantity produced (or injected) if from time zero on a pressure differential of 1 atm is maintained, *i.e.*, the pressure against the formation is reduced (or increased) by 1 atm.

The problem is solved by first expressing the time at which pressure information is required in dimensionless units, by looking up the Q_t values for that particular time, and by multiplying these by the volume conversion factor. The necessary numbers are given in Table II and graphically shown in Figure 2.

Dividing by 159,000 (the number of cubic centimeters in 1 bbl) gives the total quantity disposed of at the end of successive years. This volume increases almost proportionally to time.

If the pressure used for injection were increased by 100 lb (from 200 to 300 lb) at the end of the second year, the additional quantity injected during the third and fourth years would be half as large as the injected volume during the first 2 years, as shown in the following table.

Year	Pressure	Q_T (bbl)	Total Injected
1	200	1.33×10^6	$=1.33 \times 10^6$ bbl
2	200	2.60×10^6	$=2.60 \times 10^6$ bbl
3	300	$3.84 \times 10^6 + (0.66 \times 10)$	$=4.50 \times 10^6$ bbl
4	300	$5.05 \times 10^6 + (1.30 \times 10)$	$=6.35 \times 10^6$ bbl
5	300	$6.26 \times 10^6 + (1.92 \times 10)$	$=8.18 \times 10^6$ bbl

More Than One Well—Well Interference

Disposing of 400,000 gpd for 5 years would increase the pressure in the injection wells by 569 lb, which certainly could be considered excessive for a reservoir with an original pressure of 1,350 lb. More than one injection well

Year	t	Q_t	$200 Q_t/14.7$	Q_T (cm³)	Q_T (bbl)	Injections by Years
1	15.9×10^9	1.37×10^9	18.6×10^9	212×10^9	1.33×10^6	1.33×10^6
2	31.8×10^9	2.66×10^9	36.2×10^9	413×10^9	2.60×10^6	1.27×10^6
3	47.7×10^9	3.93×10^9	53.5×10^9	610×10^9	3.84×10^6	1.24×10^6
4	63.6×10^9	5.18×10^9	70.5×10^9	804×10^9	5.05×10^6	1.21×10^6
5	79.5×10^9	6.42×10^9	87.3×10^9	995×10^9	6.26×10^6	1.21×10^6

An injection pressure of 200 lb results in a Q_T value of

is indicated and pressure interference will result. The pressure-time relation in the forma-

TABLE II. Q_t, CUMULATIVE INFLUX (OR VOLUME INJECTED) PER ATMOSPHERE AS A FUNCTION OF THE DIMENSIONLESS TIME, t

t	Q_t	t	Q_t	t	Q_t
0.010	0.117	1.0×10^3	2.9262×10^2	1.0×10^8	1.1021×10^7
0.015	0.146	1.5×10^3	4.1489×10^2	1.5×10^8	1.6180×10^7
0.020	0.169	2.0×10^3	5.3245×10^2	2.0×10^8	2.1245×10^7
0.030	0.210	3.0×10^3	7.5848×10^2	3.0×10^8	3.1199×10^7
0.040	0.245	4.0×10^3	9.7640×10^2	4.0×10^8	4.0989×10^7
0.060	0.305	6.0×10^3	13.9659×10^2	6.0×10^8	6.0267×10^7
0.080	0.357	8.0×10^3	18.0267×10^2	8.0×10^8	7.9220×10^7
0.100	0.404	1.0×10^4	2.1989×10^3	1.0×10^9	0.9797×10^8
0.150	0.508	1.5×10^4	3.1594×10^3	1.5×10^9	1.4411×10^8
0.200	0.598	2.0×10^4	4.0904×10^3	2.0×10^9	1.8963×10^8
0.300	0.756	3.0×10^4	5.8944×10^3	3.0×10^9	2.7910×10^8
0.400	0.896	4.0×10^4	7.6460×10^3	4.0×10^9	3.6742×10^8
0.600	1.144	6.0×10^4	11.0466×10^3	6.0×10^9	5.4109×10^8
0.800	1.365	8.0×10^4	14.3536×10^3	8.0×10^9	7.1228×10^8
1.00	1.568	1.0×10^5	1.7594×10^4	1.0×10^{10}	0.8798×10^9
1.50	2.029	1.5×10^5	2.5494×10^4	1.5×10^{10}	1.3239×10^9
2.00	2.445	2.0×10^5	3.3191×10^4	2.0×10^{10}	1.7124×10^9
3.00	3.200	3.0×10^5	4.8186×10^4	3.0×10^{10}	2.5249×10^9
4.00	3.888	4.0×10^5	6.2817×10^4	4.0×10^{10}	3.3265×10^9
6.00	5.148	6.0×10^5	9.1351×10^4	6.0×10^{10}	4.9093×10^9
8.00	6.148	8.0×10^5	11.9223×10^4	8.0×10^{10}	6.4675×10^9
10.0	7.402	1.0×10^6	1.4662×10^5	1.0×10^{11}	0.8014×10^{10}
15.0	9.949	1.5×10^6	2.1366×10^5	1.5×10^{11}	1.2996×10^{10}
20.0	12.316	2.0×10^6	2.7923×10^5	2.0×10^{11}	1.7391×10^{10}
30.0	16.741	3.0×10^6	4.0746×10^5	3.0×10^{11}	2.5000×10^{10}
40.0	20.884	4.0×10^6	5.3301×10^5	4.0×10^{11}	3.3333×10^{10}
60.0	28.658	6.0×10^6	7.7874×10^5	6.0×10^{11}	4.8000×10^{10}
80.0	35.991	8.0×10^6	10.1315×10^5	8.0×10^{11}	6.4000×10^{10}
100.0	43.025	1.0×10^7	1.2568×10^6	1.0×10^{12}	0.7407×10^{11}
150.0	59.744	1.5×10^7	1.8389×10^6		
200.0	75.653	2.0×10^7	2.4099×10^6		
300.0	105.789	3.0×10^7	3.5297×10^6		
400.0	134.519	4.0×10^7	4.6289×10^6		
600.0	189.325	6.0×10^7	6.8045×10^6		
800.0	241.784	8.0×10^7	8.9280×10^6		
1,000.0	292.622				

tion around a well into which fluid is injected at unit rate is given by the exponential integral (commonly referred to as the "Ei-function"),

$$-1/2 \; \mathrm{Ei}(-r^2/4t).$$

In this formula, t is the same dimensionless time discussed before, but r is the distance between the injection wells *expressed in multiples of their radii*.

Extensive values of the Ei-function appear in "Tables of Sine, Cosine and Exponential Integrals" (Mathematical Tables Project, 1940). Figures sufficient for most work are given in Table III and shown on Figure 3. Superposition can be used as before. Therefore, the pressure increase will be computed assuming that a total of 300,000 gpd (1,135,600 l) had to be injected in three wells; this quantity is expected to increase by 300,000 gpd at the end of the second year and again at the end of the fourth year.

The pressure increase in one well can be tabulated from the preceding information.

Year	Injection Rate (gpd)	ΔP	
1	100,000	136	=136
2	100,000	140	=140
3	200,000	112 | 136	=278
4	200,000	144+140	=284
5	300,000	145+142+136	=423
6	300,000	146+144+140	=430

To these increases must be added those resulting from injection of fluid into the two neighboring wells. Suppose the wells were drilled 1,000 ft (304.8 m) apart at the corners of an equilateral triangle. This distance is equal to 4,000 times the radius of the wells, so that it is necessary to look up the numerical values of $-1/2\,\mathrm{Ei}(-16\times10^6/4t)$.

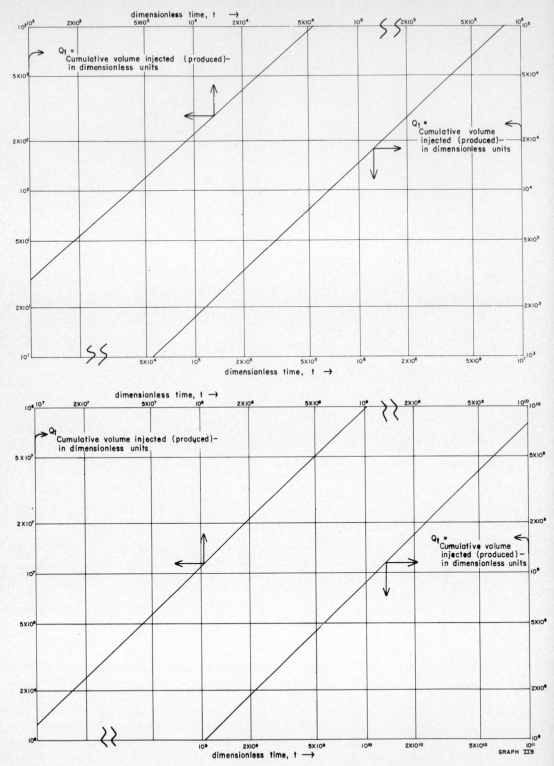

FIG. 2.—Q_t curves give cumulative volume of fluid injected into a well if from time zero a pressure differential of 1 atm is maintained. Table II gives numbers. (Note: log-log scale.)

Time (yr)	t	$r^2/4t$	$-1/2\ Ei(-r^2/4t)$		ΔP				Total Interference
1	15.9×10^9	0.000252	3.854	86				=	86
2	31.8×10^9	0.000126	4.201	94				=	94
3	47.7×10^9	0.0000839	4.404	99	+	86		=	185
4	63.6×10^9	0.0000629	4.548	102	+	94		=	196
5	79.5×10^9	0.0000503	4.660	104	+	99	+ 86	=	289
6	95.4×10^9	0.0000419	4.752	106	+	102	+ 94	=	302

The fourth column of the preceding table gives the pressure increases in atmospheres for unit injection rate in *one* of the neighboring wells. These increases must be multiplied by 0.762 to adjust for the rate's not being unity, by 14.7 to obtain pounds, and by 2 because of injection in both the neighboring wells. The

well distance, the interference effect has been computed assuming well distance of (a) 10,000, (b) 20,000, and (c) 50,000 ft. The rates of injection were assumed to increase as before. The computations are shown only for distance (a), but the total interference is shown for all three distances.

Computations for Distance (a), 10,000 ft

Year	t	$r^2/4t$	$-1/2\ Ei(-r^2/4t)$	Interference	Total		
					(a)	(b)	(c)
1	15.9×10^9	0.0252	1.564	35	35	20	5
2	31.8×10^9	0.0126	1.905	43	43	28	10
3	47.7×10^9	0.00839	2.106	47+35	82	52	18
4	63.6×10^9	0.00629	2.249	50+43	93	63	26
5	79.5×10^9	0.00503	2.360	53+47+35	135	90	36
6	95.4×10^9	0.00419	2.451	55+50+43	148	102	46

results are given in the first column of figures under the "ΔP" heading. The injection of an additional 100,000 gpd at the beginning of the third and fifth years causes the additional increases shown individually in the next two columns.

The total pressure increase in an injection well (over the original pressure) amounts to the increase resulting from injection in the well itself and the interference from both neighboring wells.

End of Year	Pressure Increase (lb) Due to		Grand Total
	Injection in Well	Interference	
1	136	86	222
2	140	94	234
3	278	185	463
4	284	196	480
5	423	289	712
6	430	302	732

Had all fluid been disposed of in only one well, the pressure would have increased 3×430 $=1,290$ lb. The use of three wells 1,000 ft apart reduces the maximum disposal pressure by $1,290-732=558$ lb at the end of the sixth year.

To provide further insight into the effect of

As can be seen from the above table, the distance between injection wells must be several miles if the interference is to be kept down to reasonable levels. The results obtained are those for the formation fluid and well characteristics previously described. They will be different if these characteristics have different values.

WELL STIMULATION—THE $\overline{P}_t$ FUNCTION

Instead of using more than one injection well, one might consider improving possible injection rates of a well by stimulation such as acidizing or shooting. To compute the effect, it is assumed that shooting or acidizing causes an enlargement of the effective borehole radius, *e.g.*, from 3 in. to 10, 20, or 50 ft. Within this radius (10, 20, or 50 ft) it is assumed that only the permeability of the formation is increased so much that it may be considered infinite in comparison to the value outside the effective radius. As a further simplification, the porosity is not considered to be affected.

The $\overline{P}_t$ curve[4] gives the pressure increase

[4] See Appendix.

TABLE III. $\overline{P}_t$ AND $-1/2$ Ei $(-x)$ REPRESENT
PRESSURE CHANGES IN ATMOSPHERES

(where x is the numerical value of $1/4t$ or $r^2/4t$)

x	$-1/2$ Ei$(-x)$	t	$\overline{P}_t$
0.010	2.019	0.010	0.01727
0.015	1.819	0.015	0.02509
0.020	1.677	0.020	0.03257
0.030	1.480	0.030	0.04675
0.040	1.341	0.040	0.06009
0.060	1.148	0.060	0.08486
0.080	1.013	0.080	0.1077
0.100	0.9115	0.10	0.1292
0.150	0.7322	0.15	0.1773
0.200	0.6113	0.20	0.2198
0.300	0.4528	0.30	0.2932
0.400	0.3512	0.40	0.3556
0.600	0.2272	0.50	0.4103
0.800	0.1553	0.60	0.4591
1.000	0.1097	0.70	0.5032
1.200	0.0792	0.80	0.5435
1.400	0.05811	0.90	0.5807
1.600	0.04315	1.00	0.6152
1.800	0.03236	1.50	0.7583
2.000	0.02445	2.00	0.8689
2.500	0.01246	2.50	0.9593
3.000	0.006524	3.00	1.036
3.500	0.003485	4.00	1.161
4.000	0.001890	6.00	1.344
4.300	0.001316	8.00	1.477
4.600	0.0009205	10.00	1.582
5.000	0.0005741	15.00	1.777
5.300	0.0004043	20.00	1.916
5.600	0.0002854	30.00	2.114
6.000	0.0001800	40.00	2.255
6.300	0.0001277	60.00	2.456
7.000	0.00005774	80.00	2.600
8.000	0.00001883	100.00	2.717
9.000	0.00006224		
10.000	0.000002078		

per unit rate of injection as a function of the time t (just like the P_t curve), taking into account the compressibility of the fluids inside the enlarged well radius. The numerical values for the curve are given in Table III; its configuration is shown on Figure 1.

If this $\overline{P}_t$ relation is to be used, the size of the enlarged radius must be obtained from pressure observations during injection tests (at constant rate) *before* and *after* shooting. It will be assumed that the radius of the well is increased from 3 in. to 100 ft, that is, enlarged 400 times. Such an increase decreases the values of the dimensionless time by a factor of $400^2 = 160,000$. Whereas the conditions given previously for P_t gave a dimensionless time t of 43.6×10^6 units for 1 day, this time now is reduced to 272.5 units. Also, whereas the pressure increase followed almost immediately the $1/2 \ln t$ relationship, after stimulation it will take the pressure in the well practically a full day to increase to the point where the $1/2 \ln t$ law prevails (Fig. 1). Hence, tests of several days duration are required to determine the improvement by stimulation. Also, as both curves can be represented by $1/2 \ln t$ functions— but one t being 160,000 times smaller than the other—the maximum improvement will

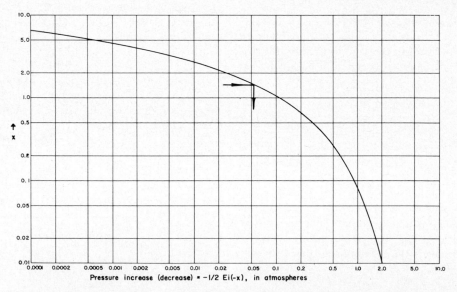

FIG. 3.—Curve represents pressure increase in a reservoir (at time t and at distance r from injection point) into which fluid is being injected at unit rate from time zero onward, where $x = r^2/4t$.

be equal to $1/2 \ln 160,000 = 5.99$ atm. For the conditions in the formation and well discussed, this improvement equals $0.762 \times 14.7 \times 5.99 = 67$ lb per 100,000 gal disposed of per day.

Assuming as before that the injection rate of 100,000 gpd during the first 2 years is increased by that amount every 2 years, a table can be set up using P_t and $\overline{P}_t$ values computed from the $1/2 \ln t$ relationship.

pressure will increase at a constant rate per unit of time. Hence, close observation of injection pressures for any indication of an acceleration in rate of increase is essential. If an unusual increase is suspected, pressure fall-off tests should be made. They are very informative and simple; it is necessary only to suspend operations and obtain accurate records of the pressure behavior as functions of the shut-down

	Well Not Stimulated			Well Stimulated			
Year	$10^{-9}t$	P_t	Pressure Increase	$10^{-9}t$	$\overline{P}_t$	Pressure Increase	Improvement
1	15.91	12.15	136 =136	99.4	6.16	69 = 69	67
2	31.81	12.50	140 =140	198.8	6.50	73 = 73	67
3	47.72	12.70	142+136 =278	298.2	6.71	75+69 =144	134
4	63.62	12.84	144+140 =284	397.6	6.85	77+73 =150	134
5	79.53	12.95	145+142+136 =423	497.1	6.96	78+75+69 =222	201
6	95.44	13.04	146+144+140 =430	596.5	7.05	79+77+73 =229	201

The beneficial effect of well stimulation is evident. The reduction in pressure remains constant at 67 lb for each 100,000 gpd disposed of.

SIZE OF RESERVOIR

In the foregoing discussion it was assumed that the reservoir could be considered of infinite extent, but this obviously is not correct. Yet work with unit functions described here in the analysis of oil-field operations—functions rigidly valid only for infinite reservoirs—has yielded trustworthy results in many cases.

It is assumed that persons in charge of disposal operations involving considerable volumes of fluids will choose undisturbed reservoirs of very large areal extent. However, the reservoirs chosen still may have such characteristics and be of such an extent that their limits interfere during disposal operations. Therefore, some means by which to recognize early indications of such problems is essential.

It is easy to understand that when fluid is injected into a circular reservoir of limited extent the early pressure increases cannot be distinguished from the increases observed in an infinite reservoir. However, after the pressure wave bounces back from the boundary, the pressure increase will accelerate (that is, deviate upward from the $P_t = 1/2 \ln t$ curve valid for operations in an infinite reservoir) and, finally, because the injection is at a constant rate, the

time. If the observed pressures are plotted *versus* the log of the shut-in time divided by the total time, the points should form a straight line. Extending this relation to the point where shut-in time divided by total time is unity should give the original reservoir pressure if no acceleration of the pressure increase has occurred. However, any excess over the original reservoir pressure at that point indicates a limited reservoir whose size can be computed from the excess pressure observed and the total quantity of fluid injected. The rate of increase will be the important factor in deciding whether operations should be resumed and, if so, for how long.

CONCLUSION

It is clear from the foregoing that the injection of waste fluids into permeable formations is feasible, and that under proper conditions considerable quantities of waste fluids can be stored safely without causing an excessive increase above the original reservoir pressure. The ensuing pressure changes at the well and at any point in the formation can be predicted because the effect of injection rate and changes in injection rate can be estimated for any point in the permeable formation. The accuracy of these estimates depends on the knowledge of the characteristics of the formation, the formation fluids, and the injected fluids.

APPENDIX

The numerical values of the three unit functions used can be obtained from the following integrals.

$$P_t = \frac{4}{\pi^2} \int_0^\infty \frac{(1 - e^{-u^2 t}) du}{u^3 \{ J_1^2(u) + Y_1^2(u) \}}$$

$$Q_t = \frac{4}{\pi^2} \int_0^\infty \frac{(1 - e^{-u^2 t}) du}{u^3 \{ J_0^2(u) + Y_0^2(u) \}}$$

$$\overline{P}_t = \frac{16}{\pi^2} \int_0^\infty \frac{(1 - e^{-u^2 t}) du}{u^5 \{ J_2^2(u) + Y_2^2(u) \}}$$

The first two of these integrals were derived by van Everdingen and Hurst (1949). Approximate formulae for obtaining the numerical values of these (and some further) functions are given in Appendix E of the article by Edwardson et al. (1962).

The possible need for the third function was brought again to the writer's notice by an article in *The Oil and Gas Journal* (1966) wherein Dowell claims the possibility of extending fractures 100 ft in all directions around a well.

The description of a pressure fall-off test is based on the method outlined by Horner (1951). He explains how to calculate the pressure in a well after an infinitely long shut-in period by using pressure data obtained during a limited time; that is, the pressure prevailing at that point in the reservoir after elimination of the effect of injection or production. The method is used throughout the oil industry.

REFERENCES

Edwardson, M. J., *et al.*, 1962, Calculation of formation temperature disturbances caused by mud circulation: Jour. Petroleum Technology, April, p. 416–426.

Everdingen, A. F. van, and W. Hurst, 1949, The application of the Laplace transformation to flow problems in reservoirs, *in* Petroleum development and technology, 1949: Am. Inst. Mining Metall. Engineers Petroleum Trans., v. 186, p. 305–324.

Horner, D. R., 1951, Pressure build-up in wells: 3d World Petroleum Cong. Proc., The Hague, sec. 2, p. 503–521.

Mathematical Tables Project, 1940, Tables of sine, cosine and exponential integrals: Federal Works Agency Works Project for the City of New York, Project No. 765-97-3-10, 2 vols., 444 p. and 225 p.

Oil and Gas Journal, 1966, Space age explosives may revive well shooting: Sept. 19, p. 82.

van Everdingen (see Everdingen).

Warner, D. L., 1965, Deep well injection of liquid waste, a review of existing knowledge and an evaluation of research needs: Cincinnati, Ohio, Div. Water Supply and Pollution Control, U. S. Public Health Service Pub. 999-WP-21.

POSSIBILITIES FOR DISPOSAL OF INDUSTRIAL WASTES IN SUBSURFACE ROCKS ON NORTH FLANK OF APPALACHIAN BASIN IN NEW YORK[1]

THOMAS P. McCANN,[2] NORMAN C. PRIVRASKY,[3]
FREDERICK L. STEAD,[4] AND JAMES E. WILSON[5]
Houston, Texas 77025; Magnolia, Arkansas 71753; and Clarksburg, West Virginia 26302

ABSTRACT

The north flank of the Appalachian basin in the state of New York was studied, with the object of determining the suitability of the region for subsurface disposal of industrial wastes, particularly liquid wastes. Permeable sandstone, salt beds that can provide leak-proof man-made caverns, and shale that can contain fluids in artificially produced fractures are especially significant.

Subsurface strata dip southward at rates between 50 and 160 ft/mi. Local deformations such as low-relief anticlines and small displacement faults are few.

Potential reservoirs for injection of liquids into permeable sandstone formations are the Potsdam and Theresa Sandstones of Cambrian age. The Potsdam has a maximum known thickness of 410 ft and an average thickness of about 100 ft; the Theresa thickness ranges from zero to 1,500 ft. Drilling depths to the Potsdam Sandstone, the lowest potential reservoir, range from 1,000 to 12,600 ft. Other possible sandstone reservoirs are present in the Silurian and Devonian Systems, but have less potential because of vagaries in porosity and permeability and because of the presence of numerous unrecorded borings in the shallower strata.

Salt beds in Silurian rocks at depths between 500 and 4,000 ft offer sites for construction of storage cavities.

Shale sections that appear to be suitable for storage of grouted wastes in hydraulically produced fractures are present in Upper Devonian and Upper Ordovician strata. There are thinner sections of possible interest for the same use in Silurian and Middle Ordovician rocks.

INTRODUCTION

The purposes of this study were as follows:

1. To locate and define the most promising sandstone reservoirs into which liquid wastes can be injected;

[1] Manuscript received, May 27, 1963; revised, November 12, 1966.

This report is respectfully dedicated to the memory of Norman C. Privrasky.

[2] Staff geologist, Shell Canadian Exploration Company.

[3] Deceased, September 14, 1963. Formerly geologist, Tidewater Oil Company, Pittsburgh, Pennsylvania.

[4] Consulting geologist.

[5] Geologist, Consolidated Gas Supply Corporation.

The original studies on which this paper was based were made for the Subcommittee on Atomic Waste Disposal of the AAPG Research Committee at the request of the U.S. Atomic Energy Commission.

The writers express their appreciation to the managements of Shell Oil Company, Tidewater Oil Company, and New York State Natural Gas Company for allowing the use of files, maps, and information, and to the geological staffs of these companies for advice, suggestions, and criticism. The writers also are indebted to Robert Stewart, Huntley & Huntley, Inc., Pittsburgh, Pennsylvania, and the late E. V. O'Rourke, Ohio State University, Columbus, Ohio, for engineering advice, and to John Broughton and the staff of the New York State Geological Survey for their assistance and cooperation.

2. To locate salt beds where solid or liquid wastes can be stored;
3. To locate and define thick shale beds into which wastes in a cement slurry can be injected by grouting;
4. To define the geographic area or areas where geologic conditions appear to be most favorable for waste disposal; and
5. To recommend the additional work needed for selection of the best local sites for experiments in a pilot waste-disposal operation.

Accordingly, this report is restricted generally to a description of present geologic and other conditions which have bearing on the problems of waste disposal.

The subsurface geology of the Appalachian basin is unique in several respects. Although the basin is the birthplace of the oil and gas industry and more than 500,000 wells have been drilled there (probably more than 7,000 in the state of New York), accurate information is very scarce in comparison to the data available on other oil- and gas-producing areas. The reason for the scarcity of data is that most of the drilling was done before 1900, when there were no regulations requiring the filing of information and the need for keeping accurate records was not recognized generally. Because most of the wells were drilled before mechanical logging methods were invented, and more than 95 percent of the wells were drilled by cable tools, mechanical logs of any type are available on only about 2 percent of the wells drilled. Only wells drilled since 1950 have been logged by methods which permit quantitative analyses of porosity, formation fluids, and other subsurface elements. Cores are very scarce and difficult to find; drill cuttings are available from perhaps 10 percent of the wells, and many of the sets of cuttings are incomplete. Because of the predominance of cable-tool drilling and, more recently, air drilling, few drill-stem tests and pressure measurements and few analyses of formation fluids are available. Fortunately, many of the deepest tests have been drilled in the recent past, and the quality and quantity of data available from these wells are generally good; however, they are still not as complete as records on tests drilled in other oil and gas provinces. Despite these inadequacies, the writers believe it is possible to make fairly accurate studies of the geology, but the evidence is mostly indirect. It will be necessary to drill tests to obtain information before any program can be initiated to store waste products in subsurface reservoirs on the north flank of the Appalachian basin in New York.

The geologic study of the area was done in four separate parts: (1) the Cambrian and Lower Ordovician section by Frederick L. Stead, (2) the Middle and Upper Ordovician section by Thomas P. McCann, (3) the Silurian System by James E. Wilson, and (4) the Devonian System by Norman C. Privrasky. The conclusions drawn from these studies are based primarily on geologic considerations, modified by such other factors as the locations of large lakes, cities, and towns.

LOCATION

This study was confined to the north flank of the Appalachian basin in the state of New York. Some of the work necessarily was carried into parts of adjacent Pennsylvania, Ohio, and Ontario, but there was no attempt to make detailed investigations in these bordering areas and conclusions stated in this paper should not be applied beyond the study area.

The area considered as potential for subsurface disposal of liquid wastes is defined on the west by the southeastern shores of Lakes Erie and On-

tario, on the north by the southern edge of the Precambrian outcrop area of the Adirondack uplift, on the east by the Hudson River, and on the south by the Pennsylvania-New York state boundary. In general, the area studied is between 74° and 80° west longitude and north of 42° latitude (Fig. 1).

The offshore areas of Lake Erie and Lake Ontario are not considered suitable for subsurface disposal of wastes because of the additional hazards of handling toxic substances in lacustrine operations where an accident could contaminate some of the largest fresh-water reservoirs in the country. The Precambrian crystalline and metamorphic rocks of the Adirondack uplift are not considered because of the generally poor reservoir qualities of such rocks and the lack of information on the movements of fluids through fracture systems in crystalline rocks. The sedimentary rocks in eastern New York are involved in complex structural deformation which has resulted in various degrees of metamorphism and generally poor reservoir conditions. Also, there is very little subsurface control in this extremely deformed area. For these reasons, eastern New York is regarded as unsuitable for subsurface storage of waste products.

GEOGRAPHY

PHYSIOGRAPHY

Western New York is mostly in the Appalachian Plateau province, but parts extend into the lacustrine plains of Lakes Erie and Ontario, the Tug Hill upland, and the lowlands of the Mohawk and Hudson River valleys. Elevations range from 246 ft (75 m) above sea level at Lake Ontario to about 2,300 ft (700 m) near the Pennsylvania border on the west, and to about 3,600 ft (1,100 m) in the Catskill Mountains on the east.

The topography becomes increasingly rugged away from the lake shores and the large river valleys. Locally, relief in the dissected plateau area is varied but averages about 400 ft (122 m) and ranges up to about 1,500 ft (457 m) in parts of the Catskill Mountains.

Several large river systems drain New York state. The Allegheny, Chemung, Susquehanna, and Delaware Rivers drain the southern part and flow southward; the Mohawk River drains the central part and flows eastward to join the Hud-

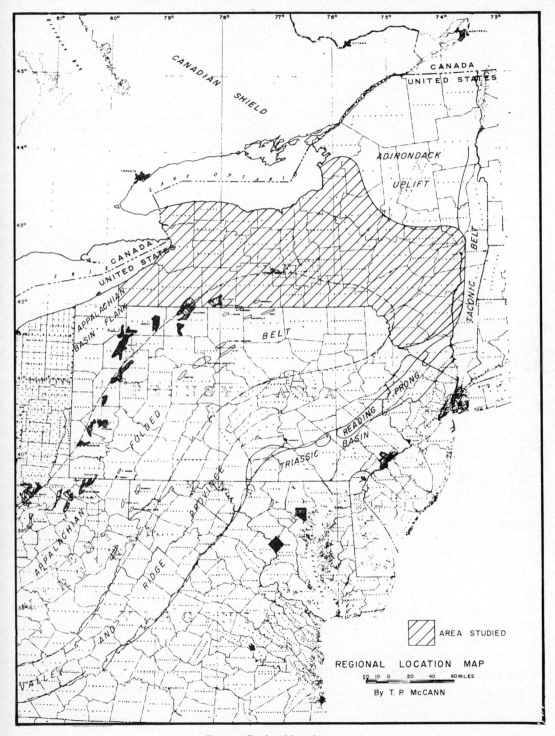

Fig. 1.—Regional location map.

son. which flows southward to the Atlantic Ocean, draining the eastern part of the state; the Black and Genesee Rivers drain the northern part of western New York and, along with several smaller streams, flow northward into Lake Ontario. In addition to Lakes Erie and Ontario, there are many large fresh-water lakes in the area (Chautauqua Lake and the Finger Lakes) and numerous smaller lakes. All of the larger lakes are used extensively for water supplies and recreational activities.

CLIMATE

The climate of western New York is varied and depends on the elevation, topography, and distance from the Great Lakes. In general, the mean temperature is about $+45°F$ ($\pm5°$) or $+7°C$; the annual rainfall is about 40 in. (102 cm); the annual snowfall varies considerably, ranging from less than 60 in. (152 cm) in places to much more than 100 in. (328 cm). Along the Great Lakes and in the higher elevations the snowfall generally averages more than 100 in.

The prevailing wind is from the northwest in the winter and from the southwest in the summer. Wind velocity varies considerably. Weather systems generally move rapidly across the state, and prolonged stationary air masses are rare. Minimum temperature is about $-50°F$ ($-45°C$) and maximum temperature is about $+100°F$ ($+38°C$).

POPULATION

Population density is considerably varied. The lacustrine plains and the lowlands in the major river valleys are heavily populated, and the high plateau areas are sparsely populated. The densely populated cities and towns are along the major rivers or on the shores of large lakes.

TRANSPORTATION

Transportation facilities range from fair to excellent. Very few places are more than a few miles from all-weather highways. Railroads which serve the area are the Lehigh Valley; New York Central;[6] New York, Ontario and Western; Dela-

[6] The New York Central and Pennsylvania Railroads are now merged under the name "Pennsylvania New York Central Transportation Company." (Ed.)

ware, Lackawanna and Western; Delaware and Hudson; Erie; Baltimore and Ohio; and Pennsylvania.[6] Few places are more than 10 mi from a railroad. Scheduled airline transportation serves the larger towns and cities.

POWER

There are no coal deposits in western New York, and the local supply of natural gas and oil is inadequate to supply the area. However, several large interstate gas-transmission lines cross western New York, and there should be no problem in obtaining natural-gas service. Coal or oil can be supplied readily. Hydroelectric power is generated from several plants at Niagara Falls and along the St. Lawrence seaway, and power-transmission lines appear to be well distributed in western New York.

LAND OWNERSHIP

Most of the land in western New York is privately owned. Tracts are small, ranging from a few acres to several hundred acres and averaging probably about 100 acres (40 hectares). The Allegheny Indian Reservation and Allegheny State Park cover a large part of the southwestern quarter of Cattaraugus County. Letchworth State Park occupies several thousand acres in Livingston and Wyoming Counties, and Catskill Park covers a large area in Ulster, Delaware, Greene, and Sullivan Counties. Few commercial land maps are available, and many of these are old and inaccurate. It probably will be necessary to make a land map of any site to be considered for waste disposal.

Titles range from poor to good. The titles of valuable land are good in most places; the titles to uninhabited land commonly are clouded.

Much of the land in western New York is under lease to oil or gas companies. Inasmuch as the status changes, the current lease situation in any area of interest should be examined.

SOIL AND VEGETATION

In general the flatland, particularly in the river valleys, is cultivated and the mountain slopes and highlands are forested. The thickness and fertility of the soil apparently are varied. Tests made at the site for the Western New York Nuclear Service Center in Cattaraugus County indicate that the pH ranges from 5.43 to 8.99 and averages about 8.3.

WATER SUPPLY

Many water-supply data are in publications of the U.S. Geological Survey. Most residents and communities utilize surface water, and most of the water wells are shallow, producing from sand and gravel of the Pleistocene drift. According to work done at the proposed site for the Western New York Nuclear Service Center, porosity, permeability, and production capabilities of Pleistocene aquifers vary considerably in short distances, and it would be futile to try to predict the shallow groundwater conditions for a specific area. Tests will have to be made after an area has been selected.

SEISMOLOGY

Western New York is reported to be an area of low seismicity, although northern New York and New England are subject to frequent minor earth shocks. Only one severe earthquake has been recorded in western New York in the past 100 years (the Attica earthquake of August 12, 1929, classified as intensity IX on the Rossi-Forel scale). The geologic map of New York (Broughton et al., 1962) indicates that numerous large faults have been mapped in and around the Adirondack uplift and in the Hudson River valley. Small faults are shown around Seneca and Cayuga Lakes in southwestern Steuben County and in southern Orleans and northern Genesee Counties. Probably there are more faults, but they cannot be seen at the surface because of the Pleistocene deposits which cover the bedrock in most of the area. Subsurface and seismic data indicate faulting associated with anticlines near the Pennsylvania border, but most of the faults seem to have maximum displacement in the Lower Devonian beds and appear to die out in the thick Upper Devonian shale. Regional gravimetric surveys suggest the presence of several large basement faults, most of which have a north-south orientation. Most of the post-Precambrian faulting in western New York probably originated in late Paleozoic time, but some geologists think faulting took place after Cretaceous time in many places.

Geomorphic evidence in places indicates that movement occurred much later than Paleozoic time, but the movement could have been a rejuvenation of older faults.

GEOLOGY
REGIONAL SETTING

The state of New York is in the northern part of the Allegheny synclinorium and is part of the north flank of the Appalachian structural basin. Precambrian metamorphic and igneous rocks are exposed on the Adirondack uplift and on the Canadian Shield in Ontario. A complex of Paleozoic metamorphic rocks, known as the "Taconic plate," forms the border of eastern New York. The regional geologic setting is shown on Figure 1.

STRATIGRAPHY

Except for the widespread cover of Pleistocene glacial drift ranging in thickness from zero to more than 1,000 ft, all of the sedimentary rocks of western New York are of Paleozoic age. Silurian and Upper Ordovician rocks crop out in eastward-trending belts across western New York, and Silurian strata also are exposed in a narrow southward-trending belt in south-central New York. Middle and Lower Ordovician and Cambrian strata are exposed around the flanks of the Adirondack uplift and in Ontario. Except for these outcrops and a very small tongue of Mississippian and Pennsylvanian rocks in southern Cattaraugus County, Devonian outcrops cover the rest of western New York (Fig. 2).

The sedimentary section ranges in thickness from a featheredge near the borders of the Precambrian outcrop area of the Adirondack uplift to more than 13,000 ft (3,962 m) in Steuben County in the southwestern part of the state (Figs. 3, 4). Devonian, Silurian, and Upper Ordovician strata are predominantly clastic, but some carbonate rock and evaporites are present in the Lower Devonian and Silurian sections. Middle and Lower Ordovician and Cambrian rocks are predominantly carbonate but include minor amounts of sandstone and shale.

The stratigraphy is complex; there are facies changes both along strike and updip. Several unconformities and disconformities are present in the section.

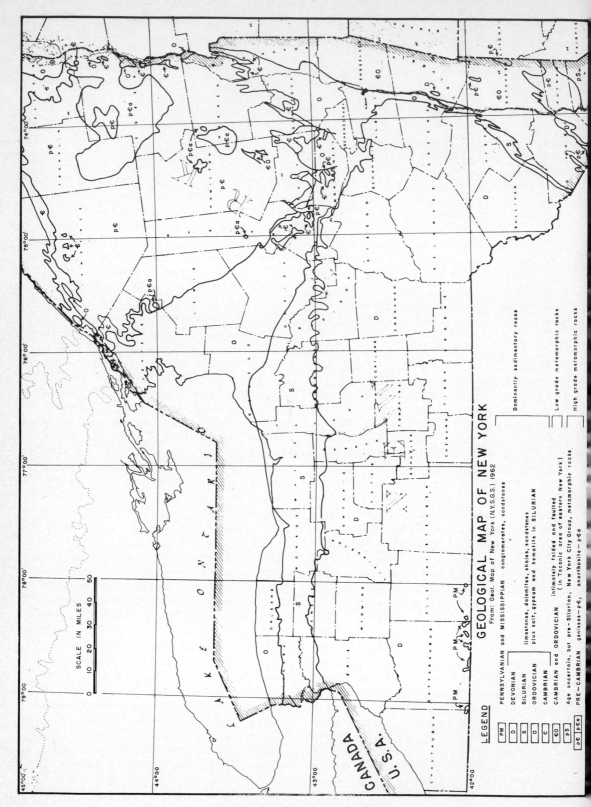

FIG. 2.—Geologic map of New York.

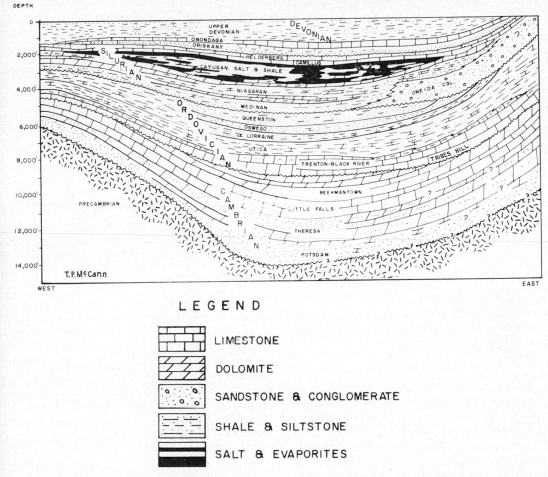

LEGEND

▦ LIMESTONE

▨ DOLOMITE

▢ SANDSTONE & CONGLOMERATE

▤ SHALE & SILTSTONE

▬ SALT & EVAPORITES

FIG. 3.—Diagrammatic structural and stratigraphic cross section along 42d parallel, western New York (not drawn to scale).

The terminology used in this paper is that commonly used by the oil and gas industry in the study area. Although these terms are recognized and well established, many other names have been used and are in use. The correlation charts published by The Geological Society of America (Cooper, 1942; Howell *et al.*, 1944; Swartz, 1942; Twenhofel, 1954) and those published by the New York Geological Survey (Broughton *et al.*, 1962; Fisher, 1959; Flagler, 1966; Rickard, 1964) provide more detailed information.

STRUCTURE

Regional dip of the surface formations in western New York is southward at about 50 ft/mi (9.5 m/km). In the subsurface, particularly on the older beds, the rate of dip increases because of convergence of the section northward, but nowhere except near faults or other local structural features does the dip exceed a few degrees.

The area studied is generally devoid of significant folding. Large-scale block faulting is present around the flanks of the Adirondack uplift, and minor faulting is associated with anticlinal features in southern New York. Probably there is more faulting in the subsurface, but it is unrecognized because of lack of information. Most of the folding is of low-order relief, and much of the structure mapped at the surface with Devonian beds as datum may be the result of differential

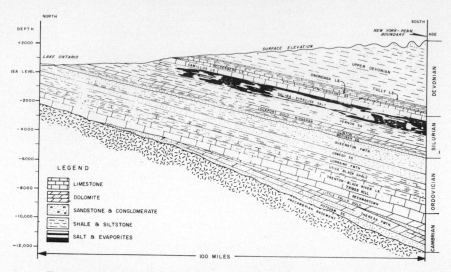

FIG. 4.—Diagrammatic cross section along 77° meridian, western New York
(not drawn to scale).

compaction or salt flowage rather than orogenic movements. The intense folding so evident in central and northern Pennsylvania dies out in southern New York (Figs. 5, 6).

GENERAL RESERVOIR CONDITIONS

Porosity and permeability of reservoirs in the Appalachian basin are generally low in comparison with porosity and permeability of reservoirs in many other geologic provinces. Porosity of rocks in the Appalachian basin commonly is less than 10 percent and permeability generally is on the order of a few millidarcys. Natural fracturing probably increases both of these parameters in places, but the evidence for this is mostly indirect. This study has been concentrated mostly on sandstone reservoirs, because the carbonate rocks in New York are generally poor reservoirs.

Except where the rocks are at very shallow depths, formation fluids are highly saline brines, methane gas, or oil. Commercial gas production has been established from Upper Devonian sandstone and shale, Silurian sandstone and carbonate rock, Middle Ordovician limestone, and Cambrian sandstone. The only known oil production in the study area is from Upper Devonian sandstone in and around the Bradford field in southwestern New York, although condensate production has been reported from a few gas wells producing from the Oriskany Sandstone (Lower Devonian).

Formation pressures found during drilling appear to be normal (expected hydrostatic pressure) or subnormal, except for abnormally high pressures reported from a few gas wells in the old Trenton fields in northern New York. It is possible that these high pressures were caused by fracture systems connected to deeper reservoirs.

Data for temperature gradients are too scarce to permit preparation of a map, but available information indicates that gradients are probably normal.

CAMBRIAN AND LOWER ORDOVICIAN

Fewer wells have penetrated the Cambrian and Lower Ordovician section and less is known about these rocks than any of the overlying shallower units. The maps, cross sections, and conclusions in this part of the study are based on subsurface information from 100 wells, as follows: 31 wells, radioactivity logs; 33 wells, sample logs; 6 wells, driller's logs; and 60 wells, scout information only. The total area involved is estimated to be 33,000 sq mi, which gives a well density of one well per 330 sq mi (855 km). It is therefore obvious that the region is relatively unexplored. Correlation of the subsurface section with the outcrop formations presents the usual problems in stratigraphy.

The well records studied date from 1886 to the present. Most of the information older than 1940 is limited both in quality and quantity. Shows of gas, oil, or salt water generally were logged, but quantitative information is very limited. Only two cores have been taken in the Cambrian and Lower Ordovician section, and apparently only a half dozen drill-stem tests. Comments on reservoir characteristics therefore are limited and, to a degree, speculative.

The Cambrian section in New York consists of rocks of Early and Late Cambrian ages, lying unconformably on an eroded basement complex of granitic and metamorphic rocks (Fig. 7). The formations which make up the Cambrian section in western New York are, in ascending order, the Potsdam Sandstone and the Theresa, Little Falls, and Beekmantown Dolomites. The Upper Cambrian is separated from the overlying Lower Ordovician Tribes Hill Limestone by a major unconformity.

REGIONAL STRATIGRAPHY

The Cambrian and Lower Ordovician sedimentary rocks in western New York are predominantly carbonate with a high clastic content. Where fossiliferous, their faunas suggest nearshore or shallow-shelf environments. The dolomite is thinly bedded and commonly interbedded with clean sandstone and light-colored shale and siltstone. All of the Cambrian strata are truncated northward and pinch out against the south flank of the Canadian Shield. Regionally they thicken basinward toward the south and southwest.

The Cambrian formations present in western New York have been correlated with other formations in several states (Howell et al., 1944; Adkison, 1966).

The subsurface Theresa and Little Falls Dolomites in New York bear only a limited relation to the surface outcrop sections described in the literature. Their several subsurface facies, however, are regionally correlative—from radioactivity logs and drill cuttings—with other formational units having wider regional acceptance and use. Thus the names "Theresa" and "Little Falls" probably need revision and redefinition.

The Lower Ordovician Tribes Hill Limestone directly overlies the Knox unconformity (see succeeding section) and is considered to be equivalent to the Chazy section in part. The Tribes Hill

is correlative with formations in Ohio, Michigan, and Ontario.

REGIONAL STRUCTURE

The dip of these deeper rocks is homoclinal, interrupted only by local south-plunging noses, synclines, and faults. The large surface anticlines of south-central New York apparently have no significance at depth. Seismograph surveys in several parts of the area show no valid relations between these surface folds and structural features in the Cambrian rocks. This fact suggests that the thick salt beds of the Upper Silurian section may have "absorbed" the deformation. The surface and shallow subsurface faulting associated with these surface anticlines also appears to die out within the Upper Silurian salt section and to bear no relation to the deeper Ordovician and Cambrian strata.

DETAILED STRATIGRAPHY

The two subsurface cross sections (Figs. 8, 9) were constructed with the top of the "Trenton" limestone as datum in order to illustrate best the specific stratigraphic relations of the Cambrian strata underlying the Knox unconformity. Both are north-south transverse sections which demonstrate the relation between the Lower Ordovician Tribes Hill Limestone and the truncated Cambrian units below it. The southern half of each of these sections underlies some of the areas of marked surface folding mentioned previously.

The paleogeologic map (Fig. 10) indicates the subcrop positions of the Potsdam, Theresa, Little Falls, and Beekmantown units at the Knox unconformity. The isopach contours show the rate of truncation northward to the Potsdam wedgeout near the south shore of Lake Ontario. The predominant facies and individual characteristics of these formations within the study area are discussed in detail in the following paragraphs.

Potsdam Sandstone.—The Potsdam is the basal sedimentary unit recognized in western New York state. The Potsdam generally is considered to be of Late Cambrian age. The formation crops out on the flanks of the Adirondack uplift. The type locality is near the village of Potsdam, St. Lawrence County, New York. The Potsdam was described originally by Emmons (1838, p. 214–217) as being 80 ft thick. The distribution of the Pots-

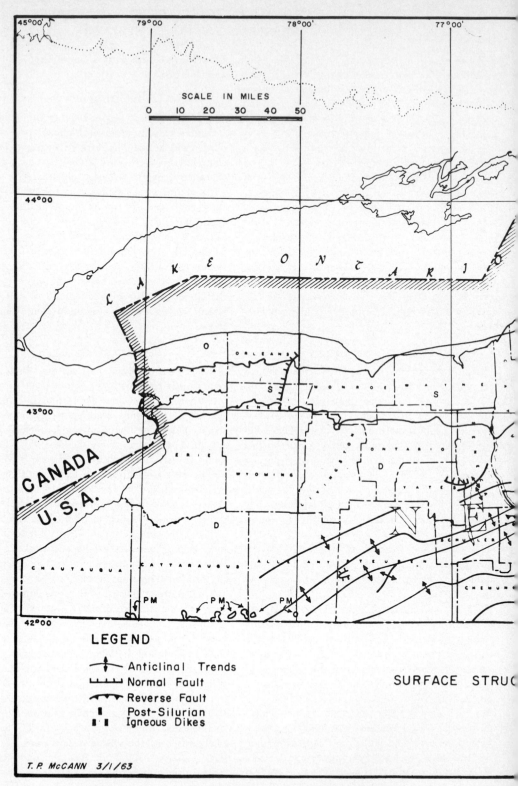

Fig. 5.—Surface structural features.

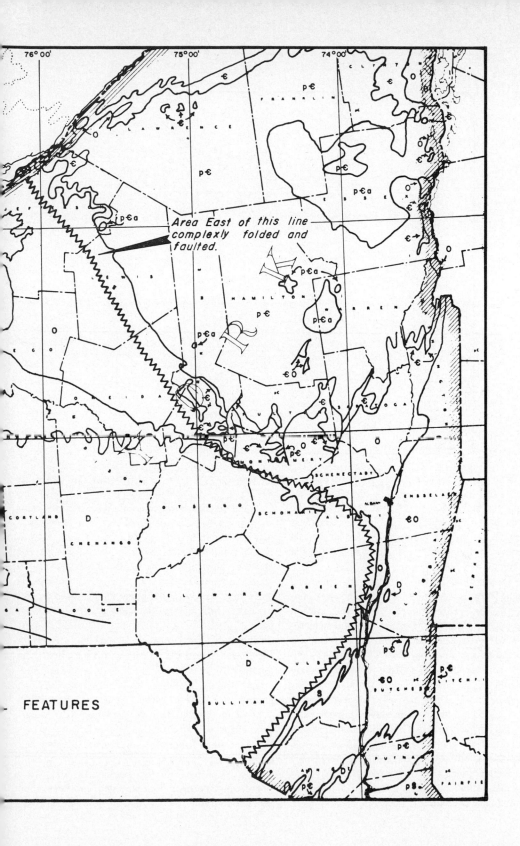

Area East of this line complexly folded and faulted.

FEATURES

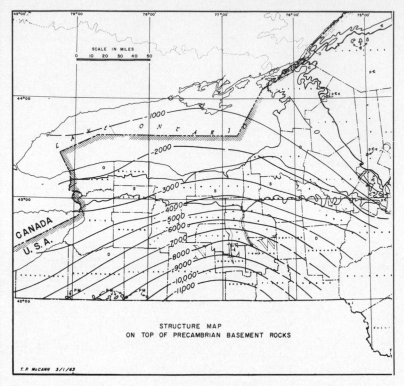

Fɪɢ. 6.—Structure map of top of Precambrian basement rocks. Contour interval, 1,000 ft (304.8 m).

dam in the subsurface is general throughout the western part of the state. The average thickness is 100 ft, but a maximum thickness of 410 ft (125 m) is found in a single well in Oneida County.

At the type locality the Potsdam was described originally (Emmons, 1838) as ". . . a true sandstone of red, yellowish red, gray, and grayish white colors, made up of grains of sand held together without a cement; intermixed with the siliceous grains are finer particles of yellowish feldspar." This description of the surface lithology and composition is fairly representative of the subsurface also. Drill cuttings have been described as very fine- to medium-grained sandstone, light brown to gray, both quartzose and dolomitic, and in places calcareous. Large frosted quartz grains, muscovite, and orthoclase feldspars —interbedded with thin layers of light-gray, very finely crystalline, porous, slightly vugular, sandy dolomite—are present.

The Potsdam Sandstone strikes generally east-west and regionally dips southward at an average rate of 100 ft/mi (about 19 m/km). It ranges in depth from 3,000 ft (915 m) in the vicinity of Buffalo, New York, to 13,000 ft (3,962 m) in southern Steuben County, near the Pennsylvania state line. In Oswego County, at the eastern end of Lake Ontario, the Potsdam is 1,500–2,000 ft deep.

The Potsdam Sandstone is differentiated from the basal sandstone stringers of the overlying Theresa Dolomite by the coarseness of the sandstone and by its "hot" radioactivity. The high gamma radiation is caused by the high feldspar content in the Potsdam. In the Gobles and Clearville fields of Ontario, Canada, on the west, this relationship is supported further by detailed logs and cores.

The basal part of the Potsdam is extremely porous and permeable. This zone has been commercially productive of natural gas in the Memphis area (1897) of Onondaga County, and 12 mi west of Buffalo in the Point Abino field (1916) of Welland County, Ontario. The same zone also has yielded salt water where tested in Cattaraugus, Wyoming, and Livingston Counties, New York. The Potsdam is a potential gas reservoir along its updip wedgeout and is the primary objective of a current drilling program in Niagara, Orleans, Monroe, and Wayne Counties, New York.

Theresa Dolomite.—The Theresa overlies the Potsdam and is of Late Cambrian age. It crops out on the flanks of the Adirondack uplift. The formation was described originally from its exposure at Theresa, New York, as having a thickness of 20–70 ft, composed of primarily sandy dolomite interbedded with "weak" sandstone (Cushing, 1908). Renamed the "Galway formation," it was redefined in 1951 to comprise "the sandy dolomites, dolomitic sandstones, and calcareous sandstones lying below the Hoyt limestone[7] and above the Potsdam sandstone" (Fisher and Hanson, 1951, p. 802). The distribution of the Theresa is general throughout the western part of the state. In the subsurface, a maximum thickness of 1,486 ft (453 m) was found in the New York Natural Gas Corp. No. 1 Robert Olin well in southern Steuben County. The subsurface Theresa Dolomite has an average thickness of 700 ft (Fig. 8).

In the subsurface the Theresa consists primarily of porous, sandy dolomite which grades into a distinct sandstone facies at its upper limits. The dolomite is buff, tan, gray, and brown; finely to medium crystalline; and contains finely disseminated subangular grains of quartz, pyrite, and biotite, and in places oölites and chert. Where the sand predominates in the samples, the cement is either calcareous or dolomitic. The clastic section at the top of the Theresa Dolomite is a white, clean sandstone with fine, subrounded grains; shows of gas and/or salt water are common. This section ranges from zero to 250 ft in thickness, depending on the degree of truncation, and appears to be developed best in the west-central part of the state. This sandstone section and the underlying sandy dolomite are correlated with formations in Ohio and Kentucky.

[7] Approximately equivalent to Little Falls Dolomite.

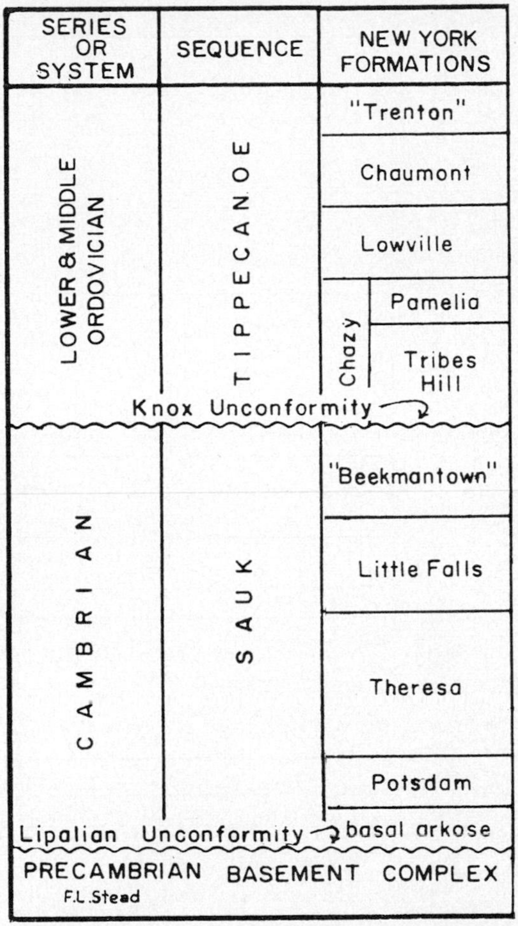

FIG. 7.—Generalized geologic column for sub-Trenton rocks of western New York. Modified after Calvert (1963b, p. 2).

The subsurface strike is east-west and the regional dip is southward at an average rate of 100 ft/mi or slightly more.

There appears to be considerable confusion among operators regarding the top of the Theresa Dolomite in the subsurface. A careful review of the available sample and radioactivity logs indicates a consistent gamma-ray "kick" at the top of the major sandstone facies in the upper part of the Theresa section (Figs. 8, 9). Because this is the only major break between the Theresa and the overlying Little Falls section, this point was used as the top of the Theresa in the cross sections and in isopach calculations.

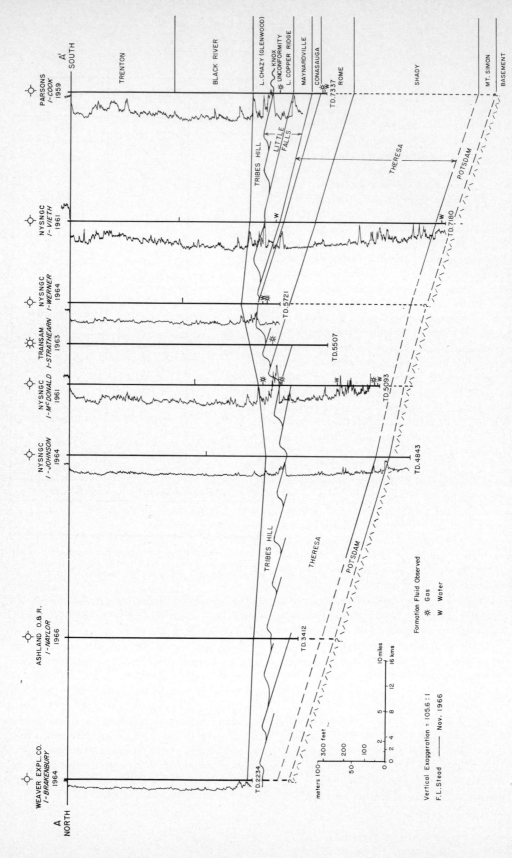

FIG. 8.—Cross section *A-A'*, Cambrian and Lower Ordovician. Trace of section shown on Figure 10.

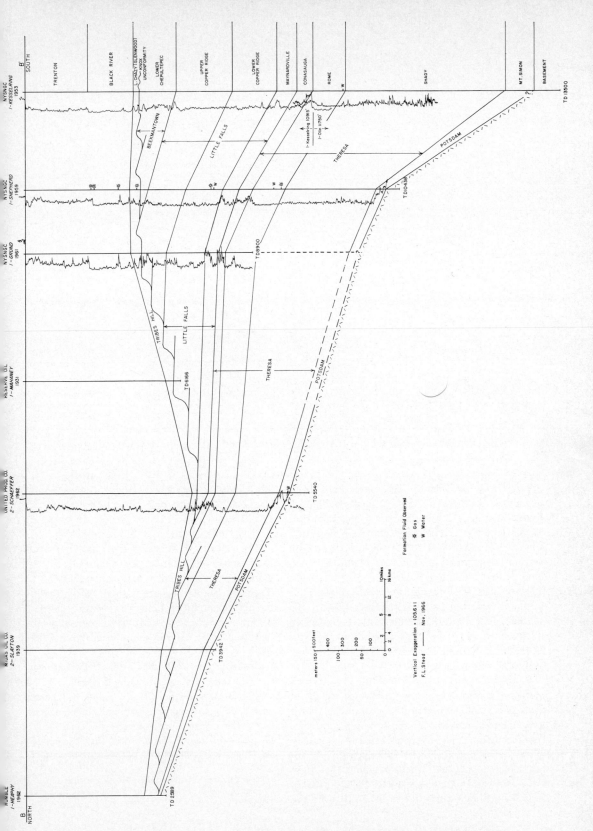

Fig. 9.—Cross section *B-B'*, Cambrian and Lower Ordovician. Trace of section shown on Figure 10.

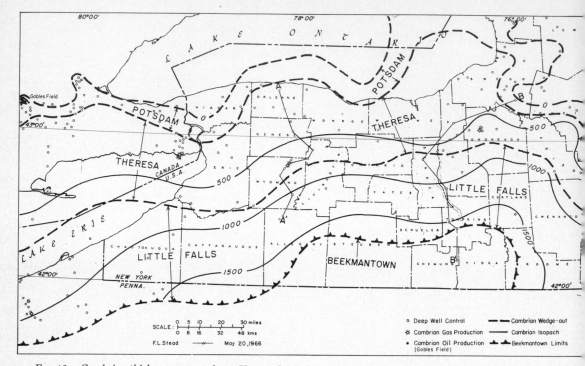

Fig. 10.—Cambrian thickness map and pre–Knox paleogeology, central and western New York. Contour interval, 500 ft (152.4 m).

Little Falls Dolomite.—The Little Falls crops out on the southern and eastern flanks of the Adirondack uplift. It was named for the exposures at Little Falls, Herkimer County, New York, where the formation is 200 ft thick. This outcrop section is composed primarily of fossiliferous dolomite and limestone directly overlying the Theresa beds. The distribution of the Little Falls in the subsurface is restricted generally to the southern half of western New York. A maximum thickness of 950 ft (290 m) is found in the New York State Natural Gas Corp. No. 1 Kesselring well in Chemung County.

In the subsurface the Little Falls consists primarily of buff to light-gray to brown, finely to medium-crystalline dolomite containing much very fine to coarse quartz sand and, in places, thin-bedded siltstone. The overall section is commonly pyritic, cherty, and oölitic. Lithologically, it appears to be fairly uniform throughout the study area. The basal part of the Little Falls is characterized by a silty-sandy facies believed to be the Maynardville equivalent. Above this section lies the oölitic dolomite which may be correlative with the "Lower" and "Upper" Copper Ridge (Trempealeau) units productive in central Ohio.

The subsurface strike of the Little Falls Dolomite is east-west across the state (Fig. 10); regional dip is southward at approximately 100 ft/mi. There are numerous porous zones within the middle and upper Little Falls which have yielded salt water in several test wells. These porous dolomite beds appear to be continuous and are considered to be potential reservoirs.

Beekmantown Dolomite.—The Beekmantown is the youngest Cambrian[8] dolomite which is preserved in the deeper parts of the Appalachian basin; it is above the Little Falls Dolomite and below the Chazy Limestone. At the type locality, near Beekmantown, New York, the exposed beds are limestone. They lie unconformably on the

[8] The Beekmantown generally is considered to be Ordovician. See references in Keroher *et al.* (1966). (Ed.)

Potsdam Sandstone because of onlap, and much of the lower section is absent. The upper part of the section also is absent because the upper surface of the Beekmantown is an unconformity overlain by the Chazy Limestone. The term "Beekmantown Group" has been used by Calvert (1962, p. 29) to designate a larger stratigraphic unit that includes the Chepultepec and Lambs Chapel Dolomites, which are present elsewhere in the Appalachian basin. Rocks equivalent to the Beekmantown have been found in the No. 1 Kesselring in Chemung County and in the No. 1 Olin in Steuben County. The subsurface relationship of this section is indicated on the paleogeologic map (Fig. 10) and on cross section *B-B'* (Fig. 9).

The Beekmantown appears to be transitional with the underlying Little Falls Dolomite and is made up of dark, very finely crystalline, silty and sandy dolomite commonly interbedded with medium- to dark-gray to black pyritic shale. These beds thicken toward the south and east and reach a maximum thickness of several thousand feet in eastern Pennsylvania and western Maryland. No shows of oil, gas, or salt water have been found in this formation.

Knox unconformity.—At the top of the Cambrian System is an unconformity of major significance. This stratigraphic break is widespread in the Appalachian basin and eastern United States. During this hiatus, the Cambrian strata were truncated in New York, Michigan, Ohio, Kentucky, Tennessee, Virginia, and other states, and in Ontario. According to Freeman (1953, p. 14), this horizon has been called the "post-Knox," "post-Arbuckle," and "post-Ellenburger" unconformity. The term "Knox unconformity" is regionally applicable to the Appalachian basin and is used in this report. According to Calvert (1962, p. 34), the "Knox Unconformity is the first major regional unconformity above the basement unconformity in the eastern United States." Because this erosional surface is associated directly with and is responsible for commercial accumulations of oil and gas throughout the basin, its true significance and relationship to rocks above and below must be recognized before the history and hydrodynamics of the Cambrian strata of the area can be understood and appreciated fully.

Tribes Hill Limestone.—The Tribes Hill is the basal unit of the Ordovician System in western New York. This section commonly has been called erroneously the "Beekmantown" by other workers in the area. The formation was named for the exposures at Tribes Hill, Montgomery County, about 30 mi east of Little Falls, on the south flank of the Adirondack uplift. The subsurface distribution of the Tribes Hill Limestone is general throughout the western part of the state. There is onlap of the strata on the north beyond the updip limits of the truncated Upper Cambrian Potsdam Sandstone.

In the subsurface the Tribes Hill consists primarily of light-gray to tan to buff, very finely crystalline, sublithographic, argillaceous, fossiliferous pyritic limestone interbedded with light-gray-green dolomitic siltstone, thin stringers of green waxy shale, and clean, white, fine-grained calcareous sandstone. Basinward, on the south, the limestone grades into dolomite with interbeds of light-green pyritic shale, light-gray to white, fine-grained sandstone, tan dolomitic siltstone, and a few stringers of black pyritic shale. The Tribes Hill unconformably overlies the Cambrian section. A basal zone of gray-green siltstone and shale containing glauconite is everywhere present at the base of the Tribes Hill. This zone is easily recognized both in drill cuttings and on radioactivity logs (Figs. 8, 9).

RESERVOIR CHARACTERISTICS

The physical data regarding porosity, permeability, mineralogy, and fluid content of the Cambrian and Lower Ordovician rocks of western New York state are extremely limited. The current status and quality of usable information about each formation are discussed in detail in the following paragraphs.

Potsdam.—No cores have been taken in the Potsdam Sandstone of New York state to the writer's knowledge. Geological Survey records show that only 48 wells have been drilled to or through this formation. Many of these are extremely old tests on which very little information is available. Most of the old records do indicate, however, that numerous shows of gas, oil, and salt water were found. These limited data strongly suggest a certain degree of primary porosity and permeability. Only 17 wells in the study area have logged this formation and neutron logs are available on only 14. Therefore, detailed log analyses regarding porosity and permeability also are extremely limited. Commercial gas production was obtained from the Potsdam in three wells in northern Onondaga County, where the section appears to have a maximum thickness of at least 300 ft (91 m). None of these wells now is producing.

Theresa.—Several random deep wildcats drilled throughout the state have found shows of gas and salt water in the Theresa section. Most of the gas shows were reported from the upper part of the formation. The Theresa yields natural gas from two wells in northeastern Wyoming County. The two wells are of low capacity and the production is marginal. In southern Wyoming County and northern Allegany County, three tests recovered significant quantities of salt water from the sandstone facies at the top of the formation. In Chemung, Tompkins, and Steuben Counties, deep drilling indicates that there are several consistent porosity zones within the lower part of the Theresa that contain salt water. Fluid recoveries from the Theresa elsewhere in the state are erratic throughout the section and show only a limited relationship between wells.

Only one core has been taken in the Theresa Dolomite. The Blair No. 1 Kennedy in Livingston County cored the Theresa from 5,660 to 5,690 ft, but the core analysis has not been released.

Little Falls.—There are no cores or core analyses of the Little Falls Dolomite in New York to the writer's knowledge. Sample and log examination indicates most of the section to be relatively dense and tight, having little intercrystalline porosity. The exception is the uppermost part of the section, which is composed of vuggy dolomite. Three wildcat tests in Madison and Chenango Counties found shows of gas and salt water in this zone. Only a few other wells in the study area had shows in this formation, possibly because of the updip truncation and removal of the porous zone.

Tribes Hill.—Shows of gas and salt water have been recorded from the Tribes Hill Limestone in the westernmost part of the state; none have been noted east of Livingston County. Gas in commercial quantities has been produced from

one well in northern Chautauqua County. Salt water has been found in Cattaraugus, Wyoming, and Livingston Counties, but not from the same zones. Because of erratic lithology, discontinuity of porosity zones, and the variety of Cambrian facies present below the Tribes Hill, the writer, on the basis of present knowledge, believes it to be unsuitable for liquid-waste disposal.

HYDRODYNAMIC DATA

There is no hydrologic information on the Cambrian and Lower Ordovician strata other than the fluid recoveries previously mentioned. Data such as volumes, reservoir pressures, and chemical analyses of fluids are not available.

A series of six drill-stem tests was taken in the Theresa section of the No. 1 Olin well in Steuben County. All tests were run below 12,000 ft. The fact that all recovered only drilling mud from the formation regardless of the time the tool was open suggests tight, low-porosity sandstone.

The Clearville field, Oxford Township, Kent County, Ontario, was discovered in 1962. This field now has 17 wells producing from Cambrian Shady and Potsdam sandstones. Imperial Oil Company, Ltd., one of the field operators, has cored these pay zones in several wells, but the results of their core analyses have not been released. The Clearville field is 150 airline miles northwest of Buffalo, New York.

The Gobles field, Blenheim Township, Oxford County, Ontario, was discovered in 1960 and produces from the Potsdam Sandstone at its updip wedgeout (Fig. 10). This stratigraphic-trap accumulation is a three-phase reservoir with net pay sections of 5–20 ft. The field now contains six gas wells and 55 oil wells. Many operators in the field have cored this pay zone, and the core data are available from the Ontario Energy Board. The field is 88 airline miles northwest of Buffalo, New York, and is the nearest productive area to the study area on which new and accurate hydrodynamic data from this Cambrian unit are available.

SELECTED DISPOSAL RESERVOIRS

On the basis of careful study of all the available data on the Cambrian and Lower Ordovician formations of western New York, the following

DISPOSAL OF INDUSTRIAL WASTES IN NEW YORK

61

units are recommended for consideration as potential underground-storage reservoirs for liquid wastes. They are listed in order of desirability.

1. *Theresa Dolomite.*—In the southwestern part of the state, all deep tests have recovered salt water consistently from the thick sandstone facies in the upper part of the formation. It is believed that these porosity zones are general in distribution and that the fluid content is predictable. The prospects for natural-gas exploration in this part of the state are limited to shallower units. Therefore, the upper Theresa section within the south-central part of the state appears attractive for disposal purposes.

2. *Potsdam Sandstone.*—In the northern part of the study area this Cambrian clastic unit is at relatively shallow depths. Available data indicate that the formation is generally porous and permeable, especially the basal part. This unit is potentially productive of oil and gas, but no commercial production has been established. On the basis of present knowledge, the formation appears attractive for disposal purposes.

3. *Little Falls Dolomite.*—The Upper Cambrian Little Falls has storage possibilities within the porous section in the uppermost part. However, because it is a carbonate reservoir, it may not be as desirable as sandstone units for injection of acidic waste liquids. In the interest of completeness the formation is included in this report, and the section warrants further investigation.

RECOMMENDED FUTURE WORK

In any area considered for deep-well injections, additional drilling will be required to supply critically needed information. Rotary tools should be used for this drilling, and adequate mud programs should be followed. The target formations should be cored if possible to supply adequate core analyses of both vertical and horizontal permeability within the prospective storage zones. The data required will be expensive to acquire, but the knowledge gained will justify the expense. Drill-stem tests and bottomhole fluid samplers run at critical intervals will provide both reservoir fluids for chemical analyses and critical pressure data. A logging program should be designed to yield the maximum data through the cored and drill-stem-tested sections.

MIDDLE AND UPPER ORDOVICIAN
GENERAL STRATIGRAPHY

Sedimentary rocks of Ordovician age are present in most of the study area. The thickness of these strata ranges from zero around the Adirondack uplift to more than 3,700 ft (1,128 m) in southern Steuben County near the Pennsylvania border. Strata of Late and Middle Ordovician ages are exposed at the surface in the northern part of the area (Fig. 2), and Lower Ordovician rocks crop out in places around the Adirondack uplift.

The Ordovician rocks can be divided into two lithologic units—an upper clastic unit consisting of shale, siltstone, and fine-grained sandstone and very minor amounts of carbonate rock; and a lower unit which is predominantly carbonate but has a few thin calcareous shale and dolomitic sandstone beds.

The Ordovician-Cambrian boundary is within the lower carbonate unit and is difficult to recognize in the subsurface. The lithologic units transgress time zones, generally becoming younger northward and westward. The Ordovician-Silurian boundary is an angular unconformity in the eastern part of the area and a disconformity in the western part of New York. In places where Silurian sandstone beds lie on Upper Ordovician sandstone the contact is obscure.

The nomenclature of the rock units is shown on the correlation chart (Fig. 11).

MIDDLE ORDOVICIAN SERIES

At the end of Cambrian time the northern part of the Appalachian basin was uplifted and eroded, then again submerged in a shallow but widespread sea which probably covered the Adirondack area and a great part of the Canadian Shield. During the period of uplift, Cambrian rocks were tilted southward and eroded.

Chazy Group sandstone and carbonate strata are present on the eastern flank of the Adirondack uplift, and Tribes Hill strata are present in the subsurface of western New York.

Black River Formation.—Black River limestone unconformably overlaps older rocks from

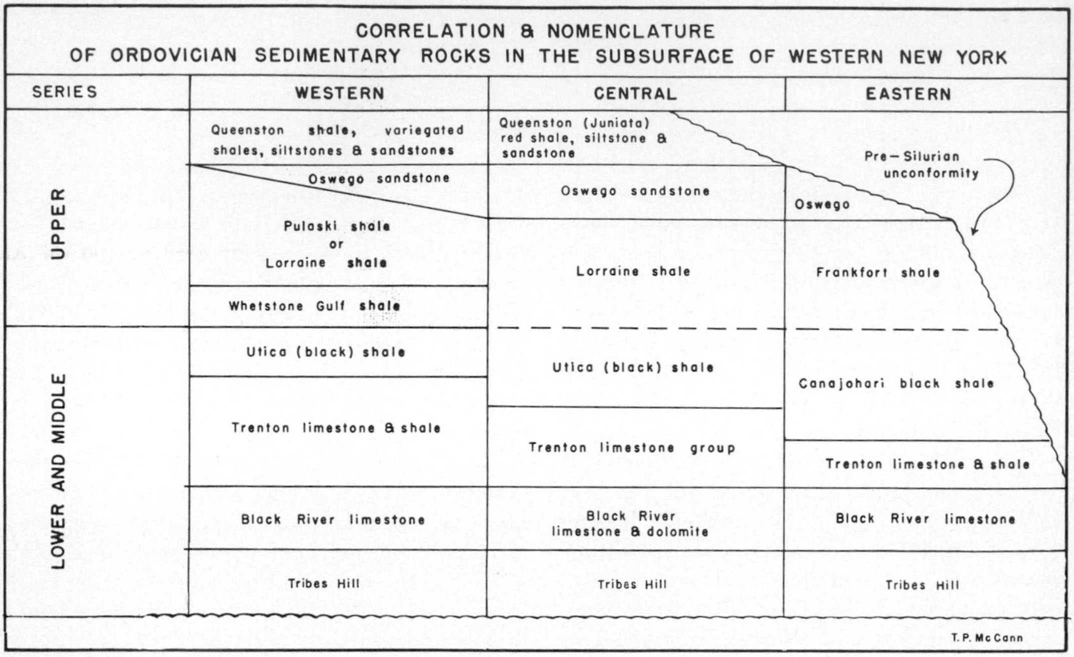

CORRELATION & NOMENCLATURE OF ORDOVICIAN SEDIMENTARY ROCKS IN THE SUBSURFACE OF WESTERN NEW YORK			
SERIES	WESTERN	CENTRAL	EASTERN
UPPER	Queenston shale, variegated shales, siltstones & sandstones	Queenston (Juniata) red shale, siltstone & sandstone	Pre–Silurian unconformity
	Oswego sandstone	Oswego sandstone	Oswego
	Pulaski shale or Lorraine shale	Lorraine shale	Frankfort shale
	Whetstone Gulf shale		
LOWER AND MIDDLE	Utica (black) shale	Utica (black) shale	Canajohari black shale
	Trenton limestone & shale	Trenton limestone group	Trenton limestone & shale
	Black River limestone	Black River limestone & dolomite	Black River limestone
	Tribes Hill	Tribes Hill	Tribes Hill

T. P. McCann

FIG. 11.—Correlation and nomenclature of Ordovician sedimentary rocks in subsurface of western New York.

south to north. Fisher (1962) indicates the lower part of the Black River strata to be older than Mohawkian. The Black River Formation consists of dark-gray to brown cherty limestone and various amounts of shale. It is slightly sandy in places. Reservoir characteristics are poor. The thickness is considerably varied, probably because of erosional relief on the depositional surface. The Black River limestone strata are not considered to have potential for the storage of liquid wastes, but the impervious character of this formation should cause it to be a good seal for the underlying beds.

Trenton Group

"Trenton" limestone, undifferentiated.—Limestone of the Black River Formation appears to be transitional with that of the overlying Trenton Group in the subsurface in most of western New York, although Kay (1948) and others indicate a hiatus between the Black River and Trenton rocks.

The undifferentiated Trenton consists of light- to dark-gray limestone beds and alternate thin, gray, calcareous shale beds. The limestone ranges from coarsely crystalline and very fossiliferous to dense and argillaceous. In a few places the limestone is silty or sandy. In the eastern part of the Mohawk Valley, Trenton limestone grades into the Canajoharie black shale facies.

The combined thickness of the Trenton-Black River rocks ranges from about 400 ft (122 m) in the north to more than 900 ft (274 m) in the southeastern part of the area studied.

Although seven methane-gas fields are productive from Trenton rocks, none of these fields has yielded significant volumes, and many geologists believe that most of the gas comes from the limestone-shale interfaces and from fractures. Some geologists think that reeflike algal structures may be effective reservoirs in Trenton rocks. Water rarely is reported from Trenton rocks in the subsurface, but at the surface numerous springs issue from extremely fractured Trenton limestone, particularly in the Mohawk Valley. The Trenton limestone in the subsurface is generally tight and is not regarded as a prospective reservoir for disposal of waste liquids.

About 400 wells have been drilled into the Trenton limestone in New York. Approximately 250 tests were drilled in the seven Trenton gas fields, and most of these test wells probably have not been plugged or were plugged improperly. Some of the gas fields reportedly had abnormally high pressures, and small-volume shows of gas commonly are found in Trenton strata. These rocks probably will be targets for oil and gas exploration for many years, particularly where the Trenton is at shallow depths.

Utica Shale.—Above the undifferentiated "Trenton" limestone is the Utica Shale. At the type locality the Utica Shale is black, carbonaceous, fissile, pyritic, and slightly calcareous, and is characterized by an abundance of graptolite fossils. In the subsurface the color ranges from gray to brown or black. Siltstone and mica are present in places, particularly in the western counties. The Utica Shale is time-transgressive, becoming progressively younger northwestward. In the eastern Mohawk Valley it is equivalent to middle Trenton rocks; as it is traced northeastward the basal units disappear and younger units appear at the top. Because the Utica Shale is transitional with the underlying Trenton limestone and with the overlying Lorraine and Frankfort Shales, the thickness figures depend partly on the opinions of the driller or geologist picking the formational boundaries. The reported thickness ranges from about 100 ft (30.5 m) to about 800 ft (244 m), the maximum being measured at the outcrop at Holland Patent, about 15 mi north of Utica. Three stratigraphic units (Ruedemann, 1947) have been established on the basis of graptolite faunas from outcrop examination, but these units are not distinguishable in the subsurface without detailed paleontological work, which rarely, if ever, is done in this area.

The Utica Shale in the subsurface has no natural reservoir properties and probably is not suitable for disposal of waste liquids. At the surface numerous springs issue from fractured Utica shale, particularly in the Mohawk Valley. Possibly the Utica Shale could be used for grouting, but the calcareous content might cause reactivity problems, and in places it may be too thin. Minor gas production has been reported from the Utica Shale, mostly in the old Trenton gas fields.

UPPER ORDOVICIAN (CINCINNATIAN) SERIES

The combined thickness of the Upper Ordovician strata is illustrated in Figure 12.

Lorraine Shale.—The Lorraine Shale, which overlies and is transitional with the underlying Utica Shale, ranges in thickness from 500 to 800 ft (152 to 244 m). It is present in the subsurface in most of western New York and crops out in the northern and eastern parts of the study area.

Twenhofel (1954) referred to the "Lorraine group" and showed the "Whetstone Gulf shale" to be the lower unit (named from outcrop in Jefferson County), but this name rarely is used in subsurface descriptions. The term "Frankfort Shale" also has been used synonymously with "Lorraine," but the New York Geological Survey now restricts the Frankfort to the lower part of the Lorraine Shale; it is considered to be equivalent to the Whetstone Gulf shale. In this paper, only the term "Lorraine" is used for these strata.

The Lorraine grades upward from dark-gray, carbonaceous, slightly calcareous, pyritic shale at the base to very fine-grained, very fossiliferous sandstone, shale, and siltstone interbedded with dark-gray, silty, micaceous shale at the top. Ruedemann (1925) described the outcropping Lorraine as "an endless alternation of shales and sandstones, the sandstones ranging [in thickness] from a few inches to a foot, and the shales from one to three feet thick; much of the rock is calcareous; often a 'sandstone' one foot thick is half crinoidal limestone and half pure sandstone and shale, barren of fossils. The sandstone exhibits ripple marks, the beds thin rapidly and fill depressions in the underlying rocks; lenticular masses of bryozoans and crinoids occur. . . ."

The Lorraine Shale is transitional with the overlying Oswego Sandstone where it is present, and the boundary commonly is difficult to recognize.

Reservoir characteristics in the Lorraine Shale are generally poor, and it does not appear to be suitable for the injection of liquid waste products. The calcareous nature of some of the sandstone might cause reactivity problems. However, the Lorraine Shale might be suitable for grouting of waste products.

Oswego Sandstone.—The Oswego Sandstone in New York is regarded as the sandstone facies of the Queenston Shale. It is present in most of

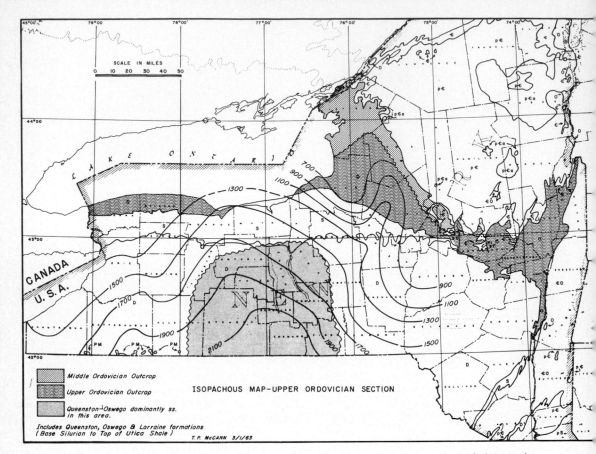

FIG. 12.—Thickness of Upper Ordovician Series, New York. Contour interval, 200 ft (60.96 m).

western New York and crops out in the northern part of the area. The thickness ranges from zero in the west, where the Oswego section is represented by silty shale of the Queenston Shale, to about 900 ft (274 m) in Chemung County (Fig. 13).

In New York the Oswego Sandstone is a monotonous sequence of fine- to very fine-grained sandstone, shale, and siltstone. Near the eastward termination in the subsurface, the Oswego is reported by Kreidler (1953) to be conglomeratic. The color ranges from dark to light gray and yellow. The sandstone is quartzose, slightly calcareous, tightly cemented with silica cement, and argillaceous in part. Thickness of beds ranges from a few inches to several feet. The lower part is fossiliferous, but the upper part is barren.

In the central part of western New York the Oswego Sandstone is overlain by sandstone, siltstone, and shale of the Queenston Shale, and the only distinction is a color change. In the easternmost counties of western New York, the Oswego Sandstone is absent because of pre-Silurian erosion, and in eastern Madison County the Oswego is overlain unconformably by the Silurian Oneida Conglomerate. Northward the Oswego probably is present under part of Lake Ontario; it is reported to be 75 ft (23 m) thick near Niagara Falls and is present in Ontario. Mineralogically, the Oswego Sandstone would be ideal for disposal of liquid waste products, but it appears to have low porosity and permeability in most places. Few shows of free liquids or gas have been reported from the Oswego Sandstone in western New York, but

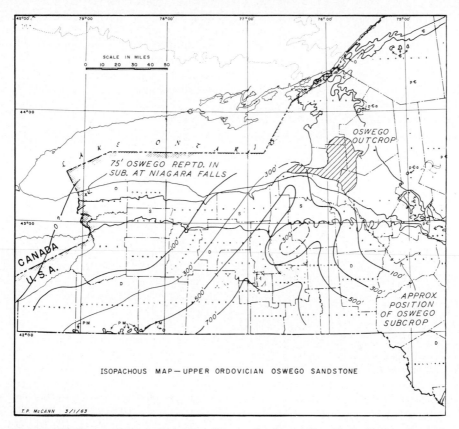

SCALE IN MILES
0 10 20 30 40 50

75' OSWEGO REPTD. IN
SUB. AT NIAGARA FALLS

OSWEGO
OUTCROP

APPROX.
POSITION
OF OSWEGO
SUBCROP

CANADA
U.S.A.

ISOPACHOUS MAP—UPPER ORDOVICIAN OSWEGO SANDSTONE

T.P. McCANN 3/1/63

Fig. 13.—Thickness of Upper Ordovician Oswego Sandstone, New York. Contour interval, 200 ft (60.96 m).

it has been penetrated by only about 400 wells and there are large areas where it has not been reached by the drill. Kreidler (1953) reports small quantities of gas produced from the Oswego Sandstone at the Fulton and Clyde fields, and states that "good porosity and adequate permeability" are present in one or two Oswego beds in the Wilson Arcade boring in Wyoming County. At the surface there are springs from the Oswego Sandstone, and wells 50–125 ft deep furnish large supplies of hard water in the northern counties.

Coring of the Oswego where it is several hundred feet thick would determine whether there are beds which have sufficient porosity and permeability to be disposal reservoirs. However, on the basis of the information available, it is doubted that the Oswego Sandstone will prove to be a suitable disposal reservoir.

Queenston Shale.—The term "Juniata" is used instead of "Queenston" by many geologists, but in this paper the term "Queenston" is used exclusively. The Queenston is a thick sequence of red, brown, gray, and green shale, siltstone, and fine- to medium-grained sandstone. In the eastern and central parts of western New York the Queenston is predominantly siltstone and sandstone; westward it grades into a slightly calcareous, brown to green, gray, and red silty shale. In general the clastic material becomes finer from east to west.

The Queenston is considered to be transitional with the underlying Oswego Sandstone where it is present. Eastward the Queenston thins because of pre-Silurian erosion, and it subcrops beneath the Oneida Conglomerate; in the west it is overlain disconformably by Medina (Silurian) sandstone. The Queenston Shale is about 800–900 ft thick in most of western New York and crops out in the northern part of the area.

Shows of gas are found commonly in the upper Queenston and minor shows of water are reported from Queenston sandstone, but in general the sandstone appears to be cemented tightly and to have poor porosity and permeability. There may be a few suitable reservoirs in medium-grained sandstone, but they would be difficult to locate. In the western counties the Queenston shale facies may be suitable for grouting.

SUMMARY OF ORDOVICIAN STRATIGRAPHY

Although as much as 1,000 ft (305 m) of sandstone is present in Upper Ordovician rocks in the central part of western New York, these beds appear to have low porosity and permeability in most places, and it is doubted that these sandstone strata are suitable for the injection of liquid waste products. Significant shows of oil, gas, or water from these rocks are rare. Because these strata are buried to depths of several thousand feet in most of the area, it would be expensive to obtain cores of the rocks and samples of formation fluids. Large areas are untested, and there may be porous, permeable Upper Ordovician sandstone in places, but the probability of finding such a sandstone is very low.

There are thick shale sections in the Upper and Middle Ordovician rocks in the western part of the area studied, and these shale beds may be suitable for the grouting of waste products in a cement slurry.

The Trenton-Black River carbonate rocks are not considered for disposal of waste products because of their poor transmissibility.

STRUCTURE

Ordovician rocks dip gently southward into the basin at less than 100 ft/mi. In the northern part of New York, where the Ordovician rocks are exposed or are at shallow depths, more than 350 wells have been drilled to the Middle Ordovician (Trenton) rocks. An interpretation of structural information from these wells, based on a 100-ft contour interval, indicates small, low-relief structural anomalies, particularly around the flanks of the Adirondack uplift. Apparently some of the faults exposed at the surface in the Adirondack Mountains extend southwestward into the subsur-

face and involve Ordovician rocks. Deeper in the basin, control is too sparse to define local structural anomalies, and a structure map with the top of the Trenton limestone as datum, and with a 1,000-ft contour interval, indicates only homoclinal structure with a few minor undulations (Fig. 14).

SILURIAN

SOURCES OF DATA

Well records.—With the advent of modern well logging in the Appalachian basin in the early 1950's, accurate information was available for the first time concerning formation depths, porosity, and water saturation. Previously, well records on many wells had been poor and commonly were not available. Because many New York wells were drilled early in the century, data commonly are unreliable or lacking. Therefore, much reliance must be placed on the more recent wells. Sample-study information is available on many tests, as well as gamma-ray and neutron logs, and these are the main sources of geologic data. Studies pertaining to hydrodynamics are definitely limited, because drill-stem tests rarely are made in the area.

Outcrop observations.—Considerable information concerning formation characteristics has been obtained from outcrops of Silurian rocks, and much of it has been published. Figure 15 shows the east-west trend of the Silurian outcrops. Glacial deposits obscure much of the bedrock, but sufficient outcrop and subsurface data are available for an adequate evaluation of stratigraphy and lithofacies across the state.

Outcrop evaluation of the Salina Group of the Cayuga Series is unsatisfactory because this section consists partly of evaporites—salt, anhydrite, and gypsum—which weather readily on exposure. Therefore, little can be concluded from outcrop data alone concerning the true nature of this section in the subsurface.

Previous investigations.—Some of the pertinent geologic reports that have been published in the past are listed in the accompanying bibliography.

STRATIGRAPHY

In the Silurian System of New York state, numerous lithologic variations resulted from erosion, nondeposition, and differences in environ-

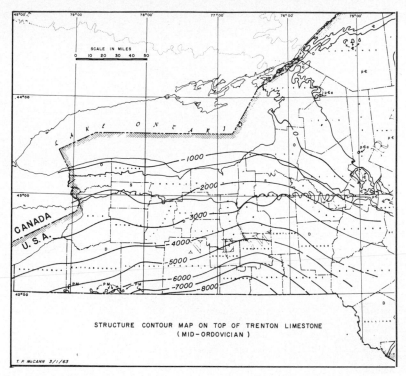

FIG. 14.—Structure contour map of top of Trenton limestone. Contour interval, 1,000 ft (304.8 m). Datum is sea level.

ment. The top of the system is placed tentatively at the top of the Manlius Limestone.[9] An unconformity separates this bed from the overlying Coeymans Limestone of the Lower Devonian Series. The base of the Silurian System is marked by an unconformity above the Lorraine, Utica, and "Hudson River" shales of the Middle and Upper Ordovician Series in east-central New York. In western New York it is delineated by the top of the Queenston red shale sequence of the Upper Ordovician Series. The intervening section of carbonate, evaporite, shale, and sandstone beds comprises the Silurian System.

Correlations within the Silurian System are shown in Figure 16. The formations listed are those which generally are accepted as representative of the geologic column. No attempt has been made to incorporate all of the numerous formation names that are used locally in the state.

[9] The Manlius now is thought to be Devonian (Fisher, 1959; Rickard, 1964). (Ed.)

Medina Series.—The Whirlpool or "White Medina" Sandstone is the basal member of the Albion Group, Medina Series, and is an almost pure, white quartzose sandstone. It extends from western to central New York, where it pinches out by onlap. Numerous gas shows, some of which have proved commercially significant, have been found in the Whirlpool Sandstone.

The Cabot Head Shale overlies the Whirlpool Sandstone in western New York, but disappears eastward by facies change and pinchout. It has little value as a reservoir bed.

The Grimsby or "Red Medina" Sandstone overlies the Cabot Head Shale in western New York and is the most prolific gas-productive unit of the Medina Series. It is approximately 100 ft (30 m) thick in west-central New York and consists of red, silty shale; red siltstone; and pink to red, fine-grained sandstone. In central New York where the Whirlpool Sandstone is not present, the contact between the base of the Grimsby Sandstone and the top of the underlying Ordovician

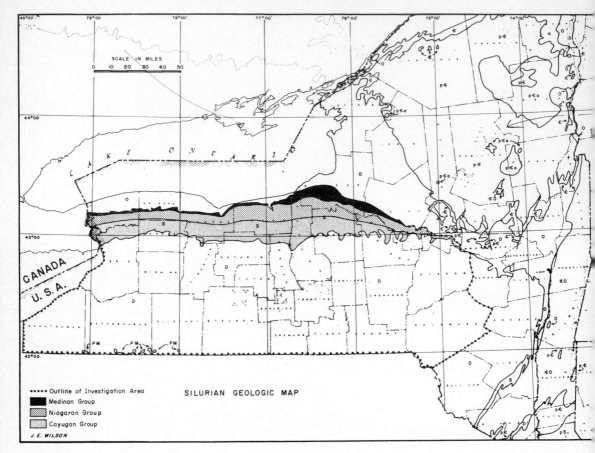

FIG. 15.—Silurian geologic map of New York.

Queenston Shale is difficult to recognize from well data because of the sandstone development of the Queenston in that area. In the eastern part of the state, the Grimsby Sandstone is absent because of nondeposition. The upper part of the Grimsby unit may be correlative with the Oneida Conglomerate.

The youngest Medina formation is the Thorold Sandstone, which overlies the Grimsby Sandstone. It is light gray, fine grained, silty, shaly, and locally dolomitic and hematitic. The Thorold Sandstone is identified easily in well cuttings and is a good marker because it is the first sandstone found below the Lockport. In eastern New York it is correlative with the Oneida Conglomerate.

The Oneida Conglomerate is the basal formation of the Clinton Group in eastern New York

and, as mentioned, is the eastern equivalent of the Thorold Sandstone. Thus it transgresses the Medina-Niagara contact. Throughout its extent it is a white, conglomeratic sandstone which is cemented tightly with silica. Shows of gas have been found in the Oneida Conglomerate, specifically in Madison County, New York, but its capacity as a reservoir seems to be relatively poor.

Niagara Series.—The stratigraphic relations of the Niagara Series are shown in Figure 17. No Clinton formation traverses the state without some change in character.

In western New York the Reynales and Irondequoit Limestones are dolomitic in character. They are true limestones in central New York and disappear by facies change in eastern New York. In the eastern area, the Reynales Limestone is cor-

SERIES NAME			WESTERN NEW YORK	WEST-CENTRAL NEW YORK	CENTRAL NEW YORK	EAST-CENTRAL NEW YORK
CAYUGA	SALINA GROUP			MANLIUS LIMESTONE	MANLIUS LIMESTONE	MANLIUS LIMESTONE
				RONDOUT LIMESTONE	RONDOUT LIMESTONE	RONDOUT LIMESTONE
			COBLESKILL DOLOMITE	COBLESKILL DOLOMITE	COBLESKILL LIMESTONE	COBLESKILL LIMESTONE
			BERTIE LIMESTONE	BERTIE LIMESTONE	BERTIE LIMESTONE	BERTIE LIMESTONE
			CAMILLUS SHALE	CAMILLUS SHALE	CAMILLUS SHALE	CAMILLUS SHALE
			SYRACUSE SALT	SYRACUSE SALT	SYRACUSE SALT	SALT ABSENT
			VERNON SHALE	VERNON SHALE	VERNON SHALE	VERNON SHALE
			PITTSFORD SHALE	PITTSFORD SHALE	PITTSFORD SHALE	PITTSFORD SHALE
NIAGARA	LOCKPORT GROUP		GUELPH	LOCKPORT DOLOMITE	LOCKPORT LIMESTONE	ILION SHALE
			LOCKPORT DOLOMITE			
	CLINTON GROUP		ROCHESTER SHALE	ROCHESTER SHALE	ROCHESTER SHALE	HERKIMER SANDSTONE
			IRONDEQUOIT LIMESTONE	IRONDEQUOIT LIMESTONE	IRONDEQUOIT LIMESTONE	KIRKLAND ORE
				WILLIAMSON SHALE	WILLOWVALE SHALE	WILLOWVALE SHALE / WESTMORELAND ORE / SAUQUOIT SHALE + SANDSTONE
			REYNALES LIMESTONE	WOLCOTT LIMESTONE	WOLCOTT LIMESTONE	
				SODUS SHALE	SODUS SHALE	ONEIDA CONGLOMERATE
			NEAHGA SHALE	BEAR CREEK	BEAR CREEK	
MEDINA	ALBION GROUP		THOROLD SANDSTONE	THOROLD SANDSTONE	THOROLD SANDSTONE	ONEIDA CONGLOMERATE
			GRIMSBY SANDSTONE	GRIMSBY SANDSTONE	GRIMSBY SANDSTONE	
			CABOT HEAD SHALE			
			WHIRLPOOL SANDSTONE	WHIRLPOOL SANDSTONE		

J.E.Wilson

FIG. 16.—Silurian correlation chart of New York.

relative with the Bear Creek Shale of the lower Clinton, and the Irondequoit Limestone merges with the Willowvale Shale of the upper Clinton. Neither the Reynales Limestone nor the Irondequoit Limestone is considered to be a reservoir formation.

The overlying Rochester Shale is approximately 100 ft thick and is gray to dark gray, dolomitic, and silty. It becomes more dolomitic toward the top and appears to be gradational with the overlying Lockport dolomite strata. In eastern New York the Rochester Shale grades laterally into the correlative Herkimer Sandstone.

The youngest rock unit of the Niagara Series is the Lockport Group. It is an excellent marker bed because of the relatively distinct contact with the Cayuga shale section above. The upper part of the Lockport in New York has been termed "Guelph," which is the name of a correlative unit in Ontario, Canada. However, the term "Lockport" is used in this paper for all strata in the Lockport Group. The Lockport is dark-gray, finely crystalline, argillaceous dolomite containing some interbedded shale. The Lockport is dolomite in the western area, but becomes more calcareous in east-central New York and grades into limestone. It shales out eastward and becomes the "Il-

ion shale" of New York state nomenclature in eastern New York. Locally the Lockport dolomite contains reef structures which have yielded gas in several pools in Seneca and Ontario Counties. The Lockport has yielded salt water contaminated with hydrocarbons and hydrogen sulfide gas from several different zones. This fluid, termed "black water" by drillers because of its dark appearance, is found extensively in the state.

In east-central and eastern New York, rocks of the Niagara Series are very different from the section described above. The formation correlative with the Rochester Shale is the Herkimer Sandstone. It ranges from a hematitic and dolomitic sandstone to a conglomeratic red and white sandstone. This formation has been productive of gas in Madison County, New York.

There are several hematitic iron beds in this vicinity, and some of them have been mined. The three most distinct beds are the Kirkland iron ore, the Westmoreland iron ore, and the Wolcott Furnace iron ore. All are red, oölitic hematite deposits, each less than 5 ft thick.

The Willowvale and Williamson Shales are mostly gray to green shale. They have not yielded any shows of water or gas.

The Sauquoit Formation of the Clinton Group

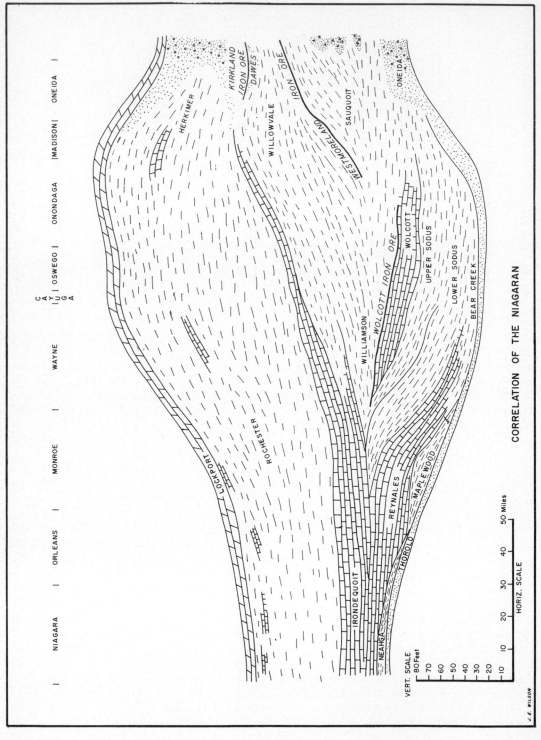

Fig. 17.—Correlations within Niagara Series, New York. Cross section adapted from Gillette (1947).

is predominantly shale west of Madison County, but elsewhere becomes more sandy and conglomeratic. It has yielded gas in seven wells, but no commercial production has been obtained. The presence of salt water in the formation indicates its permeable character.

The Wolcott Limestone is a shaly limestone with a maximum thickness of 25 ft (7.6 m). It is not considered to be a prospective reservoir bed.

The Sodus and Bear Creek Shales are calcareous in part and may be correlative with the Reynales Limestone on the west and the Oneida Conglomerate on the east. They are not deemed to be prospective oil- or gas-productive formations.

The Oneida Conglomerate is described with the Medina section. It is time-transgressive, and is of both Niagara and Medina age.

Cayuga Series.—The Pittsford Shale of the Salina Group is the lowest formation in the Cayuga Series; it is not described in all well studies. It ranges in thickness to a maximum of 20 ft (6 m) and is not present in eastern New York.

The Vernon Shale is composed of red and green shale and siltstone across the state to eastern New York, where its relationship to the Camillus Shale is not clearly defined. Coloration of the Vernon Shale is attributed to the oxidation of the iron in the clastic sediment; ferrous compounds produced greens and ferric compounds produced browns and reds. Because of the distinctive color of the formation, it is identified readily in well cuttings.

The Syracuse Salt of the Salina Group is undoubtedly the most economically important formation of the group; the salt has been mined in several localities in the state. Six salt mines have been operated, five of which were begun before 1908. Four mines are in Livingston County, one is in Genesee County, and one is in Tompkins County. The Syracuse Salt is not a homogeneous salt bed, but contains numerous interbeds of shale, dolomite, and anhydrite. The top of the formation is chosen at the top of the uppermost salt unit and the base is selected at the top of the Vernon Shale. Figure 18 shows the extent and gross thickness of the salt; the greatest thickness is in Schuyler and Chemung Counties.

The Camillus section is shaly and dolomitic. A large quantity of anhydrite and gypsum is present, and the gypsum is mined extensively. The contact with the overlying Bertie Limestone is not defined easily.

The rest of the Cayuga Series is composed of the Bertie Limestone, Cobleskill Dolomite, Rondout Limestone,[10] and Manlius Limestone; these strata consist mainly of carbonate minerals. These formations are present across the study area without gradation into other beds. They are not productive of significant amounts of gas or salt water and therefore are not considered to be prospective fluid-disposal reservoirs.

Stratigraphic summary.—It is necessary to select from the formations described those which could be considered prospective for subsurface waste storage. Because the disposal of waste can be conducted in any of three ways, the possibilities for formation storage will be considered for each and discussed further under "Reservoir Characteristics."

1. Grout injection. Grout injection probably would be conducted in shale sections. If other factors are excluded and only thickness and areal extent are considered, the most prospective Silurian shale formations are the Vernon and Rochester Shales.

2. Storage of solid waste. Solid waste would be stored in underground caverns. The Syracuse Salt would be the most favorable unit for such storage.

3. Injection of liquid waste. Liquid waste would be injected into formations which are known to have both porosity and permeability sufficient to allow free flow of fluids. On the basis of past performance, the following formations, which have yielded gas or salt water, can be considered to be prospective reservoirs: Lockport dolomite, Herkimer Sandstone, Sauquoit sandstones and shales, Oneida Conglomerate, Thorold Sandstone, Grimsby Sandstone, and Whirlpool Sandstone. Also, the Syracuse Salt, though not having native porosity and permeability, can be mined or leached out and thus made a storage reservoir for liquids.

STRUCTURE

The regional dip of the Silurian strata is shown on Figures 19 and 20. The base of the Medina and the top of the Lockport were selected for

[10] The Rondout and Manlius now are considered to be Devonian (Fisher, 1959; Rickard, 1964). (Ed.)

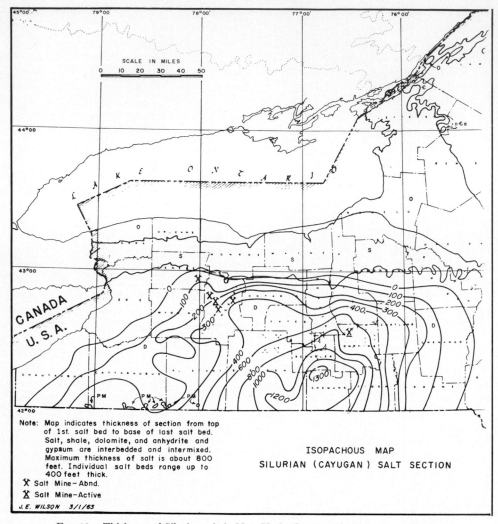

Fig. 18.—Thickness of Silurian salt in New York. Contour intervals, 100 and 200 ft.

mapping because their determination from well data is relatively clear in comparison to other formational contacts. The regional dip of the Lockport is approximately 65 ft/mi southward; the dip of the base of the Medina is approximately 80 ft/mi southward. Thus the Lockport-to-base-of-Medina interval increases 15 ft/mi southward.

Surface anticlinal axes present in the south-central part of the state are shown on Figure 5. Stratigraphic thinning tends to diminish doming with depth, however, because it raises the flank of the fold in the direction of thinning (generally the northwest flank, because all formations thin regionally toward the north and northwest). Thus, where the rate of thinning between the surface formation and a subsurface horizon is greater than the rate of northwest dip of the surface bed, the anticlinal closure will be absent in the subsurface. This is thought to be the circumstance along many of the anticlines in New York state.

Wells drilled along the major surface anticlinal trends have shown that faulting affects the Lower

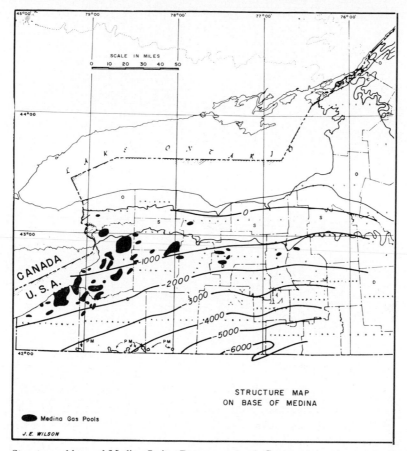

FIG. 19.—Structure of base of Medina Series. Datum, sea level. Contour interval, 1,000 ft (304.8 m).

Devonian strata. However, this is not necessarily true of the Silurian rocks, particularly the formations deposited before the Syracuse Salt. Relatively few of the many Devonian Oriskany wells have penetrated below the salt section. From those that have, data are insufficient to show the nature of faulting in the Lower Silurian section. Several persons have postulated that most faulting decreases with depth because of flowage of the salt beds. This theory appears to be plausible, but remains to be proved.

A second major area of faulting is the region adjacent to the Adirondack highland in northeastern New York. Numerous strike-slip, normal, and reverse faults have been mapped on the surface, but their southern and western extent in the subsurface is undetermined.

Elsewhere in the area of investigation, no major fault displacements have been reported. Numerous structural anomalies of small magnitude are present, but can be attributed to local warping of beds rather than to fault disturbances.

RESERVOIR CHARACTERISTICS

The formations which have been selected as prospective storage beds will be considered according to the type of disposal program.

Grout Injection

Vernon Shale.—There are no known reports of natural gas or salt water from this formation. Lithologically, it is composed of both red and green shale. Chemical analyses are given below

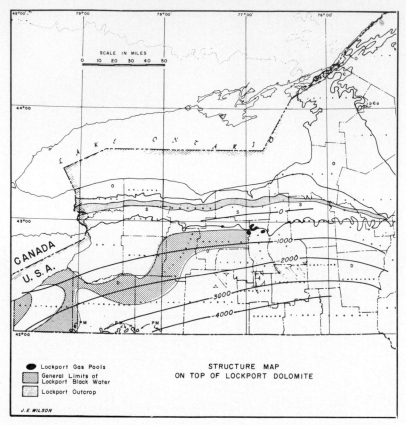

FIG. 20.—Structure of top of Lockport dolomite. Datum, sea level. Contour interval, 1,000 ft.

for a specimen of each. Both samples are from Onondaga County, New York.

Chemical Compound	Red (%)	Green (%)
SiO_2	52.30	33.14
Al_2O_3	18.85	11.26
Fe_2O_3	6.55	2.31
FeO	—	1.06
CaO	3.36	16.50
MgO	4.49	8.77
K_2O	4.65	2.56
Na_2O	1.35	1.21
CO_2	3.04	20.48
H_2O	5.30	2.88
	99.89	100.17

Porosity evaluation can be made from gamma-ray–neutron logs, but such calculations for shale are very questionable. Permeability data are not available.

Rochester Shale.—There are no known reports of natural gas or salt water from this formation. No data are available on permeability, and porosity calculations from the gamma-ray–neutron logs are very questionable. The Rochester Shale at its type locality is about 85 ft (26 m) thick. Except for the basal 10 ft which is brownish gray, the shale is dark bluish gray. The lower few feet and the upper 15 ft are relatively unfossiliferous, but the rest contains abundant fossils. In all but the lower 19 ft, limestone layers are abundant. The lower 25–30 ft of the formation is a weak shale which on exposure quickly disintegrates into a blue to brown clay. The upper 20–25 ft is more massive and more resistant, and is slightly dolomitic.

Storage of Solid Wastes

Syracuse Salt.—There are no known reports of natural gas from this formation. Salt water present in the formation may be the result of mining operations. The chemical analyses of artificial brines obtained from the salt show that sodium chloride comprises more than 95 percent of the sample, and that the rest is composed of calcium sulfate, calcium chloride, and magnesium chloride. Artificial brines are obtained by pumping fresh water into salt wells. When the water comes in contact with the rock salt, it becomes saturated with saline materials and then is forced to the surface, generally by compressed air. This is basically the method of leaching out salt cavities, and has been employed widely to extract salt commercially.

The Syracuse Salt, where pure, is essentially nonporous and impermeable and therefore can be both a storage reservoir where mined or leached out and an impermeable container, provided that the liquid to be stored will not dissolve salt. With respect to storage of hazardous waste, the following statements were made by E. G. Struxness of Oak Ridge National Laboratory (Northern Ohio Geol. Soc., 1962).

. . . the disposal of radioactive waste in properly located space obtained by the mining out of rock salt has many advantages:
1. Salt has considerable strength so that pillars left in mining may support the roof.
2. It is impervious to the passage of water because of its plasticity and crystalline structure so that mined-out space is very dry.
3. It has a sufficiently high melting point and a comparatively high thermal conductivity so that the heat generated in radioactive wastes can be dissipated in the salt without exceeding predetermined temperature rises if care is taken to design the size, shape, and spacing of waste containers.
4. The relative ease and low cost of mining out space specially designed for this purpose.

Injection of Liquid Waste

Lockport dolomite.—In west-central New York the Lockport can be considered to be a siliceous dolomite. It is made up of rhomboidal grains of dolomitic calcite, many of which enclose grains of quartz. Small quantities of chlorite, sericite, epidote, pyrite, and carbonaceous matter are present with minor percentages of feldspar, pyroxene, mica, garnet, and zircon.

Three productive gas pools have been found in reef structures in the Lockport, but no analysis of the gas produced is available. The pools, shown on Figure 20, are in Seneca and Ontario Counties, New York. Of the three, the Geneva pool—located in the town of Phelps, Ontario County, and the town of Waterloo, Seneca County—was the largest in areal extent. Forty-six wells were drilled in the pool, 26 of which were producers. No salt water was found. Individual flows ranged from 15 to 25,000 Mcf. The total pool reserve was very small, but deliverability was very high.

Lockport "black water," the general areal extent of which is shown on Figure 20, is found in several intervals within the dolomite. An analysis of a sample of this fluid collected just west of New York state showed the following characteristics.

Specific gravity	1.1728
pH	6.53
Chloride ion	161,400 ppm
Total solids	342,068 ppm

The water was being produced at the rate of 10 gal (37.85 l) per hour, which is representative of flows found elsewhere from the Lockport reservoir.

Herkimer and Sauquoit sandstones.—Production information on the Herkimer Sandstone is not available for publication. There is an appreciable gas reserve, but further exploration and development are needed. The only area in which this formation is productive is Madison County.

Sandstone of the Sauquoit Formation has yielded several gas shows in Madison and Otsego Counties, but has not proved commercial. Saltwater shows also have been obtained.

It is believed on the basis of available information that neither formation is capable of storing large volumes of fluid. Much additional drilling is required before these beds can be evaluated fully.

Oneida Conglomerate.—This formation is present only in east and east-central New York; gas shows have been found in several wells. However, its reservoir capacity is not proved, and it cannot be recommended without further drilling and evaluation.

Grimsby and Whirlpool Sandstones.—The Medina pools in New York state are outlined on Figure 19. In Ontario and Livingston Counties, the rock pressure of gas found in Medina rocks at a depth of 3,000 ft is slightly more than 600 psi. This is lower than the hydrostatic pressure for that depth, which would be more than 1,000 psi. The following analysis of the gas obtained in the Bristol pool in Ontario County is typical of the Medina gas found elsewhere in the state.

Component	Percent
Oxygen	0.02
Nitrogen	3.81
Helium	0.28
Hydrogen	Trace
Methane	92.48
Ethane	3.05
Propane	0.28
Isobutane	0.05
N-butane	0.02
Isopentane	0.01

Calculated dry heating value: 1,003 Btu
Specific gravity: 0.5911

An analysis of the salt water obtained from Medina rocks in the Leicester pool, Livingston County, is as follows.

Component	ppm
Sodium	79,000
Calcium	38,000
Magnesium	3,174
Potassium	1,376
Iron	130
Chloride	199,018
Iodide	22
Bromide	1,800

Specific gravity: 1.226 @ 68°F
pH: 4.6

This water was being produced at the rate of 150 gal per hour.

Porosity values have been computed for the Medina from gamma-ray–neutron logs in wells throughout the productive trend. The porosity averages between 7 and 10 percent as calculated from these logs. Because of the nature of the neutron tool, however, only water-filled porosity is determined, and true porosity is higher than the value calculated if water saturation is less than 100 percent. This fact is substantiated by other logging methods and by one core analysis. True Medina porosity values average between 10 and 15 percent. The only core analysis available, from a Medina well in Seneca County, shows an average porosity of 14 percent, an average water saturation of 59.4 percent, and an average horizontal permeability of 0.52 md.

Open flows from Medina rocks range from slight shows of gas to almost 10 million cu ft in wells that are fractured hydraulically. The average productive well is completed at a flow of approximately 2 million cu ft after fracture treatment. Average production for the Medina pools has been estimated to be approximately 2 million cu ft per acre for the total productive section.

The Medina sandstone strata contain a considerable quantity of shale and shaly sandstone. No chemical or mineralogic analysis of the formation was available to the writer.

SELECTED DISPOSAL RESERVOIRS

Because there is an active drilling campaign for natural gas in formations of Silurian and pre-Silurian age in New York state, care must be taken in the recommendation of prospective storage units. A waste-storage reservoir will be required to have a known set of geologic limits and an areal extent which could be covered by acquisition of leases. On this basis, the following formations are recommended as prospective in order of preference. The major limitations of each are noted.

Syracuse Salt.—The Syracuse Salt is relatively widespread through the central part of the state and the thickness is more than ample for storage. A previously mined-out cavern could be converted to specification, or a new cavern could be excavated. Location would be determined by (1) economic consideration of depth, (2) height of cavern required, and (3) presence of gas pools (these areas would be avoided).

Because of its widespread extent (Fig. 18), the Syracuse Salt is believed to be the most promising section of the Silurian.

Medina sandstone strata.—Both the Grimsby and Whirlpool Sandstones have been productive of gas in western and central New York and are prospective storage reservoirs throughout this trend. Selection of a site would depend on the estimated quantity of material to be injected underground. Reservoirs of insufficient volumetric capacity would be eliminated.

Because of current Medina drilling activity elsewhere in the state, only areas in westernmost New York are considered to be prospective for storage. However, further investigation will be required, particularly concerning the production history of the pools.

Lockport dolomite.—Prospects for storage in Lockport dolomite are very limited. The Lockport is considered only in areas where it is productive from reefs and not in the areas which have yielded "black water," because the "blackwater" rates of flow are very small. The selection of a site must be preceded by a careful investigation of the hydrodynamics of an area of interest; the drilling of test holes and measurement of fluid levels and pressures would be required.

The Lockport-reef gas pools in Seneca and Ontario Counties may be used for natural-gas storage in the future and therefore would become unavailable for waste disposal. It would then be necessary to find similar reef conditions elsewhere, which would be difficult and expensive. Thus the Lockport is prospective, but is very limited in possibilities for waste disposal.

Vernon Shale.—The Vernon Shale is recommended for its possibilities for grout injection. It is more than 800 ft (244 m) thick in Steuben County, much thicker than the Rochester Shale, which is only slightly more than 100 ft thick. These are the only Silurian shale sections which are continuous throughout the state. The Camillus shales are too impure to warrant consideration.

The Vernon Shale contains a large quantity of iron oxides, and the chemical suitability for grout injection must be determined.

Because of its large areal extent, the Vernon Shale is available for injection in the entire area of investigation south of the outcrop of the youngest Niagara rocks.

DEVONIAN

NUMBER AND QUALITY OF WELL DATA

Location descriptions and other information are available for about 1,500 wells within the area of interest. It is estimated that nearly as many wells have been drilled in northern Chautauqua and Cattaraugus Counties and in Erie and Wyoming Counties. Only critical wells in the latter area were plotted and used.

Data are available for about 300 wells for which specific locations are not known. Most of these wells are in the western counties of New York.

About 47 mechanical logs, 62 Geo-Log sample

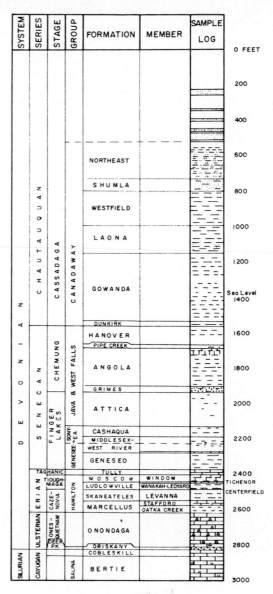

FIG. 21.—Correlation chart of Robert Bates No. 1 well. Adapted from Donnerstag and McDonald (1952). Terminology altered to conform to geologic map of New York (Broughton *et al.*, 1962).

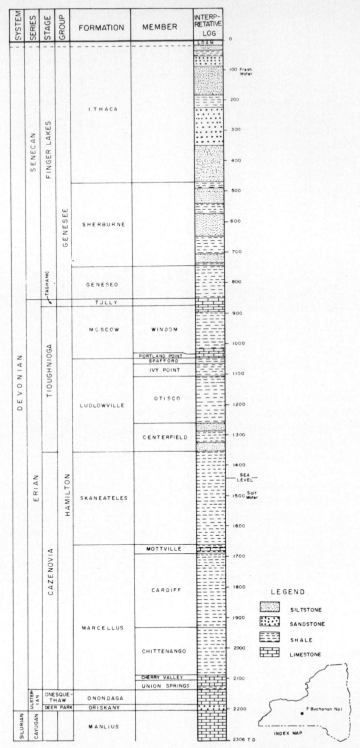

FIG. 22.—Correlation chart of F. E. Buchanan No. 1 well. Adopted from Wiggins (1954). Terminology altered to conform to New York State geologic map (Broughton *et al.*, 1962).

Westfield- Clymer	Dunkirk- Chautauqua	Silver Creek- Cherry Creek- Jamestown	Eden- Cattaraugus- Randolph	Springville- Ellicottville- Salamanca	Arcade- Franklinville- Olean	Portage- Angelica- Belmont	Nunda- Canaseraga- Wellsville	
PANAMA	PANAMA·	PANAMA	PANAMA	PANAMA	PANAMA	PANAMA	PANAMA	CONEWANGO GROUP
ELLICOTT DEXTERVILLE	ELLICOTT DEXTERVILLE	ELLICOTT DEXTERVILLE	• •	• • CUBA	"BUTT'S Zone 9" "BUTT'S Zone10" "BUTT'S Zone II" CUBA	• • CUBA	GERMANIA WHITESVILLE HINSDALE WELLSVILLE CUBA	CONNEAUT GROUP
NORTHEAST SHUMLA WESTFIELD LAONA GOWANDA (Concealed)	NORTHEAST SHUMLA WESTFIELD LAONA GOWANDA SOUTH WALES DUNKIRK	NORTHEAST SHUMLA WESTFIELD LAONA GOWANDA SOUTH WALES DUNKIRK	"MACHIAS" "MACHIAS" • SOUTH WALES DUNKIRK	"MACHIAS" • SOUTH WALES DUNKIRK	"MACHIAS" • HUME CANASERAGA SOUTH WALES DUNKIRK	"MACHIAS" RUSHFORD CANEADEA HUME CANASERAGA SOUTH WALES DUNKIRK	"MACHIAS" • CANASERAGA SOUTH WALES DUNKIRK	CANADAWAY GROUP
(Concealed)	HANOVER	HANOVER	HANOVER	HANOVER	HANOVER	WISCOY	WISCOY	JAVA AND WEST FALLS GROUPS

N.C. Privrasky

• = Undifferentiated

FIG. 23.—General relationship of members of Upper Devonian Series in southwestern New York.

descriptions, and 37 descriptions from other sources were available for examination. These represent 113 wells throughout the state of New York that could be used for correlation purposes and for identifying lithologic units of the Devonian System. However, many descriptions are incomplete.

Driller's logs were not used in any interpretation because of their inadequacy.

For the stratigraphic phase of the study, Geo-Log sample descriptions were relied on for control because of their widespread distribution and relative abundance. This method insured a measure of consistency in the sample descriptions. However, the other available descriptions were examined and incorporated where practical.

INTERVAL STUDIED

Only in the southernmost parts of Cattaraugus and Allegany Counties and the southeastern corner of Chautauqua County is the entire Devonian section found in drilling; this is the only area in New York underlain by Mississippian rocks. The total thickness of Devonian rocks in this area is about 3,500 ft (1,067 m) compared to an expected thickness of 8,000–10,000 ft (2,438–3,048 m) in southern Broome and Delaware Counties. In the latter area the Mississippian rocks are absent, probably because of erosion, and the thick-

ness of the missing section cannot be determined with certainty.

REGIONAL STRATIGRAPHIC RELATIONSHIPS

The geologic literature regarding the Devonian System of New York is replete with the names of lithologic units that have been defined and redefined. The stratigraphic correlation chart of the Devonian System being completed by the New York State Science Service was not available at the time of this writing (May 1963).[11]

Facies changes make lateral correlation difficult, especially in the subsurface where fossils are sparse or where mutilation by the drill bit has made their identification difficult if not impossible. The attempt by two authors to correlate subsurface units with the stratigraphic nomenclature of nearby areas is shown on Figures 21 and 22. Figure 21 represents the section found in the No. 1 Robert Bates, Chautauqua quadrangle, Chautauqua County, and Figure 22 represents the section penetrated by the New York State Natural Gas Corp. No. 1 F. E. Buchanan well, Moravia quadrangle, Tompkins County, New York. The two wells are about 160 mi (257 km) apart.

Figure 23 shows the correlation of the Upper Devonian Series of southwestern New York. The

[11] See Rickard (1964). (Ed.)

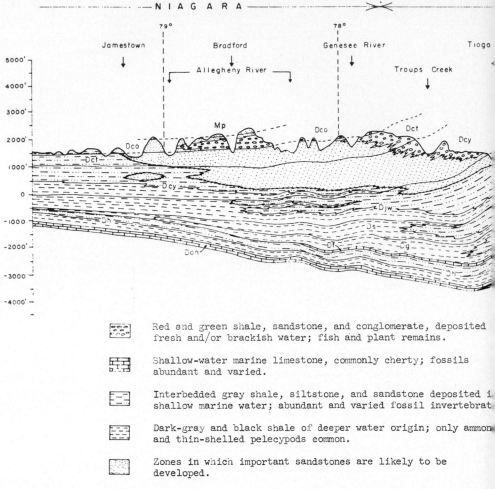

Red and green shale, sandstone, and conglomerate, deposited fresh and/or brackish water; fish and plant remains.

Shallow-water marine limestone, commonly cherty; fossils abundant and varied.

Interbedded gray shale, siltstone, and sandstone deposited i shallow marine water; abundant and varied fossil invertebrat

Dark-gray and black shale of deeper water origin; only ammon and thin-shelled pelecypods common.

Zones in which important sandstones are likely to be developed.

FIG. 24.—Cross section of Devonian strata along New York–Pennsylvania border showing relationships of facies and approximate zones of sandstone development in Upper Devonian Series. Modified after Broughton *et al.* (1962).

section extends from western Chautauqua County to western Steuben County. The writer attempted to adopt stratigraphic nomenclature which conforms to the terminology used on the geologic map of New York (Broughton *et al.*, 1962).

The Devonian System is composed of marine and nonmarine rocks. The nonmarine redbed sequence has been referred to broadly as the "Catskill facies," which is the predominant facies in eastern New York. Figure 24 shows the relation of the "Catskill facies" to the several marine units in the western part of the state. Figure

24 also shows the correlation of the several lithologic units of the Devonian System. Zones in which sandstone development can be expected also are shown.

STRATIGRAPHY

Lower Devonian Series.—The Lower Devonian Series is composed predominantly of limestone, the Oriskany Sandstone being at the top where present. At the outcrop the base of this series is placed above the top of the Cobleskill Dolomite and within the Chrysler (Rondout) Limestone.

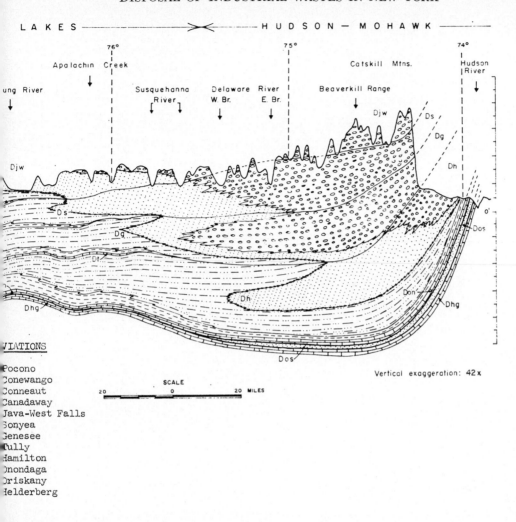

LAKES ——————— >< ——— H U D S O N — M O H A W K ———

Vertical exaggeration: 42x

SCALE

20   0   20 MILES

VIATIONS

Pocono
Conewango
Conneaut
Canadaway
Java-West Falls
Sonyea
Genesee
Tully
Hamilton
Onondaga
Oriskany
Helderberg

These units are difficult to identify in the subsurface, and there may be considerable doubt about the position of the Silurian-Devonian contact.

The thickness of the Lower Devonian Series, including the Oriskany Sandstone, ranges from a featheredge in southwestern New York to possibly 800 ft in the southeastern part of the state.

The Oriskany Sandstone is quartzose sandstone that ranges in thickness from a wedge edge to 70 ft (21 m) or more in the south-central part of New York. Figure 25 shows the distribution of the Oriskany Sandstone in New York.

The Oriskany contains both silica and calcite cement. In New York, as elsewhere in the Appalachian basin, this sandstone appears to contain primary porosity within the siliceous zones and seems to be tight throughout the very calcareous zones.

The recoverable reserves of gas, measured in cubic feet per acre, vary substantially among the fields. This variance is independent of the total thickness of the Oriskany Sandstone, suggesting that the net effective porosity varies laterally and may be very different in adjacent areas, both in

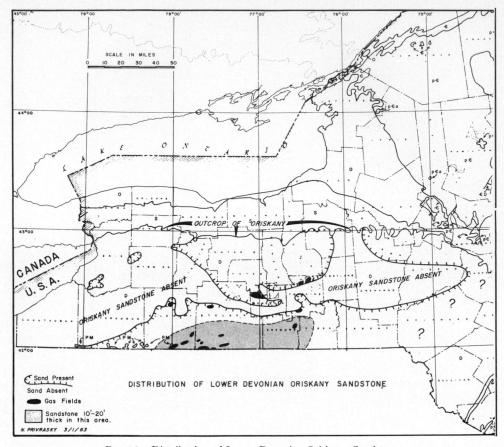

FIG. 25.—Distribution of Lower Devonian Oriskany Sandstone.

total effective thickness and in stratigraphic position within the sandstone zone.

Middle Devonian Series.—The Middle Devonian Series is composed of the Tully Limestone
at the top, the Onondaga Limestone at the base,
and an intervening shale section.

Although reefs have been identified in outcrops
of the Onondaga Limestone in east-central New
York, none has been identified in the subsurface.

The intervening shale section has been divided
into the Moscow-Ludlowville, Skaneateles, and
Marcellus shales at the outcrop, but may be referred to more conveniently as the "Hamilton
Group" (Fig. 21). This shale sequence grades
eastward into a predominantly siltstone facies and
a sandy siltstone facies (Fig. 24).

The Tully Limestone is a very argillaceous

limestone that is present throughout much of
southern New York. Gas production has been reported from the Tully Limestone and the Hamilton Group, but only in small quantities; the gas
is consumed locally.

Upper Devonian Series.—The Upper Devonian
Series consists of interbedded shale, siltstone, and
sandstone. These units are outlined broadly in
Figure 24. The series contains several fresh-water
aquifers and, because it is at relatively shallow
depth, has been penetrated by numerous borings.
The records of many old wells have been lost,
and because most of the wells probably were
plugged inadequately or were left open, they provide possible avenues of escape for injected
fluids. Because of the risk of contamination of
fresh-water aquifers, rocks of the Upper Devo-

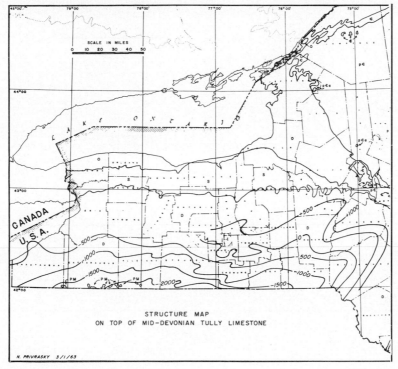

SCALE IN MILES
0 10 20 30 40 50

STRUCTURE MAP
ON TOP OF MID–DEVONIAN TULLY LIMESTONE

N. PRIVRASKY 3/1/63

FIG. 26.—Structure of top of Tully Limestone. Datum is sea level. Contour interval, 500 ft (152.4 m).

nian Series are considered to be inappropriate for use as disposal reservoirs.

STRUCTURE

Regional dip is generally southward; the rate increases from about 60 ft/mi in western New York to about 160 ft/mi in south-central New York, as shown by the structural contours of the top of the Tully Limestone (Fig. 26).

The several major interruptions in the regional dip are principally in south-central New York. The structural configuration of the Tully Limestone is known to decrease in intensity northward and westward.

There appears to be some difference between the structural configuration mapped from surface exposures and that mapped in the subsurface. This difference is illustrated in Figure 27, where both surface and subsurface structural contours are shown. The difference may be more apparent than real because of inadequate structural control. However, the selection of a waste-disposal

site will depend on detailed subsurface analysis rather than on surface mapping.

RESERVOIR CHARACTERISTICS

Oriskany Sandstone.—A relationship has been reported between structure and porosity in the Oriskany Sandstone in some of the gas fields of New York. Porosity appears to be confined to the structurally highest part, and there is perhaps only a small quantity of salt water downdip. Farther downdip the Oriskany Sandstone is nonporous and devoid of gas and water.

The average porosity of the Oriskany Sandstone in New York is reported to be about 9 percent. In the more productive fields the sandstone is very permeable, and it seems to be an accepted fact that this permeability is caused by open fractures. No core analyses are available for the Oriskany Sandstone in New York.

Upper Devonian sandstones.—Figure 28 shows the several sandstone beds present in the Upper Devonian Series of New York. There are about

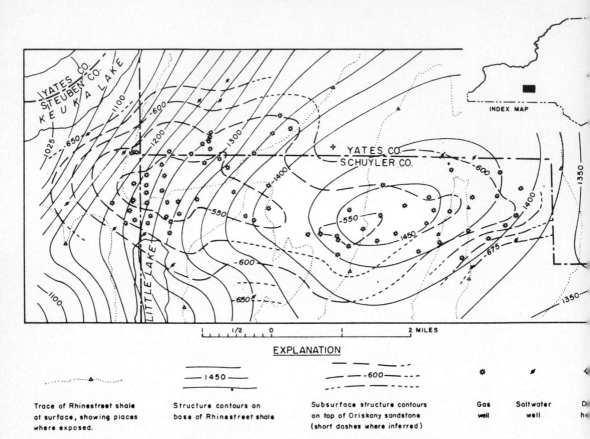

Fig. 27.—Map of Wayne-Dundee gas field showing relations between surface and subsurface structure. Datum is mean sea level. Contour interval, 25 ft (7.62 m). Only wells that were used for control of subsurface structure are shown. Adapted from Bradley and Pepper (1938).

20 oil-productive sandstone bodies, some of which may be correlative with one another. The main oil sands in Cattaraugus County are the Bradford Third and the Chipmunk. The Richburg is the main productive sand in Allegany County. Many of the oil sands are said to be "dry," that is, no mobile salt water is present. In such areas the oil commonly is found in synclines.

In some places there are salt-water-bearing sandstone beds above and below the main productive sandstones. For example, there is a salt-water-bearing sandstone 30 ft below the top of the Chipmunk sandstone, and care must be taken not to penetrate the water zone in the event of production from the Chipmunk.

The following are average porosity values for Upper Devonian sandstones.

Unit	Percent
Chipmunk	22.5
Bradford Second	16.1
Bradford Third	14.5
Richburg	13.0

The permeability of the Richburg sandstone ranges from 3 to 10 md, and that of the Bradford Third sandstone ranges from 5 to 15 md.

Table I is a core analysis of the Bradford Third sand and Table II is a core analysis of the Chipmunk sand. Both cores are from the South Penn Oil Co. No. 282 Rumsey-Devonian well in the Bradford field. Many more core analyses are available for the productive sandstones of the Bradford field.

The individual sandstone beds are relatively

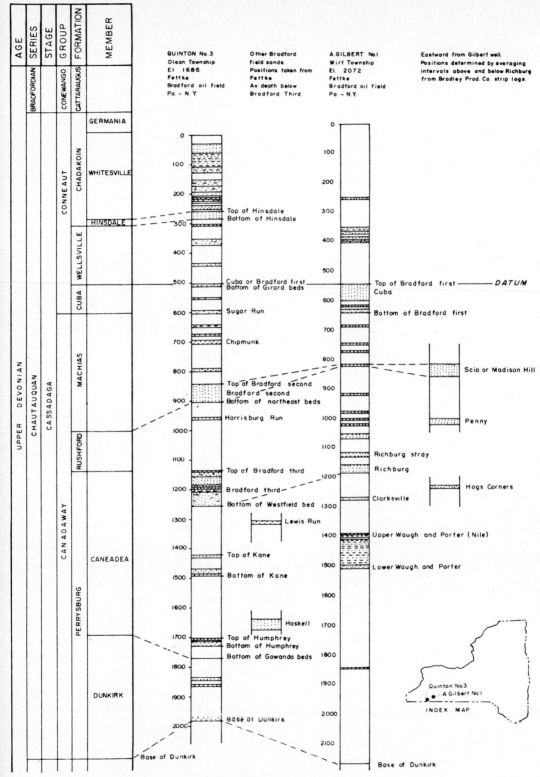

FIG. 28.—Correlations, relative positions, thicknesses, and depths of the several Upper Devonian sandstone units. Adapted from Kreidler (1953).

TABLE I. CORE ANALYSIS OF BRADFORD THIRD
SAND, SOUTH PENN OIL CO. WELL No. 282
RUMSEY-DEVONIAN

Depth (ft)	Porosity (%)	Permeability (md)	Water Saturation (%)	Oil Saturation (%)
1,219.8	9.82	0.44	36.5	18.7
1,220.8	5.24	0.13	32.7	38.1
1,222.8	5.76	0.05	17.8	58.1
1,251.5	8.48	0.05	15.1	52.2
1,253.5	6.47	0.05	21.8	57.1

thin, but the combined thickness is significant, as shown in Figure 29.

The average rock type of the Bradford sandstone sequence is described as containing 30 percent rock fragments (older Paleozoic rocks), 3–4 percent biotite and muscovite, 5–12 percent clayey material (mostly shreds of biotite and sericite), practically no feldspar, and 60–65 percent quartz grains.

HYDRODYNAMIC DATA

No data were available to the writer for evaluation of the hydrodynamic qualities of the reservoirs. A thorough inquiry among the several companies operating in the area may yield valuable information.

SELECTED DISPOSAL RESERVOIRS

Lower Devonian carbonate rocks.—The Lower Devonian carbonate rocks are not considered for the injection of waste material. However, work in any specific area may prove them to be of value as secondary objectives.

Oriskany Sandstone.—The Oriskany Sandstone is a prospective reservoir for waste disposal, but because of the apparently erratic porosity and permeability of this sandstone, considerably more analytical work must be done before a disposal site can be selected. Although the sandstone body may be sufficiently thick, the porosity and permeability may prove to be too low to allow its use for waste disposal. The character of the natural fracturing of the sandstone must be understood thoroughly before artificial fracturing is attempted.

Middle Devonian shales.—Grout injection into the relatively thick shale sequence of the Hamilton Group is possible. The small volumes of gas obtained from this shale attest to the presence of natural fractures.

Upper Devonian sandstones.—Although the individual sandstone beds in the Upper Devonian Series are thin, the cumulative sandstone thickness is sufficient to allow the injection of waste liquids in significant quantities. The relatively shallow depths, the numerous shallow wells for which locations are not available, and the erratic nature of the individual sandstone beds would be major considerations in the selection of reservoirs for waste-disposal injection. However, for reasons already given, Upper Devonian sandstones probably should not be considered for disposal reservoirs.

Upper Devonian shales.—The relatively thick shale sequence is desirable for the injection of waste by grouting. However, this unit is considered to be only a secondary objective.

TABLE II. CORE ANALYSIS OF CHIPMUNK SAND,
SOUTH PENN OIL CO. WELL No. 282
RUMSEY–DEVONIAN

Depth (ft)	Porosity (%)	Permeability (md)	Water Saturation (%)	Oil Saturation (%)
780.5	11.69	0.23	18.5	29.8
781.5	8.94	0.24	18.0	44.7
783.5	13.69	0.73	17.9	27.3
786.5	15.95	5.00	38.5	20.3
787.5	17.61	11.90	45.3	17.3
788.5	18.53	3.53	44.2	17.3
789.5	15.14	0.80	31.4	23.8
790.5	13.18	1.27	27.5	29.6
791.5	14.12	0.63	23.6	27.5
792.5	14.34	0.44	26.1	26.3
793.7	10.50	0.48	13.4	38.1
795.0	10.21	0.37	26.8	32.6
797.5	12.30	0.93	24.3	28.1
798.5	12.71	1.17	26.4	30.2
802.0	12.33	0.50	28.1	32.6
803.0	14.32	1.32	33.7	31.4
804.0	13.52	0.98	27.7	31.1
805.0	9.89	0.32	34.1	27.9
806.0	14.16	1.07	28.1	33.0
807.0	12.99	1.02	30.9	34.9
808.0	13.21	0.87	29.1	32.1
823.5	8.66	0.32	27.1	37.1
835.4	10.53	0.20	29.5	40.1
842.5	11.84	0.29	26.4	31.9
843.5	11.94	0.42	25.6	41.7

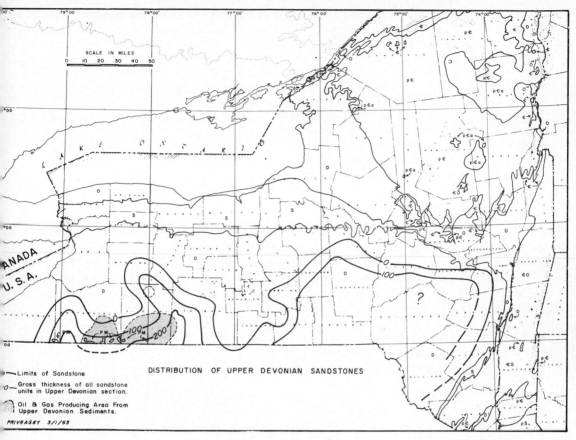

SCALE IN MILES
0 10 20 30 40 50

DISTRIBUTION OF UPPER DEVONIAN SANDSTONES

Limits of Sandstone

Gross thickness of all sandstone
units in Upper Devonian section.

Oil & Gas Producing Area From
Upper Devonian Sediments.

PRIVRASKY 3/1/63

Fig. 29.—Total thickness of combined Upper Devonian sandstone units. Contour interval, 100 ft.

SUMMARY OF POTENTIAL RESERVOIRS

SANDSTONE RESERVOIRS

Upper Devonian sandstone beds are restricted to southern New York, where they crop out at the surface and dip southward into the subsurface to a maximum depth of about 3,000 ft at the Pennsylvania-New York boundary. The sandstone generally is shaly and lenticular and ranges from very fine grained to conglomeratic. At shallow depths the beds are fresh-water aquifers; deeper in the subsurface they contain salt water, gas, or oil. Thousands of wells have been drilled to these objectives, but most of the drilling was done before 1920, and the location and status of many wells are unknown. Considerable data are available for these reservoirs in the Bradford field. Gross sandstone thickness is estimated to be a maximum of 200 ft (61 m). Thickness of individual beds rarely exceeds 20 ft.

The Middle Devonian Oriskany Sandstone is restricted to southern New York. Maximum thickness is 50 ft and average thickness is between 10 and 20 ft. Distribution is irregular, and reservoir conditions range from very poor to good. The sandstone is clean, well sorted, quartzitic, slightly to moderately calcareous, and fine to medium grained. The Oriskany crops out at the surface and dips southward into the subsurface to a depth of about 4,000 ft at the New York-Pennsylvania boundary. Several gas fields produce from this reservoir in New York, and numerous wells have found salt water in the Oriskany. Hundreds of wells have drilled through the Oriskany and many data are available, especially from some of the gas-storage pools.

Lower Silurian (Medina) sandstone beds are present in the subsurface in most of western New York. These beds, generally called "Thorold," "Grimsby," and "Whirlpool" Sandstones, are gas reservoirs in the western counties. Elsewhere they are generally tight, and water flows are not found commonly in them. The Medina sandstone beds crop out at the surface and dip southward to a depth of about 6,000 ft in south-central New York. The sandstone is generally shaly, quartzitic, slightly calcareous, and fine to medium grained. Thousands of wells have been drilled to Medina sandstone beds, most of them before 1920. Data from old wells are poor or lacking; data from recently drilled tests are good. A few of the old gas fields still are producing, many are used for gas storage, and others apparently are completely abandoned.

The Cambrian Theresa Dolomite is present in the subsurface in most of the southern part of western New York. It subcrops below Black River (Middle Ordovician) limestone at a depth of about 4,000 ft (1,219 m) and dips southward to a depth of about 11,000 ft (3,353 m) in Steuben County. No hydrocarbons have been found in this formation in commercial quantities, but several wells have found substantial flows of salt water in it. It is sparsely tested, having been penetrated by fewer than 50 wells. The thickness of the sandstone beds ranges from zero to 250 ft. Available data are fair to good.

The Cambrian Potsdam Sandstone is the most widespread reservoir in New York. It subcrops beneath Black River limestone at a depth of 1,000 ft or less and dips southward to a depth of more than 12,000 ft at the New York-Pennsylvania boundary. The Potsdam Sandstone is as thick as 410 ft and averages 200 ft in thickness in much of the area. There is minor gas production from this reservoir in the northern area, and many wells have had flows of salt water from it. Fewer than 50 wells have penetrated the Potsdam Sandstone, but most of these are old shallow tests; therefore, data are scarce. The Potsdam Sandstone crops out in Ontario and in places around the edge of the Adirondack uplift. The sandstone is fine to medium grained, dolomitic and calcareous in places, and poorly to well sorted.

The Potsdam and Theresa sandstones appear to be the most promising reservoirs for the disposal of liquid wastes. However, the other units described may be adequate in places. There may be other suitable sandstone bodies in some areas, but generally the sandstones appear to lack sufficient porosity and permeability.

SALT BEDS

An estimated 8,500 sq mi in western New York is underlain by beds of rock salt of Silurian (Cayuga) age. The beds range up to 548 ft (167 m) in thickness and are interbedded and intermixed with shale, dolomite, and anhydrite. Depth to the salt ranges from about 500 ft to more than 4,000 ft. The salt is reported to start creeping at a depth of about 3,000 ft. Several shafts have been sunk to mine salt, but only two mines are active. Numerous wells have been drilled through the salt. Data are fair but are mostly from around the mines; elsewhere, details are lacking. The Silurian salt beds offer possibilities for storage of wastes in insoluble, solid form. It also may be possible to store very toxic liquid wastes in salt jugs.[12]

CARBONATE RESERVOIRS

Certain limestone and dolomite beds in western New York are reservoirs in places and may be of interest. These are the Silurian Lockport dolomite in western New York (reef zones) and the Cambrian Little Falls sandy dolomite in Madison and Chenango Counties. These carbonate reservoirs may be suitable for disposal of liquid wastes. Other carbonate reservoirs have porosity locally, but none appear to have continuous porous zones over large areas.

SHALE SECTIONS

Up to 3,000 ft of Upper Devonian shale and more than 2,000 ft of Upper Ordovician shale and siltstone offer possibilities for grout injection in much of western New York. Waste products in insoluble form also might be stored in rooms mined in the Upper Devonian shale section. Thinner shale beds are present in the Silurian and

---

[12] Man-made cavities or chambers in salt which are used for storage of natural gas, LPG, liquid and other industrial wastes, *etc.*

Middle Ordovician rocks, and these may be suitable for grout injection.

SELECTED REFERENCES

Adkison, W. L., ed., 1966, Stratigraphic cross section of Paleozoic rocks, Colorado to New York: Tulsa, Oklahoma, Am. Assoc. Petroleum Geologists Cross Sec. Pub. 4, 58 p., 7 pls.

Alling, H. L., 1928, The geology and origin of the Silurian salt of New York State: New York State Mus. and Sci. Service Bull. 275.

—— and L. I. Briggs, 1961, Stratigraphy of Upper Silurian Cayugan evaporites: Am. Assoc. Petroleum Geologists Bull., v. 45, no. 4, p. 515–547.

Amsden, T. W., 1955, Lithofacies map of Lower Silurian deposits in central and eastern United States and Canada: Am. Assoc. Petroleum Geologists Bull., v. 39, no. 1, p. 60–72.

Anonymous, 1961, Action in Appalachian basin sets fast pace: Oil and Gas Jour., v. 59, no. 44 (Oct. 30), p. 214–215.

Atomic Energy Commission, 1960, Management of radioactive wastes: Ann. Rept. to U.S. Congress, January 1960.

Bernard, Harold, 1962, New developments in the management of low and intermediate level waste: Transcript of talk presented at 17th Ann. Purdue Industrial Waste Conf., May 1–3, Lafayette, Indiana.

Bizal, R. B., 1962, Gas storage capacity spurts: Oil and Gas Jour., v. 60, no. 20 (May 14), p. 125–138.

Bordne, E. F., 1960, Water resources of a western New York region (a case study of water resources and use in the Genesee valley and western Lake Ontario basin): Syracuse Univ. Press.

Bradley, W. H., and J. F. Pepper, 1938, Geologic structure and occurrence of gas in part of southwestern New York: U.S. Geol. Survey Bull. 899-A.

Brewer, Charles, Jr., 1933, Oil and gas geology of the Allegany State Park, 1931: New York State Mus. and Sci. Service Circ. 10.

Broughton, J. G., et al., 1962, Geologic map of New York—1961: New York State Mus. and Sci. Service Geol. Survey Map and Chart Ser. No. 5, 5 map sheets, scale 1:250,000, 42 p. text.

Brown, W. B., III, 1960, Appalachian spotlight—New York State: Producers Monthly, v. 24, no. 10, p. 10.

Burgess, R. J., 1962, Cambrian hydrocarbon traps on the northwest rim of the Appalachian basin: Proc. Tech. Sess., Ontario Petroleum Inst., v. 1, p. 1–24.

Caley, J. F., 1940, Paleozoic geology of the Toronto-Hamilton area, Ontario: Canada Dept. Mines and Resources, Geol. Survey Mem. 224.

Calvert, W. L., 1962, Sub-Trenton rocks from Lee County, Virginia, to Fayette County, Ohio: Ohio Div. Geol Survey Rept. Inv. No. 45, 57 p.

—— 1963a, A cross-section of sub-Trenton rocks from Wood County, West Virginia, to Fayette County, Illinois: Ohio Div. Geol. Survey Rept. Inv. No. 48, 32 p.

—— 1963b, Sub-Trenton rocks of Ohio in cross-sections from West Virginia and Pennsylvania to Michigan: Ohio Div. Geol. Survey Rept. Inv. No. 49.

—— 1964a, Sub-Trenton rocks from Fayette County, Ohio, to Brant County, Ontario: Ohio Div. Geol. Survey Rept. Inv. No. 52.

—— 1964b, Pre-Trenton sedimentation and dolomitization, Cincinnati Arch province; theoretical considerations: Am. Assoc. Petroleum Geologists Bull., v. 48, no. 2, p. 166–190.

—— 1964c, Morrow County, Ohio, area has about 100 active rigs: World Oil, v. 158, no. 2, p. 79–80.

—— 1964d, Cambrian erosional remnants yield oil in central Ohio: World Oil, v. 158, no. 4 (Feb.-Mar.), p. 78–84.

—— 1965, Cambrian correlations in the Appalachian region: Proc. Tech. Sess., Ontario Petroleum Inst., v. 4, paper 2, p. 1–11.

Chadwick, G. H., 1935, Chemung is Portage: Geol. Soc. America Bull., v. 46, p. 343–354.

—— 1936, History and value of the name "Catskill" in geology: New York State Mus. and Sci. Service Bull. 307 (Jan.).

Colton, G. W., 1956, Bedrock geology of the Hamburg quadrangle, New York: U.S. Geol. Survey Map GQ-97.

—— 1961, Geologic summary of the Appalachian basin, with reference to the subsurface disposal of radioactive waste solutions: U.S. Geol. Survey Trace Elements Inv. Rept. 791 (June).

Cooper, G. A., chm., 1942, Correlation of the Devonian sedimentary formations of North America: Geol. Soc. America Bull., v. 53, p. 1729–1794.

Cushing, H. P., 1908, Lower portion of the Paleozoic section in northwestern New York: Geol. Soc. America Bull., v. 19, p. 155–176.

Davis, G. H., III, 1953, The contact between the Manlius limestone and the Coeymans limestone in upper New York State: New York State Mus. and Sci. Service Circ. 35 (Oct.).

de Laguna (see Laguna).

De Witt, Wallace, Jr., 1956, Bedrock geology of the Eden quadrangle, New York: U.S. Geol. Survey Map GQ-96.

—— 1960, Java formation of Late Devonian age in western and central New York: Am. Assoc. Petroleum Geologists Bull., v. 44, no. 12, p. 1933–1935.

—— and G. W. Colton, 1953, Bedrock geology of the Silver Creek quadrangle, New York: U.S. Geol. Survey Map GQ-30.

Donnan, B. C., 1957, Great Lakes leases offer new drilling area: Oil and Gas Jour., v. 55, no. 41 (Oct. 14), p. 301–312.

—— 1959, Tempo quickens on Lake Erie: Oil and Gas Jour., v. 57, no. 43 (June 1), p. 222–227.

Donnerstag, Phillip, 1949, Recent petroleum exploration in New York State: Appalachian Geol. Soc. Bull., v. 1, p. 303–306.

—— 1950, Sample study and correlation of the C. C. Lobdell No. 1 well: New York State Mus. and Sci. Service Circ. 28.

—— and R. McDonald, 1952, Sample study and correlation of the Robert Bates No. 1 well: New York State Mus. and Sci. Service Circ. 30.

Emmons, E., 1838, Report of the second geological district of the State of New York: New York Geol. Survey, 2d Ann. Rept., p. 185–252.

Everhart, G. M., 1953, Map of northern part of Appalachian basin showing location of selected deep wells: U.S. Geol. Survey Oil and Gas Inv. Map OM-136.

Fettke, C. R., 1933, Subsurface Devonian and Silurian sections across northern Pennsylvania and southern New York: Geol. Soc. America Bull., v. 44, p. 601–660.

—— 1948, Subsurface Trenton and sub-Trenton rocks in Ohio, New York, Pennsylvania, and West Virginia: Am. Assoc. Petroleum Geologists Bull., v. 32, no. 8, p. 1457–1492.

Finn, F. H., 1949, Geology and occurrence of natural gas in Oriskany sandstone in Pennsylvania and New York: Am. Assoc. Petroleum Geologists Bull., v. 33, no. 3, p. 303–335.

Fisher, D. W., 1954, Stratigraphy of the Medinan Group, New York and Ontario: Am. Assoc. Petroleum Geologists Bull., v. 38, no. 9, p. 1979–1996.

—— 1956, The Cambrian System of New York State, in El Sistema Cambrico, su paleogeografia y el problema de su base: 20th Internat. Geol. Cong., v. 2, no. 2, p. 321–351.

—— 1959, Correlation of the Silurian rocks in New York State: New York State Mus. and Sci. Service Geol. Survey Map and Chart. Ser. No. 1, 1960.

—— 1962a, Correlation of the Cambrian rocks in New York State: New York State Mus. and Sci. Service Geol. Survey Map and Chart Ser. No. 2.

—— 1962b, Correlation of the Ordovician rocks in New York State: New York State Mus. and Sci. Service Geol. Survey Map and Chart Ser. No. 3.

—— and G. F. Hanson, 1951, Revisions in the geology of Saratoga Springs, New York, and vicinity: Am. Jour. Sci., v. 249, p. 795–814.

Flagler, C. W., 1966, Subsurface Cambrian and Ordovician stratigraphy of the Trenton Group-Precambrian interval in New York State: New York State Mus. and Sci. Service Map and Chart Ser. No. 8.

Freeman, L. B., 1949, Regional aspects of Cambrian and Ordovician subsurface stratigraphy in Kentucky: Am. Assoc. Petroleum Geologists Bull., v. 33, no. 10, p. 1655–1681.

—— 1951, Regional aspects of Silurian and Devonian subsurface stratigraphy in Kentucky: Am. Assoc. Petroleum Geologists Bull., v. 35, no. 1, p. 1–61.

—— 1953, Regional subsurface stratigraphy of the Cambrian and Ordovician in Kentucky and vicinity: Kentucky Geol. Survey, 9th ser., Bull. 12, 352 p.

Gillette, Tracy, 1947, The Clinton of western and central New York: New York State Mus. and Sci. Service Bull. 341.

Grabau, A. W., 1913, Early Paleozoic delta deposits of North America: Geol. Soc. America Bull., v. 24.

Green, D. A., 1957, Trenton structure in Ohio, Indiana, and northern Illinois: Am. Assoc. Petroleum Geologists Bull., v. 41, no. 4, p. 627–642.

Harding, R. W., 1950, Correlation of Bradford Third and Richburg sands, Pennsylvania and New York: Am. Assoc. Petroleum Geologists Bull., v. 32, no. 8, p. 1866–1873.

—— 1966, An independent looks at New York's Oriskany: Oil and Gas Jour., v. 64, no. 12 (March 21), p. 130–136.

Hartnagel, C. A., 1938, Medina and Trenton of western New York: Am. Assoc. Petroleum Geologists Bull., v. 22, no. 1, p. 79–99.

—— and D. H. Newland, 1932, Recent natural gas developments in south-central New York: New York State Mus. and Sci. Service Circ. 7.

—— and W. L. Russell, 1929, New York oil fields, in Structure of typical American oil fields, v. 2: Tulsa, Oklahoma, Am. Assoc. Petroleum Geologists, p. 269–289.

Haught, O. L., 1956, Probabilities of the presence of reservoirs in the Cambrian and Ordovician of the Allegheny synclinorium: Kentucky Oil and Gas Assoc., Proc. Tech. Sess., May 25; Kentucky Geol. Survey, Ser. 9, Spec. Pub. 9, p. 7–16.

Heald, M. T., and R. C. Anderegg, 1960, Differential cementation in the Tuscarora sandstone: Jour. Sed. Petrology, v. 30, no. 4, p. 568–577.

Heck, E. T., 1948, New York subsurface geology: Am. Assoc. Petroleum Geologists Bull., v. 32, no. 8, p. 1449–1456.

Henich, J. P., 1949, Empire oil: New York, Dodd, Mead and Co., 457 p.

Hess, H. H., et al., 1957, The disposal of radioactive waste on land: Washington, D.C., Natl. Acad. Sci.–Natl. Research Council.

Howell, B. F., et al., 1944, Correlations of the Cambrian formations of North America: Geol. Soc. America Bull., v. 55, p. 993–1003.

Ingham, A. I., 1960, Oil and gas frontiers in the east: Geotimes, v. 4, no. 6 (March), p. 14–16, 33–34.

Isachsen, Y. W., 1962, Unpublished description of Precambrian lithologies in New York deep wells: Albany, New York.

Kay, Marshall, 1937, Stratigraphy of the Trenton Group: Geol. Soc. America Bull., v. 48, p. 233–301.

—— 1942, Development of northern Allegheny synclinorium and adjoining regions: Geol. Soc. America Bull., v. 53, p. 1601–1658.

—— 1948, Summary of Middle Ordovician bordering Allegheny synclinorium: Am. Assoc. Petroleum Geologists Bull., v. 32, no. 8, p. 1397–1416.

Keroher, G. C., et al., 1966, Lexicon of geologic names of the United States: U.S. Geol. Survey Bull. 1200.

King, P. B., 1951, The tectonics of middle North America: Princeton, New Jersey, Princeton Univ. Press.

Kornfeld, J. A., 1961, A new look at an old province: World Oil, v. 153, no. 6 (Nov.), p. 110–112.

Kreidler, W. L., 1953, History, geology and future possibilities of gas and oil in New York State: New York State Mus. and Sci. Service Circ. 33.

—— 1957, Occurrence of Silurian salt in New York State: New York State Mus. and Sci. Service Bull. 361, p. 1–56.

—— 1959, Selected deep wells and areas of gas production in eastern and central New York: New York State Mus. and Sci. Service Bull. 379, p. 1–243.

—— 1960, Developments in New York State in 1959: Am. Assoc. Petroleum Geologists Bull., v. 44, no. 6, p. 683–687.

Laguna, Wallace de, 1959, What is safe waste disposal?: Bull. Atomic Scientist, v. 15, no. 1, p. 35–43.

Lanning, David, 1947, A study of the Oswego sandstone and a consideration of its productive possibilities: Unpub. M.S. thesis, Univ. Pittsburgh.

Love, J. D., and Linn Hoover, 1960, A summary of the geology of sedimentary basins of the United States, with reference to the disposal of radioactive wastes: U.S. Geol. Survey Trace Elements Inv. Rept. 768 (May).

Lytle, W. S., and W. R. Wagner, 1960, Pre-Upper Devonian stratigraphy of Kardosh No. 1 well, Crawford County, Pennsylvania: Am. Assoc. Petroleum Geologists Bull., v. 44, no. 6, p. 698–699.

McGuire, W. H., and Paul Howell, 1963, Oil and gas possibilities of the Cambrian and Lower Ordovician in Kentucky: Lexington, Kentucky, Spindletop Research Rept., 128 p.

Meinzer, O. E., et al., 1942, Water levels and artesian pressure in observation wells in the United States in 1940, Part 1, Northeastern states: U.S. Geol. Survey Water-Supply Paper 906.

Moore, T. V., et al., 1958, Problems in the disposal of radioactive waste in deep wells: Dallas, Texas, Am. Petroleum Inst., Div. Production.

Newland, D. H., 1921, The mineral resources of the State of New York: New York State Mus. and Sci. Service Bulls. 223, 224.

——— and C. A. Hartnagel, 1908, Iron ores of the Clinton formation in New York State: New York State Mus. and Sci. Service Bull. 123, p. 1–76.

——— and ——— 1932, Review of the natural gas and petroleum developments in New York State: New York State Mus. and Sci. Service Bull. 295.

——— and ——— 1936, The mining and quarry industries of New York State for 1930 to 1933: New York State Mus. and Sci. Service Bull. 305.

——— and ——— 1939, The mining and quarry industries of New York State for 1934 to 1936: New York State Mus. and Sci. Service Bull. 319.

——— et al., 1933, The Paleozoic stratigraphy of New York: Internat. Geol. Cong., 26th Sess., U.S., Guide Book No. 4, Excursion A-4, Washington, D.C.

Northern Ohio Geological Society, 1962, Abstracts of Symposium on salt: May 1962.

Oliver, W. A., Jr., 1954, Stratigraphy of the Onondaga limestone (Devonian) in central New York: Geol. Soc. America Bull., v. 65, p. 621–652.

——— 1956, Biostromes and bioherms of the Onondaga limestone in eastern New York: New York State Mus. and Sci. Service Circ. 45.

Patel, K. S., 1963, Interrelation of velocity, density difference, viscosity ratio and transition zone length for vertical miscible displacement in a consolidated porous medium: Unpub. Master's thesis, Pennsylvania State Univ.

Patterson, J. R., 1961, Ordovician stratigraphy and correlations in North America: Am. Assoc. Petroleum Geologists Bull., v. 45, no. 8, p. 1364–1377.

Pepper, J. F., 1954, Bedrock geology of the Hornell quadrangle, New York: U.S. Geol. Survey Map GQ-37.

——— and W. De Witt, Jr., 1951, The stratigraphy of the Perrysburg formation of Late Devonian age in western and west-central New York: U.S. Geol. Survey Oil and Gas Inv. Chart OC-45.

——— and G. W. Colton, 1956, Stratigraphy of the West Falls formation of Late Devonian age in western and west-central New York: U.S. Geol. Survey Oil and Gas Inv. Chart OC-55.

Pounder, J. A., 1964, Cambrian of Ontario, Canada: Proc. Tech. Sess., Ontario Petroleum Inst., v. 3, p. 1–24.

Richardson, G. B., 1941, Subsurface structure in part of southwestern New York and mode of occurrence of gas in the Medina Group, Pt. 2 of Geologic structure and occurrence of gas in part of southwestern New York: U.S. Geol. Survey Bull. 899-B, p. 69–93.

Rickard, L. V., 1962, Late Cayugan (Upper Silurian) and Helderbergian (Lower Devonian) stratigraphy in New York: New York State Mus. and Sci. Service Bull. 386.

——— 1964, Correlation of the Devonian rocks in New York State: New York State Mus. and Sci. Service Geol. Survey Map and Chart Ser. No. 4.

Rodgers, John, 1949, Evolution of thought on structure of middle and southern Appalachians: Am. Assoc. Petroleum Geologists Bull., v. 33, no. 10, p. 1643–1654.

Roliff, W. A., 1949, Salina-Guelph fields of southwestern Ontario: Am. Assoc. Petroleum Geologists Bull., v. 33, no. 2, p. 153–188.

Rothrock, H. E., 1949, Mayfield pool, Cuyahoga County, Ohio: Am. Assoc. Petroleum Geologists Bull., v. 33, no. 10, p. 1731–1746.

Ruedemann, Rudolf, 1925, The Utica and Lorraine formations of New York, Pt. 1, Stratigraphy: New York State Mus. and Sci Service Bull. 258.

——— 1947, Graptolites of North America: Geol. Soc. America Mem. 19, 652 p.

Sanford, B. V., 1961, Subsurface stratigraphy of Ordovician rocks in southwestern Ontario: Geol. Survey Canada, Paper 60–26.

——— and R. G. Quillian, 1959, Subsurface stratigraphy of Upper Cambrian rocks in southwestern Ontario: Geol. Survey Canada, Paper 58–12.

——— et al., 1958, Geological map of southwestern Ontario showing oil and natural gas producing areas: Geol. Survey Canada.

Schramm, M. W., Jr., 1961, Oil and gas possibilities of the northern Appalachian basin: Producers Monthly, v. 25, no. 4 (April), p. 22–24.

Stevenson, R. E., 1948, Geologic structures of the Middle Devonian rocks of Otsego County: New York State Mus. and Sci. Service Rept. Inv. No. 1.

——— 1949, Geologic structures of the Lower Devonian rocks of central New York: New York State Mus. and Sci. Service Rept. Inv. No. 3.

Sutton, R. G., 1957, Lithofacies map of Upper Devonian in eastern United States: Am. Assoc. Petroleum Geologists Bull., v. 41, no. 4, p. 750–755.

——— 1959, Structural geology of the Dryden and Harford quadrangles, New York: New York State Mus. and Sci. Service Prelim. Rept.

——— 1960, Stratigraphy of the Naples Group (Late Devonian) in western New York: New York State Mus. and Sci. Service Bull. 380, p. 1–56.

Swain, J. F., 1950, Geology and occurrence of oil in Medina sand of Blue Rock–Salt Creek pool, Ohio: Am. Assoc. Petroleum Geologists Bull., v. 34, no. 9, p. 1874–1886.

Swartz, C. K., 1923, Correlation of the Silurian formations of Maryland with those of other areas: Maryland Geol. Survey, p. 183–232.

——— chm., 1942, Correlation of the Silurian formations of North America: Geol. Soc. America Bull., v. 53, p. 533–538.

Swartz, F. M., 1948a, Late Ordovician and Silurian facies, conditions of deposition and paleogeography in north-central Appalachians (abs.): Am. Assoc.

Petroleum Geologists Bull., v. 32, no. 11, p. 2160.

——— 1948b, Trenton and sub-Trenton of outcrop areas in New York, Pennsylvania, and Maryland: Am. Assoc. Petroleum Geologists Bull., v. 32, no. 8, p. 1493–1595.

——— 1950, Subsurface projection of Cambro-Ordovician sediments in the Pennsylvania–New York region: Pennsylvania Topog. Geol. Survey Bull. G25.

Tesmer, I. H., 1955, Restudy of Upper Devonian (Chautauquan) stratigraphy and paleontology in southwestern New York State: New York State Mus. and Sci. Service Circ. 42.

——— 1957, Sample study and correlation of three wells in Chautauqua County, New York: New York State Mus. and Sci. Service Bull. 362.

Thomas, R. N., 1951, Devonian shale gas production in central Appalachian area: Am. Assoc. Petroleum Geologists Bull., v. 35, no. 10, p. 2249–2256.

Torrey, P. D., 1935, Summary of geology of natural gas fields of New York and Pennsylvania, in Geology of natural gas: Tulsa, Oklahoma, Am. Assoc. Petroleum Geologists, p. 949–988.

Trainer, D. W., 1932, The Tully limestone of central New York: New York State Mus. and Sci. Service Bull. 291, p. 1–43.

Twenhofel, W. H., chm., 1954, Correlation of the Ordovician formations of North America: Geol. Soc. America Bull., v. 65, no. 3, p. 247–298.

Ulrich, E. O., 1913, The Ordovician boundary: 12th Internat. Geol. Cong., Compte Rendu, Toronto, Canada.

Van Tyne, A. M., 1960, New York oil and gas developments, 1959: Internat. Oil Scouts Yearbook, v. 30, p. 356–358.

Wagner, W. R., 1958, Emma McKnight No. 1 well, Pymaturing Township, Mercer County, Pennsylvania: Pennsylvania Topog. Geol. Survey, Well Sample Record 40.

Weaver, O. D., 1964, Next major Cambrian province: Oil and Gas Jour., v. 62, no. 32 (Aug. 10), p. 114–119.

——— 1965a, North flank of Appalachian set for testing: Oil and Gas Jour., v. 63, no. 36 (Sept. 6), p. 216–219.

——— 1965b, New York offers multiple strat-trap potential in Cambro-Ordovician sediments: Oil and Gas Jour., v. 63, no. 37 (Sept. 13), p. 166–170.

Wedel, A. A., 1932, Geologic structure of the Devonian strata of south-central New York: New York State Mus. and Sci. Service Bull. 294, p. 1–73.

Weisnet, D. R., 1961, Composition, grain size, roundness and sphericity of the Potsdam sandstone (Cambrian) in northeastern New York: Jour. Sed. Petrology, v. 31, no. 1, p. 5–14.

Wiggins, J. W., 1954, Sample study and correlation of the F. E. Buchanan No. 1 well: New York State Mus. and Sci. Service Circ. 38 (Oct.).

——— 1959, Sample study and correlation of the E. C. Kesselring No. 1 well: New York State Mus. and Sci. Service Circ., unnumbered (Sept.).

Willard, Bradford, 1961, Stratigraphy of the Cambrian sedimentary rocks of eastern Pennsylvania: Geol. Soc. America Bull., v. 72, no. 12, p. 1765–1776.

Wilmarth, M. G., 1938, Lexicon of geologic names of the United States, Pts. 1, 2: U.S. Geol. Survey Bull. 896.

Woodruff, J. G., 1942, Geology of the Wellsville quadrangle, New York: New York State Mus. and Sci. Service Bull. 326, p. 1–133.

Woodward, H. P., 1957a, Chronology of Appalachian folding: Am. Assoc. Petroleum Geologists Bull., v. 41, no. 10, p. 2312–2327.

——— 1957b, Structural elements of northeastern Appalachians: Am. Assoc. Petroleum Geologists Bull., v. 41, no. 7, p. 1429–1440.

——— 1958, Emplacement of oil and gas in Appalachian basin, in Habitat of oil: Tulsa, Oklahoma, Am. Assoc. Petroleum Geologists, p. 494–510.

——— 1961a, Reappraisal of Appalachian geology: Am. Assoc. Petroleum Geologists Bull., v. 45, no. 10, p. 1625–1633.

——— 1961b, Preliminary subsurface study of southeastern Appalachian interior plateau: Am. Assoc. Petroleum Geologists Bull., v. 45, no. 10, p. 1634–1655.

Yeakel, L. S., Jr., 1962, Tuscarora, Juniata, and Bald Eagle paleocurrents and paleogeography in the central Appalachians: Geol. Soc. America Bull., v. 73, p. 1515–1540.

POSSIBILITIES FOR SUBSURFACE WASTE DISPOSAL IN A STRUCTURAL SYNCLINE IN PENNSYLVANIA[1]

JOHN E. HARDAWAY[2]
Westwood, New Jersey 07675

ABSTRACT

Results of a study of a small structural syncline on the western perimeter of the central Appalachian Mountains of Pennsylvania suggest that the area may be suitable for the injection of liquid wastes into deep subsurface reservoirs. The study was performed under the auspices of the AAPG, the U.S. Atomic Energy Commission, and Princeton University.

The bowl-shaped syncline forms a basin just north of Bedford, Bedford County, and occupies about 45 sq mi (116.5 sq km) of the county. The total thickness of Paleozoic strata is more than 7,000 ft (2,134 m). The reservoir aquifer considered suitable for disposal is the Lower Silurian Tuscarora Sandstone, a clean quartzose sandstone. The investigation showed that the syncline has sufficient structural closure to warrant consideration as a reservoir. The selected sandstone aquifer crops out along two-thirds of the syncline's perimeter and is approximately 3,700 ft (1,128 m) beneath the center of the basin. It apparently is not faulted, and it may be treated as a confined aquifer because it is bounded by shale and shaly, silty sandstone which probably have much lower permeability.

Porosity measurements of Tuscarora and Juniata sandstones gave values of 15 and 10 percent, respectively. The probability of the presence of connate brine in the Tuscarora is enhanced by the fact that it is present in a deep well near Bedford. The Tuscarora strata are described as a "salaquifer" which will not promote harmful chemical interactions.

The shale beds of the area were studied similarly and are regarded as favorable for the injection, into artificially created fractures, of wastes that have been incorporated in cement slurries. However, grouting in shale appears less promising for large-scale injection than disposal in permeable sandstone.

GENERAL GEOLOGY AND GEOGRAPHY

The study region is primarily along the northeast-southwest-trending Appalachian Mountain system of Pennsylvania, West Virginia, and Maryland. Of specific interest are the local isolated synclines in the Valley and Ridge province.

Three separate synclinal features in Pennsylvania were considered. One is east of Hollidaysburg, Pennsylvania; another extends for considerable distances through the Broad Top coal field of Huntingdon and Bedford Counties; and the third is north of Bedford, Pennsylvania, in the Dunning Cove area. The Hollidaysburg area was excluded from the study because of recently substantiated faulting. The Broad Top syncline was eliminated because of its large size, the lack of geologic mapping in the area, and the presence of undetermined coal reserves.

The third area, henceforth referred to as the "Dunning Cove syncline," was selected for study because the bowl-shaped syncline appeared to offer a permeable aquifer at depth—the Tuscarora quartzose sandstone, which is confined sufficiently by less permeable strata (the overlying Clinton shales and the underlying Juniata sand-

[1] Manuscript received, June 10, 1963. Revised, September 20, 1966, from a thesis presented to the Department of Geological Engineering, Princeton University, in partial fulfillment of the requirements for the degree of Master of Science in Engineering.

[2] Isotopes, a Teledyne company.

The writer gratefully acknowledges the guidance and counsel of John C. Maxwell, Chairman, Department of Geological Engineering, Princeton University, and the assistance of John E. Galley, Chairman, AAPG Subcommittee on Atomic Waste Disposal. Most of the expense of this report was defrayed by the Atomic Energy Commission through the AAPG Subcommittee. The writer is indebted to the Department of Geological Engineering, Princeton University, for the use of its vehicles and facilities. Thanks also are due Addison S. Cate, Pennsylvania Geological Survey; Peoples Natural Gas Company of Pittsburgh, Pennsylvania; and Cumberland and Allegheny Gas Company of Pittsburgh for their response to inquiries. Edward Watson of Bryn Mawr College provided advice and support during the initiation of this report. The response of the many colleges and universities consulted on the problems of waste disposal is greatly appreciated. Especially valued is the assistance of the writer's wife during the research, field work, and writing of the report.

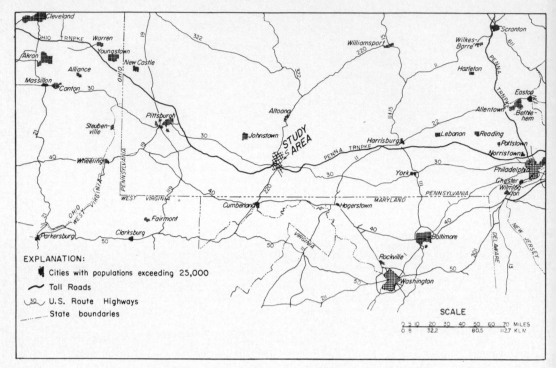

Fig. 1.—Location map of study area, major highways, and cities.

stone, siltstone, and shale) to contain injected liquids. Previous work indicated that the area had structural closure and an isolated hydrologic regimen. The syncline also appeared to contain a large quantity of shale, and this was examined for the ion-exchange properties and hydraulic-fracturing potential necessary for grouting.

The study involved both a literature search and field work because the large-scale Geologic Map of Pennsylvania (Gray et al., 1960) was the only source of information initially available to the writer. The syncline was studied primarily with respect to its stratigraphy and structure, and secondarily with respect to the surface and subsurface hydrology, lithology, and economic development.

Field work was done during November 1962 and February-March 1963. A short trip also was made to the area in April 1963.

PHYSIOGRAPHY

The study area is in south-central Pennsylvania, colinear with the westernmost part of the Valley and Ridge province and in the central Ap-

palachian Mountains of Bedford County (Figs. 1, 2). On the west edge of the area, a broad northeast-trending structural depression separates the folded Appalachians, in which the syncline lies, from the warped border of the geosyncline beneath the Appalachian Plateau (Kay, 1942). The study area is a small bowl-shaped syncline delineated by concentric arcs of Ordovician, Silurian, and Devonian strata (Fig. 3). The syncline is in the east-central part of Bedford County, and Bedford, the largest town in the county, is within the syncline.

Topographically, the maximum relief in the Dunning Cove syncline is 1,300 ft (396 m); the elevation ranges from about 1,100 ft (335 m) to 2,400 ft (731 m) above sea level. The syncline is bordered on the north and east by Evitts Mountain and on the west by the north-plunging anticline of Wills Mountain and the south-plunging anticline of Dunning Mountain. Certain areas of the syncline, especially along the prominent Tuscarora sandstone ridges of the mountains, are inaccessible to vehicles without extensive clearing of the vegetation and talus.

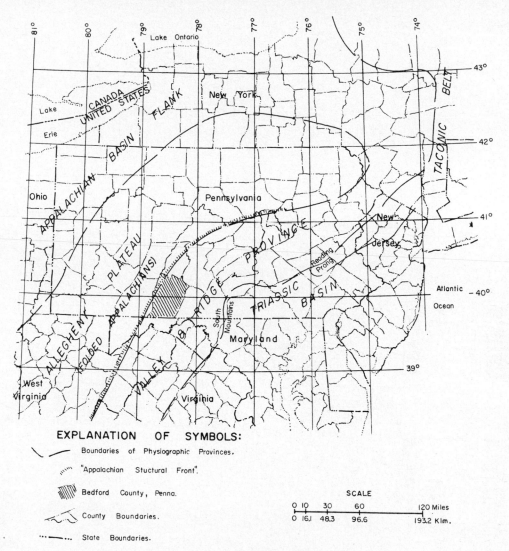

FIG. 2.—Physiographic map of Pennsylvania.

GENERAL GEOLOGY

The geologic and structural pattern of the Bedford area is by no means resolved completely, though extensive efforts by Stevenson (1882), Butts (1945), and more recently by several oil and gas companies have helped to clarify the pattern.

Outcrops near and in the Dunning Cove syncline include strata of Late Ordovician (Reeds-ville) through Middle Devonian (Hamilton Group) age. Subsurface rocks include Ordovician, Cambrian, and Precambrian strata. West of Bedford, Late Devonian and younger rocks constitute most of the outcrops. The stratigraphic section of greatest concern to this study includes the Reedsville Shale (Upper Ordovician) through the Mahantango Formation of the Hamilton Group (Middle Devonian).

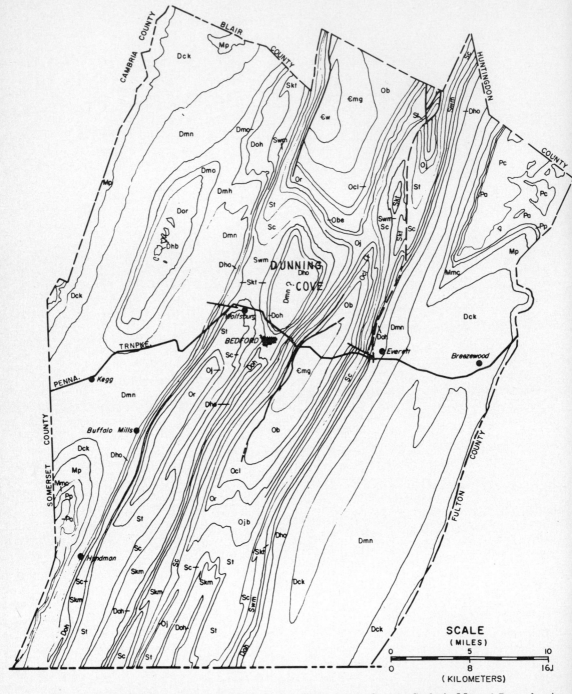

FIG. 3.—General geologic map of Bedford County, Pennsylvania. Source: Geologic Map of Pennsylvania (Gray *et al.*, 1960); published by permission of Pennsylvania Geol. Survey. Location of Dunning Cove area is shown.

EXPLANATION OF GEOLOGIC SYMBOLS USED ON
FIGURE 3

PENNSYLVANIAN
 Pm Monongahela sandstone, shale, limestone
 Pc Conemaugh shale, siltstone
 Pa Allegheny (Group) sandstone, shale, limestone
 Pp Pottsville (Group) sandstone, conglomerate
MISSISSIPPIAN
 Mmc Mauch Chunk shale, sandstone
 Mp Pocono (Group) conglomerate, sandstone
DEVONIAN
 Dck Catskill shale, sandstone
 Dmn "Chemung" and "Portage" shale, sandstone
 Dmh Mahantango shale
Dho Marcellus shale
       Onondaga shale } Dmo
Doh Dor Oriskany sandstone, limestone
     Dhb Helderberg limestone
SILURIAN
      Skt Keyser limestone
           Tonoloway limestone
Skm   Wills Creek shale
      Swm Bloomsburg redbeds
           McKenzie shale and limestone
     Sc   Clinton (Group) shale
     St   Tuscarora sandstone
ORDOVICIAN
Ojb Oj   Juniata redbeds
     Obe Bald Eagle conglomerate, sandstone
     Or   Reedsville shale
     Ocl Coburn through Loysburg limestone
     Ob   Beekmantown (Group) dolomite
CAMBRIAN
€mg Cg   Mines dolomite
           Gatesburg dolomite
     €w   Warrior dolomite

SURFACE HYDROLOGY

The Dunning Cove syncline is drained by the Raystown Branch of the Juniata River and its tributaries. The syncline is a part of the Susquehanna watershed because the Juniata joins the Susquehanna at Harrisburg, Pennsylvania. Figure 4 shows the major drainage channels in the study area.

The primary tributary of the drainage system of the syncline is Dunning Creek, which enters the study area from the west at the town of Cessna. At this location the plunging anticlines of Dunning and Wills Mountains probably reach their deepest subsurface elevation. Most of Bedford County is drained by the Susquehanna and Potomac River systems (Fig. 4), the former draining most of the county toward the north and east and the latter draining toward the south. The Ohio River system drains the county along its westernmost boundary. The Susquehanna and Juniata Rivers are both the result of post–Appalachian revolution erosion (Thompson, 1939).

Dunning Creek and the Raystown Branch of the Juniata River have reached local and regional base level, inasmuch as their courses contain numerous meanders which are shifting continuously. Such meanders are evident in all the major streams. The lack of zones of weakness of linea-

tions along the drainage routes suggests that the water gaps such as those at Bedford and Wolfsburg were formed as a result of slow and continued uplift. Thompson (1939) points out this fact, noting that the drainage of the southern Appalachians does not follow geomorphologic boundaries. A single exception is the postulated fault in the Everett (Pennsylvania) water gap to the east (Fig. 3).

Most of the public and industrial water supply of the Bedford area is from artificial reservoirs, and a smaller quantity is from the natural streams. Though no recent enumeration was available from the municipal water companies, water wells provide a small percentage of the potable water supply to both industry and homes. Water wells and springs in the county of Bedford in the early 1930's are shown on Figure 4. The principal aquifers broached for potable water are the Oriskany Sandstone and the stratigraphically adjacent limestone beds.

CLIMATE

The climate of the Bedford area includes relatively hot summers and cold winters. Visher (1954) reports temperatures as high as 111°F (44°C; from recordings before 1945) and as low as −45°F (−43°C; from readings before 1952) for Pennsylvania. He concludes further that the temperature in the Dunning Cove area ranges from a low of about −40°F (−40°C) to a high of approximately 95°F (34°C).

Total precipitation is normally on the order of 45 in. (114 cm) a year and averages less than 4 in. (10 cm) a month. The late fall and early winter months generally have the least rainfall of the year, though February is often the driest month. There generally are about 100 days with from 0.01 to 0.25 in. (0.025 to 0.635 cm) of rain throughout an average year and about 45 days a year with from 0.25 to 0.50 in. of rain. Fifty-five percent of the rain generally falls during the spring and summer months. Occasional dry spells may persist for several months in the area, during which less than 0.25 in. of rain falls.

Wind velocity averages 8 mi (13 km) per hour in the vicinity of Bedford; wind generally is west-by-northwest or west-by-southwest across the basin. Occasional strong winds are common,

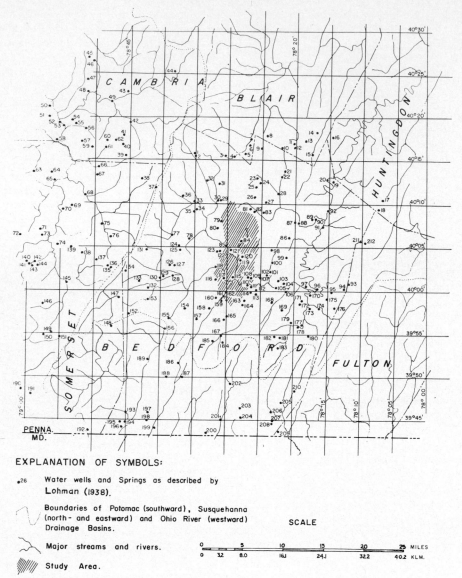

FIG. 4.—Locations of domestic and industrial water wells (1933–1934) and of major surface streams. Source of some data: Lohman (1938), *in* Pennsylvania Topog. Survey Bull. W5; published by permission.

and one to three winds of tornado intensity are likely each year, generally during May and June (Visher, 1954).

Many low-pressure centers travel across the study area, primarily southwest to northeast. High-pressure centers are predominant directly south of Bedford, traveling from west to east. Hurricanes have not been recorded regularly in the immediate area, but could be expected to

travel northward toward and across the Dunning Cove syncline.

Snow flurries begin as early as November, and there are generally about 40 days or more of notable snowfall each year. Snowfalls of 1 in. (2.5 cm) or more commonly begin in the middle of December and occur through early March; the total average snowfall is about 30 in. (76 cm) per year. The Bedford area has received as much as

55 in. (1.4 m) of snow in one year, and Somerset County on the west has received up to 88 in. (2.24 cm) in a year (Kauffman, 1960). Snowfall generally constitutes 10 percent of the total annual precipitation in the area.

Alternate freezing and thawing is very common in the study area, although the configuration of the mountains serves to prolong colder temperatures. Only four months are generally frostfree. The soil commonly freezes to depths of 18–36 in. (46–92 cm).

There is dense fog during a substantial part of the day approximately 30 times each year in the Bedford area. Mist and fog are augmented by the quantities of relatively stagnant water, the lowlands, and the wind-shielding mountains.

Evaporation from pans averages 38 in. (97 cm) per year and evaporation from reservoirs and shallow lakes averages 30 in. (76 cm) per year (Visher, 1954). The annual excess of precipitation over evaporation is normally about 20 percent, and years in which evaporation exceeds precipitation are rare.

In general, the climate conditions of the Dunning Cove area lead to considerable soil erosion, and stringent practices of soil conservation are necessary. Although extensive flooding is rare, large tracts of bottom land along the meandering streams are inundated periodically during the spring thaws. Ice damage to the fields and buildings is common.

SOIL AND VEGETATION

Soils in the area of the Dunning Cove syncline range from moderately productive to subproductive. Less than 5–10 percent of the basin has been mapped with respect to the residual and alluvial soil types.

Natural vegetation in the Bedford area consists predominantly of scrub and immature trees, few more than 40 ft high. The area was forested in the late 1800's, but there has been no commercial lumbering since that period. Growth of underbrush around the perimeter of the area is limited by talus from the Tuscarora ridges.

Most of the area that might provide economic crop and pasture land has been cleared. With the support of the federal government, an attempt is being made to rehabilitate some of the claimed land for recreational areas and to institute soil-rejuvenation programs.

The scrub growth camouflages many of the probable geologic outcrop locations inside the basin, especially those of the Devonian strata. The fact that the sandy Juniata, Tuscarora, and Oriskany outcrop areas have proliferous growths of oaks and the limestone ridges have growths of chestnut trees is useful in geologic mapping.

LAND OWNERSHIP AND ECONOMICS

The area of the Dunning Cove syncline, excluding the town of Bedford and the seven smaller towns, is occupied chiefly by small and medium-sized farms, generally individually owned and of average or below-average productivity and profitability in comparison to the rest of the county. The average size of a farm in Bedford County is 161 acres (64.4 hectares), and farms in the basin generally are smaller.

DENSITY AND DISTRIBUTION OF POPULATION

The largest town in the study area is Bedford, with a population of 3,696 as of 1960. The borough of Bedford, which is the county seat of Bedford County, is surrounded by the township of Bedford, which is the largest township in the county (1960 population of 3,977). Part of East St. Clair Township, which had a population of 1,664 in 1960, and a small corner of Napier Township on the south are within the Dunning Cove syncline.

Bedford County has a population density of 41.8 people per square mile. It contains no "urbanized" areas, but is on the easternmost edge of the Pittsburgh-Johnstown-Altoona urban area. Although the study area includes the most densely populated area of the county, it still is an area of relatively sparse population. Furthermore, the size of the populated areas is remaining constant.

TRANSPORTATION FACILITIES

The Bedford area is served by a good system of highways and two divisions of the Pennsylvania Railroad.[3] The primary highway is the Pennsylvania Turnpike. Supplementary to it is U.S. Route 30, which generally parallels the toll road through the southern part of the study area. A

[3] The Pennsylvania and New York Central Railroads now are merged under the name "Pennsylvania New York Central Transportation Company." (Ed.)

two-lane highway, U.S. Route 220, runs generally north-south from Altoona, Pennsylvania, to Cumberland, Maryland. Route 220 diagonally crosses the two plunging anticlines which delineate the western boundary of Dunning Cove syncline.

Most county and township roads in the study area are macadamized. Approximately 30 percent of the local roads in the basin are constructed entirely of local granular and clayey materials and are graded and drained, but may become treacherous during the winter months and after heavy rains.

The nearest airfield is the Blair County Airport, approximately 32 mi (59.26 km) by road north of Bedford, near Martinsburg, Pennsylvania.

STRATA EXPOSED IN STUDY AREA

Rock outcrops of formations studied in the Bedford area (Fig. 5) are moderate in number and small in extent; thus, correlation and interpretation of structure are difficult. Extensive weathering makes porosity and permeability tests of the outcrops questionable and structural measurements inaccurate.

Relatively unweathered outcrops of the Tuscarora Sandstone can be found along the turnpike on the north side of the water gap through Evitts Mountain east of Bedford. In this exposure are the only fresh outcrops of the older Juniata and Bald Eagle Formations found in the Dunning Cove area. Shallow exposures of the Juniata also are found east of St. Clairsville and are present with the Bald Eagle at scattered places on the east slope of Evitts Mountain.

Only 145 ft (44 m) of Tuscarora is exposed along the turnpike (Cleaves, 1949); the rest is covered by talus along the west flank of Evitts Mountain. The Juniata section probably is complete at this location, and measures about 1,050 ft (320 m) along the turnpike cut. There is limited faulting in the exposure. The Bald Eagle Formation is repeated by faulting at the east end of the cut.

The Tuscarora also is exposed along the face of an abandoned quarry on the north side of the Raystown Branch gap, 0.5 mi west of Wolfsburg. Because of the nearness of the heavily traveled Pennsylvania Turnpike to the other exposure, the quarry location provides better sampling conditions.

Measurable outcrops of the Clinton strata are limited mostly to extremely weathered excavations and cuts in Rose Hill shale in the vicinity of the turnpike near Wolfsburg.

The McKenzie and Bloomsburg Formations are found in a few outcrops which are limited similarly in horizontal extent. The most accessible exposure of the two formations and their contact is just west of the Bedford interchange along the north side of the turnpike.

The Wills Creek Shale is present in shallow outcrops along U.S. Route 220 and the adjacent county roads where the highway crosses the anticlines of Dunning and Wills Mountains south of Cessna. It is commonly difficult to differentiate the Wills Creek exposures from similar argillaceous limestone beds of the Tonoloway, McKenzie, and Oriskany (Shriver) units except by their geographic location and a knowledge of the regional structure.

Formations younger than the McKenzie are exposed in the interior of the Dunning Cove syncline as well as west of the study area. The Tonoloway is found in good outcrops on the east side of U.S. 220 north of Bedford and along the northeast side of the turnpike on the western rim of the syncline.

The most representative exposure of the Keyser Limestone is in an abandoned quarry about 4.5 mi (7.2 km) west of Bedford on U.S. Route 30 and approximately 0.3 mi (0.5 km) north of Napier. The Tonoloway also is exposed here and can be compared with the Keyser rocks. Outcrops of the Keyser are limited within the Dunning Cove area; the generally thin strata are present along the fairly inaccessible wooded ridges of the interior hills.

The Helderberg was identified tentatively in a highly weathered road-material excavation on an unpaved county road extending north across the west rim of the syncline from Bedford. The red and white silty limestone debris of road fill is generally characteristic of the Helderberg, although differentiation from the overlying Shriver Chert Member of the Oriskany is difficult.

A few small exposures of the Ridgeley Sandstone Member of the Oriskany were found; however, this sandstone is weathered easily to a friable soil and no competent sandstone was found exposed. Geologic measurement of the outcrops is inaccurate because the sandstone weathers so easily.

The Onondaga Limestone and the Marcellus Shale were examined in a drainage-ditch excavation on the southwest side of the northern access road to the Bedford turnpike service area. The poor resistance of these two formations to weathering·and their relative thinness have limited the outcrops elsewhere in the study area. Shale beds were identified tentatively as Onondaga at a fairly large abandoned quarry northwest of the basin near St. Clairsville, although they are also similar to Mahantango shale. One of the limited but competent limestone beds of the Onondaga was found inside the basin east of Belden.

There are excellent exposures of the Mahantango Formation of the Hamilton Group on the west side of the county road along the west bank of Dunning Creek. A good exposure of the Mahantango-Marcellus contact and of the concretions in the Marcellus Shale is found near a road-material quarry 3.5 mi northeast of Bedford. Strata of the Hamilton Group also are exposed in an extensive roadcut along U.S. 220 south of St. Clairsville.

Younger formations such as the Harrell Shale (Late Devonian) and Tully Limestone (Late or Middle Devonian) were not identified inside the structural basin. Such outcrops are present west and northeast (Broad Top area) of the study area. Strata older than the Bald Eagle are present east and south of the Dunning Cove area.

STRATIGRAPHY

As summarized in Figure 6, the relevant stratigraphic column of the Dunning Cove area includes rocks of Late Ordovician through Middle Devonian age. The Precambrian, Cambrian, and Lower and Middle Ordovician strata were not studied in detail because the deepest formation considered for disposal of liquid wastes is the Tuscarora Sandstone of Early Silurian age. No Upper Devonian strata were mapped.

PRECAMBRIAN AND CAMBRIAN

Rocks of Precambrian age are not exposed in Bedford County. East of the study area, on the east edge of the Valley and Ridge province, metamorphosed basalt and rhyolite of Precambrian age are found. It is probable that these strata extend beneath the Bedford area, in a somewhat less deformed and metamorphosed condition.

The oldest Cambrian unit exposed in Bedford County is the Warrior Limestone, which here is fine-grained dolomite with shaly partings. It is overlain by crystalline dolomite and sandstone of the Gatesburg Formation. The next younger unit is the Mines Dolomite (Early Ordovician), an oölitic, crystalline dolomite. Figure 7 shows isopach maps of the Middle and Upper Cambrian, Lower Ordovician, and Middle Ordovician rocks.

Cambrian rocks older than the Warrior unit which are present in the subsurface in the study area include the Pleasant Hill Limestone and the Waynesboro Formation.

ORDOVICIAN

Pre-Reedsville.—The oldest Ordovician strata beneath the Dunning Cove syncline are in the Beekmantown Group, composed of four formations—the basal Stonehenge Limestone or Larke Dolomite, overlain successively by the Nittany Dolomite, the Axemann Limestone, and the uppermost Bellefonte Dolomite. This normally unexposed sequence of Lower Ordovician limestone and dolomite is about 2,600 ft (792 m) thick in the Hollidaysburg quadrangle of Blair County (Butts, 1945) and about 3,000 ft (914 m) thick in the area of Sinking Valley, also in Blair County (Moebs and Hoy, 1959).

Above this carbonate sequence is approximately 600 ft (183 m) of additional limestone including strata of the so-called Chazy and Black River Groups and the Trenton Group (Fig. 8). The Loysburg Formation is overlain by the Curtin Limestone and the Nealmont, Salona, and Coburn Formations, in ascending stratigraphic order. These beds consist primarily of impure limestone.

The Middle Ordovician sequence is combined by Kay (1944) under the following groups, listed in descending order, which are believed to be applicable to the area of Bedford County.

Trenton Group
    Coburn (?) Formation
    Salona Formation
    Nealmont Formation

(Continued on page 106)

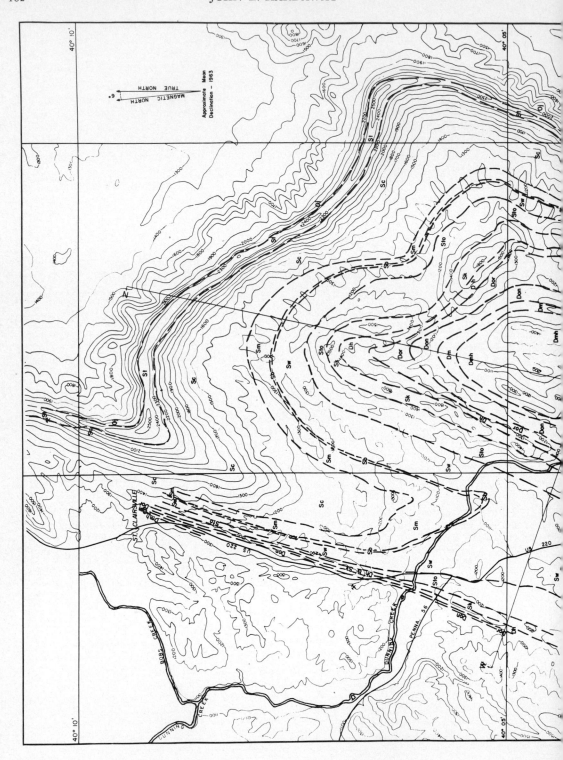

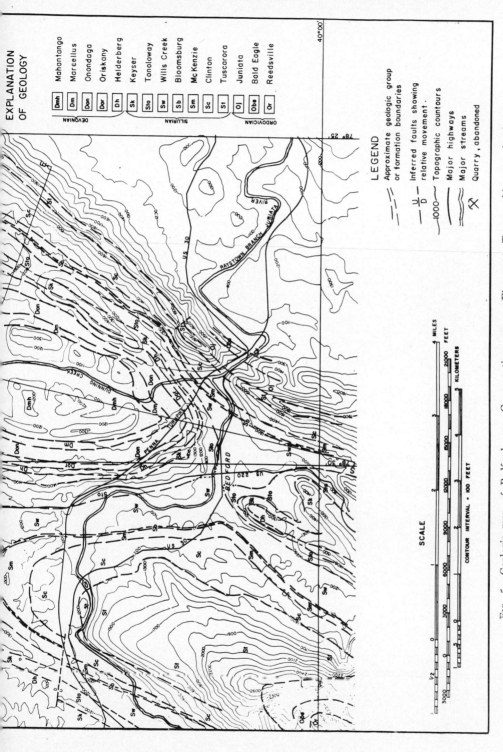

Dmh	Mahantango
Dm	Marcellus
Don	Onondaga
Dor	Oriskany
Dh	Helderberg
Sk	Keyser
Sto	Tonoloway
Sw	Wills Creek
Sb	Bloomsburg
Sm	McKenzie
Sc	Clinton
St	Tuscarora
Oj	Juniata
Obe	Bald Eagle
Or	Reedsville

DEVONIAN

SILURIAN

ORDOVICIAN

LEGEND

Approximate geologic group
or formation boundaries

Inferred faults showing
relative movement.

—1000— Topographic contours

Major highways

Major streams

Quarry, abandoned

SCALE

CONTOUR INTERVAL = 100 FEET

Fig. 5.—Geologic map of Bedford area. Cross sections are on Figure 14. Topographic control taken from U.S. Geological Survey 15-minute quadrangle maps: Bedford (1910), Clearville (1931), Everett (1900), Hyndman (1931).

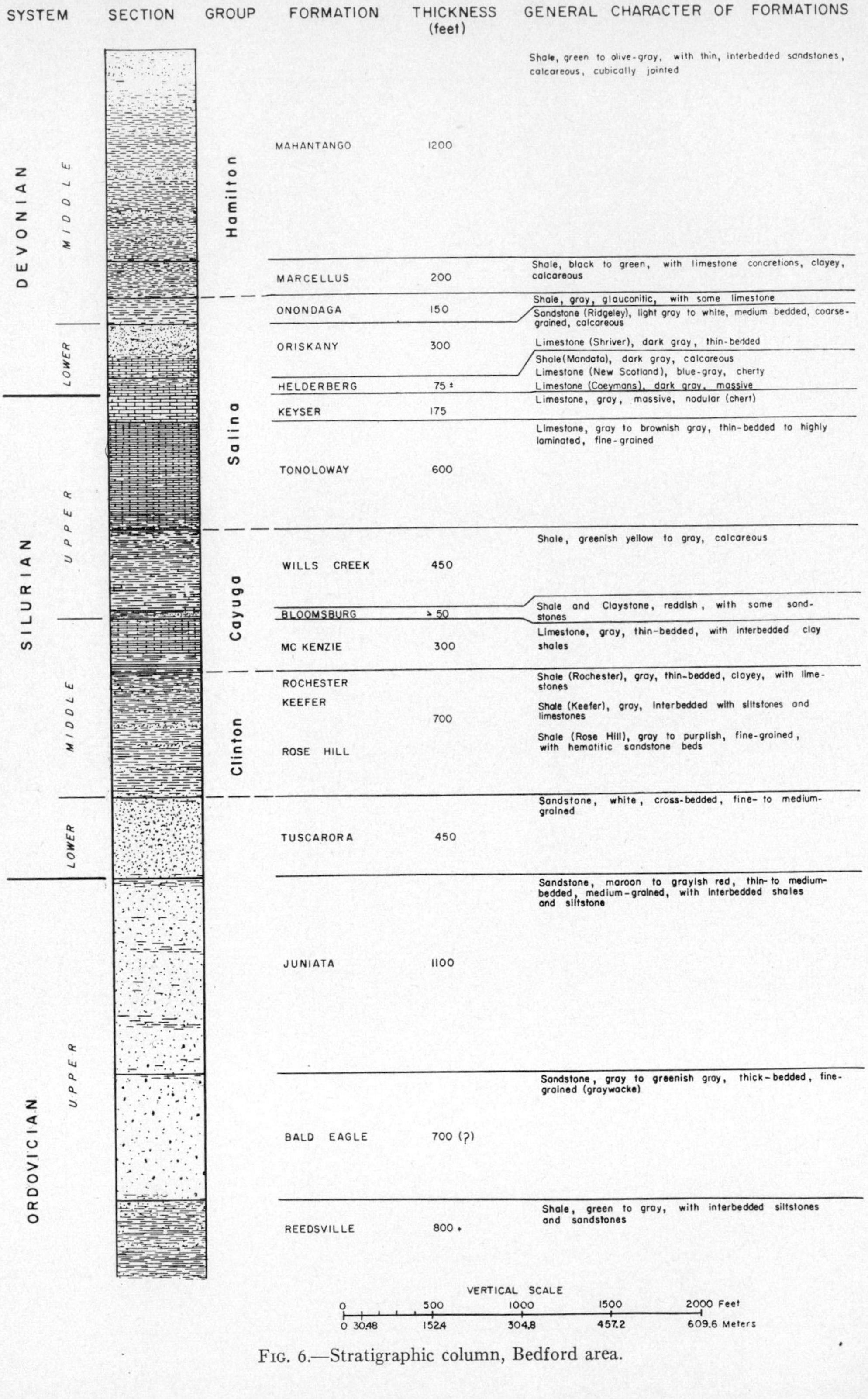

SYSTEM	SECTION	GROUP	FORMATION	THICKNESS (feet)	GENERAL CHARACTER OF FORMATIONS
					Shale, green to olive-gray, with thin, interbedded sandstones, calcareous, cubically jointed
DEVONIAN	MIDDLE	Hamilton	MAHANTANGO	1200	
			MARCELLUS	200	Shale, black to green, with limestone concretions, clayey, calcareous
	LOWER		ONONDAGA	150	Shale, gray, glauconitic, with some limestone
					Sandstone (Ridgeley), light gray to white, medium bedded, coarse-grained, calcareous
			ORISKANY	300	Limestone (Shriver), dark gray, thin-bedded
			HELDERBERG	75 ±	Shale (Mandata), dark gray, calcareous / Limestone (New Scotland), blue-gray, cherty / Limestone (Coeymans), dark gray, massive
SILURIAN	UPPER	Salina	KEYSER	175	Limestone, gray, massive, nodular (chert)
			TONOLOWAY	600	Limestone, gray to brownish gray, thin-bedded to highly laminated, fine-grained
		Cayuga	WILLS CREEK	450	Shale, greenish yellow to gray, calcareous
			BLOOMSBURG	≥ 50	Shale and Claystone, reddish, with some sand-stones
			MC KENZIE	300	Limestone, gray, thin-bedded, with interbedded clay shales
	MIDDLE	Clinton	ROCHESTER		Shale (Rochester), gray, thin-bedded, clayey, with lime-stones
			KEEFER	700	Shale (Keefer), gray, interbedded with siltstones and limestones
			ROSE HILL		Shale (Rose Hill), gray to purplish, fine-grained, with hematitic sandstone beds
	LOWER		TUSCARORA	450	Sandstone, white, cross-bedded, fine- to medium-grained
ORDOVICIAN	UPPER		JUNIATA	1100	Sandstone, maroon to grayish red, thin- to medium-bedded, medium-grained, with interbedded shales and siltstone
			BALD EAGLE	700 (?)	Sandstone, gray to greenish gray, thick-bedded, fine-grained (graywacke)
			REEDSVILLE	800 +	Shale, green to gray, with interbedded siltstones and sandstones

VERTICAL SCALE

```
0        500        1000       1500       2000 Feet
0  30.48    152.4      304.8      457.2      609.6 Meters
```

FIG. 6.—Stratigraphic column, Bedford area.

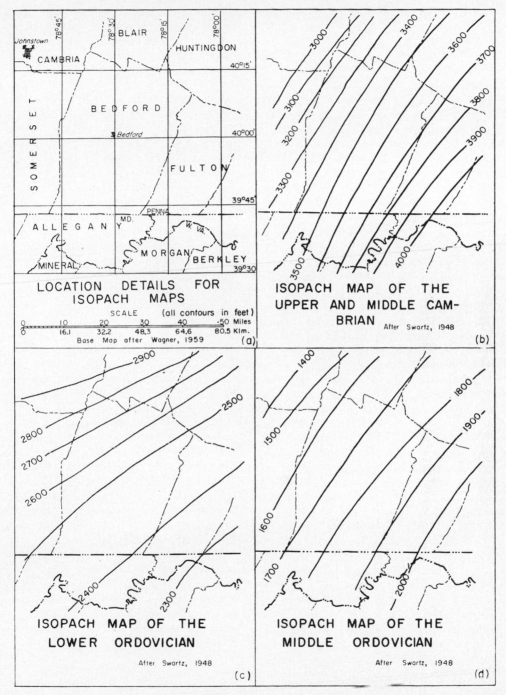

FIG. 7.—Index map and isopach maps of Middle and Upper Cambrian, Lower Ordovician, and Middle Ordovician strata, Bedford area. Base map published by permission of Pennsylvania Geol. Survey from Inf. Circ. 16.

Black River Group
  Curtin Limestone
  Benner Limestone
Chazy Group
  Hatter Formation
  Loysburg Formation

Reedsville Shale (Cincinnati Series).—The next
youngest formation, the Reedsville Shale, is not
well exposed in the study area, but is described
because of its probable significance as a barrier to
the flow of liquid wastes. An outcrop of limited
extent, which is faulted, is found at the easternmost end of the Bedford Narrows cut on the
Pennsylvania Turnpike.

The Reedsville is a sequence of green to gray
shale beds and interbedded subordinate siltstone
and thin sandstone layers. Both the top and the
base of the formation are gradational with the adjoining strata. Precise information on the thickness of the Reedsville Shale is not available, but
a thickness of 1,000 ft (305 m) is probable in the
study area.

The Reedsville is generally clayey and carbonaceous in south-central Pennsylvania and is faulted
extensively near the Bedford area; along the
Friends Cove fault, the Lower Ordovician and
Upper Cambrian strata have been thrust westward over younger shale beds. This faulting is apparent east of Evitts Mountain on the regional
geologic map (Fig. 3) and the regional structure
map (Fig. 12).

Bald Eagle Formation (Cincinnati Series).—
The Bald Eagle Formation is a dark-gray to greenish-gray sandstone which contains visible specks
of iron carbonate. It contains minor gradational
beds of greenish-gray, silty shale. The Bald Eagle
is thickly bedded and crossbedding is well developed; it has fine, poorly sorted, well-cemented
grains. It generally is considered to be a gray-
wacke (Swartz, 1950), but it is commonly conglomeratic at the base. A few lenses of milky-white
quartz pebbles have been reported in the area
(Cleaves, 1949).

Minor partings of reddish shale are present and
are most conspicuous in the upward transition
into the overlying Juniata Formation. The Bald
Eagle becomes increasingly shaly with depth in
its lower third. It is estimated to be about 700 ft
(213 m) thick, although there is no complete section in the study area. The Bald Eagle is transi-

tional with the underlying Reedsville Shale and
intertongues upward with the Juniata strata.

No porosity measurements were made of Bald
Eagle sandstone; however, the porosity and permeability of the strata are probably very low because of the presence of interstitial chlorite and
iron carbonate, which generally tend to block the
possible channels of flow (Swartz, 1950).

Topographically, the Bald Eagle forms ridges
subordinate to the predominant Tuscarora ridges,
and supports benches and flat-topped spurs separated by deep ravines.

Juniata Formation (Cincinnati Series).—The
Juniata Formation is a maroon to grayish-red
sandstone which becomes gray-green toward the
base. The formation in places is brick red and is
generally interbedded with similarly colored shale
and siltstone. The Juniata is a thin- to average-
bedded lithic sandstone, which contains many
platy to flaggy beds and distinct crossbedding and
other current structures, according to Yeakel
(1962).

The sandstone of the Juniata is both coarse
and fine grained, consisting primarily of well-
rounded quartz grains and minor chert, accessory
limonite-hematite, and subspherical concretions of
siderite in microscopic section. The formation is
locally conglomeratic.

The thickness of the Juniata redbeds is estimated to be about 1,100 ft (335 m) in the Dunning Cove area (Fig. 8). The top and bottom of
the Juniata are gradational with the overlying
Tuscarora and the underlying Bald Eagle.

The Juniata forms a bench between the Bald
Eagle and Tuscarora outcrops or is exposed along
the escarpment ridge of the Tuscarora; it weathers to a thin, rocky, sandy soil.

The factors which decrease the porosity and
permeability of the older Bald Eagle also should
cause the Juniata porosity and permeability to be
low. Limited measurements of porosity for a single specimen of the Juniata Sandstone are reported in the section on "Detailed Lithology and
Porosity."

SILURIAN

*Tuscarora Sandstone (Albion(?)-Medina(?)
Series).*—The Tuscarora is a light-gray, almost
white, quartzitic sandstone, in places pink or

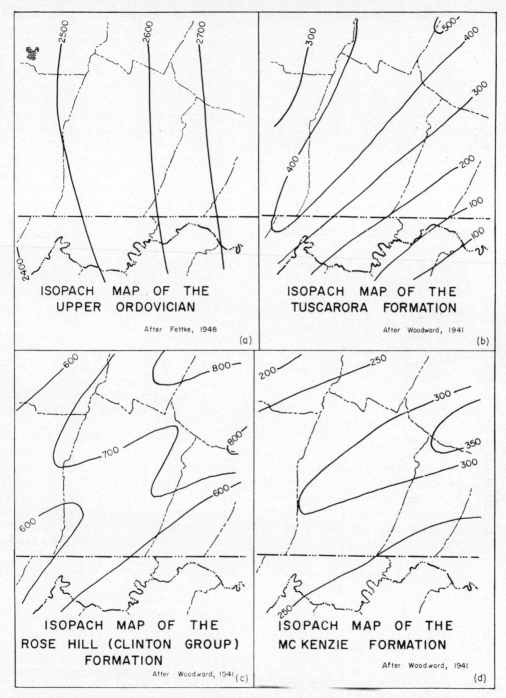

ISOPACH MAP OF THE
UPPER ORDOVICIAN

After Fettke, 1948

(a)

ISOPACH MAP OF THE
TUSCARORA FORMATION

After Woodward, 1941

(b)

ISOPACH MAP OF THE
ROSE HILL (CLINTON GROUP)
FORMATION

After Woodward, 1941 (c)

ISOPACH MAP OF THE
MC KENZIE FORMATION

After Woodward, 1941

(d)

FIG. 8.—Isopach maps of Upper Ordovician, Tuscarora (Lower Silurian), Rose Hill (Middle Silurian), and McKenzie (Middle Silurian) strata, Bedford area. Maps after Woodward (1941) published by permission of West Virginia Geol. and Econ. Survey. Figure 7a is index map.

greenish gray; however, the latter colors are not regionally traceable, but rather are gradational. The sandstone is interbedded with minor gray to dark-gray, silty, slightly calcareous shale beds toward the top. The sandstone is fine to medium grained and generally massive, although in places it is flaggy. The water-worn sand grains are well sorted and subrounded, having some microstylolite development and authigenic overgrowths. According to Yeakel (1962), the most common cement is authigenic quartz.

Few thickness measurements of the Tuscarora, as recorded from outcrops and wells in the vicinity of Bedford, are in agreement. The writer believes that the value of 450 ft (137 m) used in this preliminary study is representative of, if not very close to, the actual thickness (Fig. 8).

The Tuscarora grades into Juniata-type red sandstone, siltstone, and shale at the base and grades upward into shale of the Rose Hill Formation of the Clinton Group. The Tuscarora is widespread and thins regionally west of Bedford and the Allegheny Front.

The Tuscarora is the major ridge-forming sandstone near Dunning Cove; it occupies the crests of tree-covered mountains and has more than 1,400 ft (427 m) of topographic relief. Tuscarora ridges overwhelm the adjacent strata with large quantities of talus, which generally conceals possible fresh surfaces of the topographically lower Rose Hill, Juniata, Bald Eagle, and even Tuscarora outcrops. The overlying soil is generally thin, sandy, and unproductive.

Heald and Anderegg (1960) imply that the Tuscarora Sandstone of Pendleton County, West Virginia, and Highland County, Virginia, about 80 mi south of the Dunning Cove area, is characterized generally by low permeability. They attribute the low permeability (especially in the fine-grained beds) to pressure solution. They state that locally the Tuscarora contains alternate layers of tightly cemented sandstone and thinner layers of essentially uncemented argillaceous sandstone. Clay in the argillaceous layers prevented secondary growth of quartz. They conclude that, if pressure solution had not occurred, porosity in some beds would have been high; moreover, the clay coating prevented cementation in other beds. There are uncemented or slightly

cemented lenses within tightly cemented beds. Pockets of gas prevented waters from completely cementing the lenses (Heald and Anderegg, 1960).

The writer believes that the permeability indicated by the porosity measurements (reported in the section on "Detailed Lithology and Porosity") and the presence of large quantities of salt water at depth (summarized under "Hydrodynamics and Presence of Brine") show that there is a negligible amount of clay in the Bedford area.

The Tuscarora is quarried for use in the manufacture of silica brick. On the west and north, the stratigraphic equivalents of the Tuscarora, such as the "Clinton" and Whirlpool, are prime gas-productive sands (Cate, 1961), but the Tuscarora has not been proved petroleum-productive in the Valley and Ridge province.

Clinton Group (Niagara Series).—The Clinton Group, because of its stratigraphic location, its relative weakness, and the cover of Tuscarora debris, is difficult to divide into constituent formations. Therefore, it generally is considered herein as a group.

The Clinton is composed of possibly four separate formations; however, it is primarily shale. In ascending order, these formations are the Thorold Sandstone, Rose Hill Formation, Keefer Sandstone, and Rochester Shale.

The Thorold Sandstone in the subsurface is thin-bedded gray shale, in part silty, with interbeds of fine-grained, light-green to gray, quartzitic and slightly calcareous sandstone. The sandstone becomes cleaner toward the base. In the Allegheny Plateau the Thorold is a thin sandy unit containing glauconite, chamosite, leptochlorite, and oölitic hematite; it becomes finer grained eastward toward Bedford (Cate, 1961).

The overlying Rose Hill Formation probably contains the Thorold Sandstone as mapped (Fig. 8), but complete exposures including the Clinton-Tuscarora contact are not present. The Rose Hill is a sequence of light-gray-green shale beds, in places purplish gray and greenish gray, interbedded with green-gray siltstone and characteristically brick-red hematitic limestone and oölitic, hematitic sandstone which may cap topographic ridges. These sandstone beds are a few inches to several feet thick. The Rose Hill becomes finer grained, greenish, and sandy toward its base, where it includes the hematitic red sandstone referred to as the "Block Ore," so named because of its blocky character and commercial mining in colonial days. Where the several nonpersistent hematite beds crop out, they form intermediate ridges on the Tuscarora-supported slopes. The "iron sandstones" commonly are present in two separate ridges. The Rose Hill is irregular in thickness, but makes up most of the Clinton Group.

The Keefer Sandstone in the study area is predominantly gray shale interbedded with green-gray siltstone and finely clastic limestone. It is very calcareous in outcrops and becomes calcareous sandstone at its base. Although in the Bedford area the Keefer is not identified readily, it may be present as a medium- to coarse-grained, quartzose to calcareous sandstone, locally interbedded with siltstone and shale, all dark gray. The Keefer is transitional with the underlying Rose Hill Formation and is irregular in thickness. Topographically, the shale forms sharp ridges or benches along ridges of the Tuscarora or Rose Hill. The sandstone beds are similar to those of the Tuscarora.

The uppermost formation of the Clinton Group is the Rochester Shale, a dark-brown-gray calcareous and fossiliferous unit consisting of very thin lenticular shale beds and fine-grained, clastic, gray limestone interbeds. The Rochester grades into limestone toward the top and is probably equivalent to the Lockport Dolomite of the Allegheny Plateau. The Rochester forms a topographic bench below the overlying McKenzie and above the Keefer ridge, where the latter is present, but Rochester shale rarely is exposed. The formation thins regionally toward the west and north.

The entire Clinton Group is estimated to be about 700 ft (213 m) thick. The Clinton strata thicken east of Bedford County where the sandstone percentage increases. The upper Rochester is gradational with the younger McKenzie Formation.

McKenzie Formation (Niagara Series).—The McKenzie Formation is gray to dark-gray, in places blue, thin bedded, argillaceous limestone, interbedded with gray and greenish-brown calcareous clay shale similar to that of the underlying Rochester Shale. The basal McKenzie includes an intraformational limestone breccia which is overlain by gray, fine-grained, fossiliferous limestone. The upper McKenzie contains lighter gray to greenish-gray shale and siltstone and very fine-grained sandstone.

The McKenzie is estimated to be nearly 300 ft (91 m) thick in the Dunning Cove syncline (Fig. 8). It is gradational in its contact with both the younger Bloomsburg and the older Rochester.

Bloomsburg Formation (Cayuga Series).—The Bloomsburg Formation consists of gray-red to reddish-gray shale and claystone. It is thin in the Dunning Cove area, rarely more than 50 ft (15 m) thick (Fig. 9). The redbeds thicken eastward. Wherever the Bloomsburg is of sufficient extent, it may form low topographic ridges which are wooded; otherwise it produces typically barren soil.

Wills Creek Shale (Cayuga Series).—The Wills Creek Shale is greenish-yellow to light-green-gray and dark-gray, thin-bedded, calcareous shale which is interbedded with brown-gray argillaceous limestone. The formation is cherty toward the top and the limestone interbeds contain calcite, quartz veins, and quartz vugs. Red zones are common in the lower part of the Wills Creek, and a distinct sandstone zone is found locally at the top of the shale sequence. Minor anhydrite in thin veins is characteristic of the formation. The thickness of the Wills Creek (Fig. 9) is estimated to be 450 ft (137 m).

The Wills Creek Shale normally is eroded easily and therefore forms low valleys between the Tuscarora ridges as well as low, sinuous ridges which reflect the extremely complex folding of the incompetent strata. Because of its incompetent nature, the shale probably absorbed much of the regional as well as local deformation.

Tonoloway Limestone (Cayuga Series).—The Tonoloway is a light-gray to brownish-gray limestone with alternate zones of fine-grained limestone and dolomite and numerous argillaceous layers. The limestone has many thin interbeds which contain calcite veins and druses and some anhydrite.

The most important diagnostic feature of the formation is its many fine laminations, especially apparent on weathered surfaces, which give rise

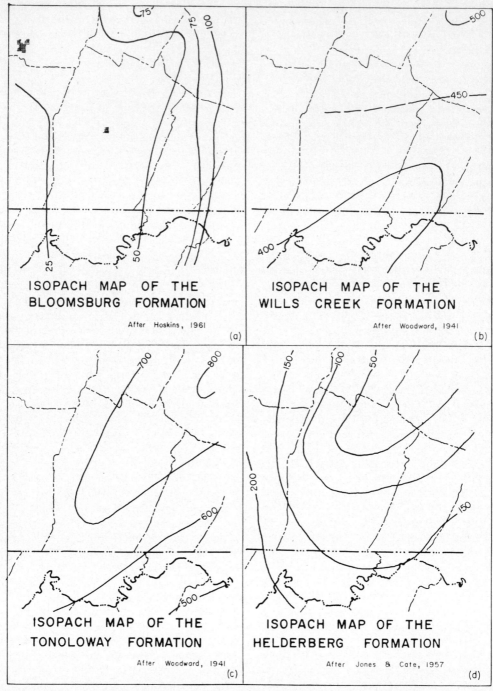

FIG. 9.—Isopach maps of Bloomsburg, Wills Creek, Tonoloway (all Upper Silurian), and Helderberg (Lower Devonian) strata, Bedford area. Maps after Woodward (1941) published by permission of West Virginia Geol. and Econ. Survey. Maps of Bloomsburg and Helderberg from Pennsylvania Geol. Survey Bull. G36 (Hoskins, 1961) and Spec. Bull. 8 (Jones and Cate, 1957); published by permission. Figure 7a is index map.

to the designation "Ribbon limestone." In places the top of the Tonoloway is cherty and massive; it tends to become pink crystalline limestone toward the base. The Tonoloway is described as "lithographic" where its fine-grained character predominates. The formation is estimated to be more than 600 ft (183 m) thick near Bedford (Fig. 9).

The Tonoloway generally underlies complexly folded Silurian valleys of the Valley and Ridge province and forms the lower and middle escarpments of the Helderberg-Oriskany ridges. Both Tonoloway and Keyser limestones are quarried for agricultural lime and are used locally as a road aggregate. The Tonoloway forms a clayey, fertile soil.

Keyser Limestone (Cayuga(?) Series).—Commonly included as the lower member of the Helderberg Group (Swartz, 1926; Slaughter and Darling, 1962), the Keyser is mapped herein as a separate formation in agreement with current practice of the Pennsylvania Geological Survey. In this form the Keyser, where thick enough, is divided into three so-called "units."

The lower unit is gray to brownish-gray, lumpy or nodular limestone, thickly bedded and crystalline; the nodules consist of chalcedonic chert. The middle unit is medium-gray, very fossiliferous limestone which is medium to thickly bedded. The upper unit is dark-gray argillaceous limestone which is medium to thickly bedded. The total thickness of the Keyser near Bedford is probably 175 ft (53 m).

The Keyser is transitional with the underlying Tonoloway. On the Allegheny Plateau, a widespread disconformity (Jones and Cate, 1957) separates the top of the Keyser from the overlying Coeymans Limestone Member of the Helderberg Limestone.

The Keyser generally is present as an escarpment along the upper Oriskany-Helderberg slopes and commonly forms independent resistant ridges. North of Bedford in the Hollidaysburg quadrangle, the limestone is quarried for lime for agricultural use and is used for crushed stone.

DEVONIAN

Helderberg Limestone.—In the Dunning Cove area it is possible in places to divide the Helderberg Limestone into three members.

The lower or Coeymans Limestone Member is dark-gray to black, argillaceous (silty) limestone which is generally more massive and crystalline than the underlying Keyser Limestone. The Coeymans is locally arenaceous and siliceous, and may contain sparry inclusions of calcite wherever the underlying Keyser is of a pelletoid texture (Cate, 1961).

The middle or New Scotland (Limestone) Member is also limestone, but is generally blue-gray, both thickly and thinly bedded, fine grained, and coarsely crystalline. The limestone contains white to brown-gray and blue-gray semichalcedonic, subchalcedonic, and chalcedonic chert in thin layers. The chert is present primarily in the fine-grained denser limestone of the New Scotland.

These two limestone members are overlain by the Mandata (Shale) Member, a dark-gray silty shale which is black in places and ranges from notably calcareous to extremely calcareous in outcrops.

All lithologic boundaries are apparently gradational, both at the base of the Helderberg and between the Coeymans, New Scotland, and Mandata Members.

The Helderberg is thus predominantly limestone and is present in the vicinity of Bedford in varied thicknesses; the thickness in the Dunning Cove area is estimated to be about 75 ft (23 m). In Bedford County, the formation contains a high percentage of limestone along the northeast-southwest-trending axis of greatest deposition (Fig. 9). The shale content decreases west of Bedford and coarse clastics increase eastward.

The Helderberg generally forms the crests of ridges in conjunction with the underlying limestones of the Keyser and Tonoloway. The Helderberg weathers to a rich, clayey soil which is cherty near the hilltops, emphasizing the resistant nature of the cherty New Scotland Member.

Oriskany Formation.—The Oriskany Formation is composed of two identifiable members, the Shriver Chert Member at the base and the Ridgeley Sandstone Member at the top.

The Shriver Member in the study area is dark-gray to black, siliceous limestone which also may be described as very calcareous siltstone. The limestone is underlain by minor beds of black shaly limestone or calcareous shale. The Shriver also contains dark-gray to black chert in thin beds and nodules. The limestone is thinly bedded to laminated, and is very fossiliferous. It is generally difficult to distinguish the Shriver from the underlying Helderberg limestone and calcareous shale (Mandata), both in outcrops and in well cuttings (Jones and Cate, 1957).

The Ridgeley Member is light-gray to white, commonly yellowish-brown sandstone, somewhat similar to the older Tuscarora, but generally less durable on weathered surfaces. The Ridgeley is normally medium to coarse grained, somewhat calcareous, and sporadically cherty. The silica grains are generally subrounded to well rounded and cemented by both primary and secondary silica and/or calcite. The sandstone is commonly jointed to some degree. Where the Ridgeley is notably calcareous, weathering has produced small pockets which are filled with silicified fossils.

The Ridgeley is locally conglomeratic north of Bedford near Hollidaysburg (Butts, 1945) and in Maryland (Slaughter and Darling, 1962), and it probably is locally conglomeratic in the Dunning Cove area.

The thickness of the Oriskany Formation is estimated to be about 300 ft (91 m) in the study area; the Ridgeley and Shriver are approximately equal in thickness (Fig. 10).

Both of the contacts of the Oriskany are gradational. The Shriver is gradational with the underlying Helderberg, but the black splintery shale of the Mandata can be identified in places. The Ridgeley is gradational with the younger Onondaga shale and limestone, and the boundary zone commonly is filled with siliceous, glauconitic, and limy material.

The Shriver thins regionally both east and west, and the Ridgeley thins and thickens abruptly in local areas of structural relief. Whichever member is slightly thicker (generally the Shriver near Bedford) normally forms the crests of minor wooded ridges. The Shriver weathers to a cherty soil and residual white clay in parts of Pennsylvania. The Ridgeley weathers to a light-yellow-brown sandy soil which is recognizable and, in combination with the sandstone debris, indicative of the member's presence.

The Oriskany is a primary source of gas on a commercial scale in the Pavia field of Bedford and Blair Counties and the Five Forks and Purcell fields of southeastern Bedford County (Fig. 13). However, where penetrated in Napier Township the sandstone-limestone sequence is not commercially productive because of its synclinal structure. The Ridgeley has been used as a source of glass sand.

Because of the importance of the Oriskany Formation to the oil and gas industry, much information is available regarding its lithology.

Onondaga Limestone.—The Onondaga can be divided into two members, the Needmore Shale Member below and the "Selinsgrove Limestone Member"[4] above. The Needmore, where found, is light-gray to dark shale, in places green gray; it is thinly bedded and contains interbeds of glauconite. The Selinsgrove is represented by a few beds of light- to dark-gray limestone in the Bedford area. This limestone is argillaceous, thinly bedded, and contains beds of chert and chert nodules.

The Onondaga represents different conditions of deposition than the underlying Ridgeley sandstone. It generally thickens east of Bedford and thins irregularly toward the west. The Onondaga is about 150 ft (46 m) or less thick in the Dunning Cove area (Fig. 10). On the Allegheny Plateau the formation contains local unconformities.

The Onondaga commonly is topographically lower than the Oriskany and Hamilton ridges. The limestone forms soft, clayey soil.

Hamilton Group.—In the Bedford area, the Hamilton generally is divided into two mappable formations, the Marcellus Shale at the bottom and the Mahantango Formation at the top.

The Marcellus is black to dark-gray, soft and clayey, carbonaceous shale, calcareous in part and becoming olive green upward toward the overlying Mahantango. The Marcellus is thinly bedded or in places laminated, a characteristic which results in fissile outcrops. The surfaces are generally wrinkled in a manner similar to that of gneiss, and large, dark limestone concretions and minor pyrite are common.

The overlying Mahantango is green to olive-

[4] The term "Selinsgrove" generally has been abandoned, but no new name has been proposed for the rocks in the study area here classified as Selinsgrove. (Ed.)

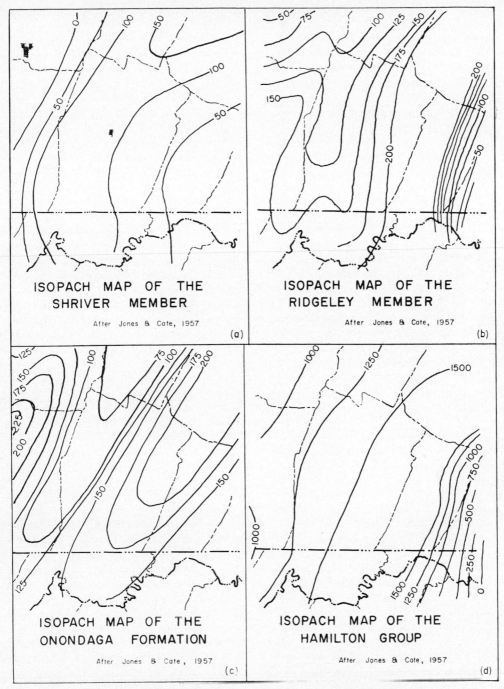

ISOPACH MAP OF THE
SHRIVER MEMBER

After Jones & Cate, 1957

(a)

ISOPACH MAP OF THE
RIDGELEY MEMBER

After Jones & Cate, 1957

(b)

ISOPACH MAP OF THE
ONONDAGA FORMATION

After Jones & Cate, 1957

(c)

ISOPACH MAP OF THE
HAMILTON GROUP

After Jones & Cate, 1957

(d)

FIG. 10.—Isopach maps of Shriver, Ridgeley (both Lower Devonian), Onondaga, and Hamilton (both Middle Devonian) strata, Bedford area. Source: Pennsylvania Geol. Survey Spec. Bull. 8; published by permission. Figure 7a is index map.

gray, slightly carbonaceous and calcareous shale; thin, sporadic sandstone zones thicken eastward from the study area. Minor limestone lenses are present. The sandstone beds generally are in the middle section of the Mahantango and are hard, platy, olive gray to tan, medium grained, and a few inches thick.

A common distinguishing characteristic of the Hamilton is its cubic or rhomboid jointing (Willard, 1935a).

The thickness of the Hamilton Group is varied, but averages about 1,400 ft (427 m) in Bedford County (Fig. 10). The Marcellus is thin in comparison to the Mahantango; it averages between 175 and 200 ft (53 and 61 m) in thickness, and the Mahantango is about 1,200 ft (366 m) thick. The Hamilton strata thin regionally westward.

The Hamilton is transitional at its base with the Onondaga shale and limestone. The Marcellus is similarly gradational upward into the Mahantango.

The Marcellus is too thin to show any mappable geomorphologic pattern other than the depressions caused by its susceptibility to weathering. The Mahantango normally forms a belt of uneven width—along stream depressions or along the slopes of hills—as small cliffs such as those along the west side of Dunning Creek. The black shale weathers to brownish-red-stained fragments and is very dark when wet. The upper shale of the Hamilton weathers to claylike, green-gray, soft chunks of shale.

Susquehanna Group.—The nomenclature of the post-Hamilton strata in Pennsylvania is indefinite. Butts (1918) considered the Burket to be the basal member of the Harrell Shale. Arndt *et al.* (1959) placed the Burket in the Rush Formation, the Tully Limestone Member being at the base. Willard (*in* Willard *et al.*, 1939) also considered the Burket to be a member of the Rush Formation and said there is a definite line of separation between it and the Harrell Shale Member of the Fort Littleton Formation. The U.S. Geological Survey now classifies the Harrell and Brallier Shales, of Late Devonian age, as formations in the Susquehanna Group (Keroher *et al.*, 1966). The Tully Limestone generally has been considered to be the basal unit in the Susquehanna

Group, but it may be of Middle Devonian age (Cooper, 1942).

The writer did not map the Susquehanna strata because they were not identified by him in preliminary field work. However, they are shown on the Geologic Map of Pennsylvania (Gray *et al.*, 1960).

The Tully is very thin in Bedford County and thins southward (Fig. 11); thus it probably is not present in the Dunning Cove basin. Where present, the Tully is medium- to light-gray limestone which may be represented only by thin transitional beds in the upper few feet of the gray Mahantango shale. The limestone is fine grained to crystalline, although it may be impure or silty locally. The Burket also is thin in Bedford County (about 40 ft or 12 m; Willard, 1935b). The Burket-Tully strata generally erode to topographic valleys or crop out along the perimeters of such valleys.

The Harrell is overlain by the Brallier Shale, which is not found in Dunning Cove but is known to be present in southern Bradford County near the town of Hewlett (Willard, 1935b).

If these Upper Devonian strata are present within the Dunning Cove syncline, the structural closure of the reservoir is greater than shown; the Tuscarora at the center of the basin would be about 600 ft deeper than shown in Figure 14. Therefore, the Dunning Cove area would be more favorable for the injection of waste liquids.

STRUCTURE
REGIONAL RELATIONSHIPS

The physiographic location of Dunning Cove —on the western perimeter of the Valley and Ridge province—is in a narrow region of structural transition from the complexly folded anticlines and synclines of the Appalachian Mountains westward into the less intensely folded and undulate strata of the Allegheny Plateau (Fig. 2). The large anticlines and synclines trend in generally linear northeast-southwest patterns parallel with the east and west boundaries of Bedford County (Fig. 12). Most of the deformation occurred during the Appalachian orogeny near the end of the Paleozoic Era.

The Dunning Cove syncline is anomalous along

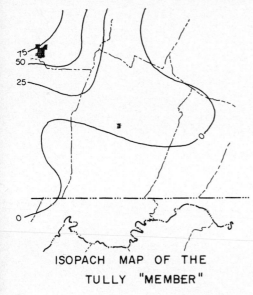

ISOPACH MAP OF THE
TULLY "MEMBER"

After Jones & Cote, 1957

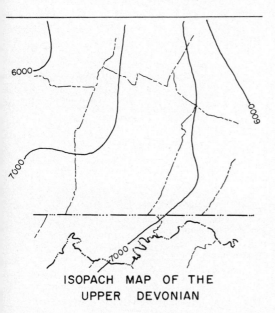

ISOPACH MAP OF THE
UPPER DEVONIAN

After Jones & Cote, 1957

FIG. 11.—Isopach maps of Tully Limestone (Middle or Upper Devonian) and Upper Devonian strata, Bedford area. Source: Pennsylvania Geol. Survey Spec. Bull. 8; published by permission. Figure 7a is index map.

the strike of the alternate synclines and anticlines. It forms the northern terminus of a long, narrow valley which extends southward from Bedford through Cumberland, Maryland. This structural and topographic lineament also is designated the "Cumberland valley" or the "Bedford syncline" along its entire length (Fettke and Fairall, 1953).

The Dunning Cove syncline is bounded on the east and north sides by the convex (to the west) west limb of the Roaring Spring anticline, which broadens extensively north of the Bedford area (Figs. 5, 12).

The Wills Mountain anticline either originates as a separate anticline along the western limit of the study area or very possibly is related to the northward-rising Dunning Mountain anticline. The topography and geology of the Cessna area suggest, by a slight offset of topographic slopes, that the two anticlinal noses are not folded along a single axis but that their axes are nearly parallel and in close proximity (within a few thousand feet at the surface). However, if a line parallel with the eastern outcrop along Evitts Mountain were drawn from the south along Wills Mountain, the resulting convex (to the west) curvature of the line would be sufficient to connect with the strike of Dunning Mountain. The value of additional exploration at this junction is considered in the discussion of site evaluation. It is believed that the nearness of the two anticlines allows temporary representation of the two uplifts as combined.

FAULTS

Faulting is recorded both in surface exposures and by subsurface drilling in Bedford County (Figs. 3, 12, 13). The structural front of the deformed Appalachians is characterized by complex and undetermined fault patterns. Nevertheless, the study area does not appear to be affected adversely by discontinuities of great extent or intensity. The extensive thrust faults east and north of the syncline (Figs. 3, 12) do not disturb the Tuscarora or invade Dunning Cove syncline.

The Friends Cove fault cuts the surface about 1,000 ft due east of Evitts Mountain, where it has thrust Gatesburg (Upper Cambrian) and

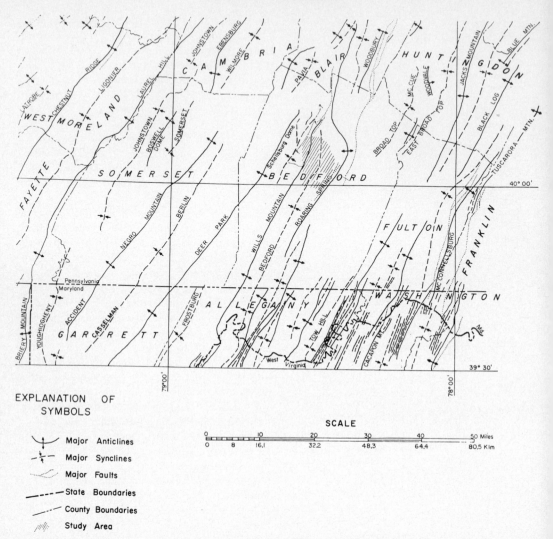

EXPLANATION OF
SYMBOLS

⌄ Major Anticlines

⌃ Major Synclines

Major Faults

State Boundaries

County Boundaries

Study Area

SCALE

0   10   20   30   40   50 Miles
0   8   16.1   32.2   48.3   64.4   80.5 Klm

FIG. 12.—Major structural features in vicinity of Bedford. Source: Pennsylvania Geol. Survey Bull. G27 (Fettke, 1954); published by permission.

Mines (Upper Cambrian?) strata westward over the younger (Ordovician) Beekmantown Group and part of the Benner, Curtin(?), Nealmont, Salona, and Coburn sequence of limestone beds. No effect or continuation of this thrusting was found on the west toward Bedford.

On the north, a thrust fault along the east side of Dunning Mountain separates the younger Bald Eagle Formation from the westward-thrust sequence of Warrior-Gatesburg-Mines dolomite beds. This fault and the Friends Cove fault are

many miles in horizontal extent. Careful study of the area was imperative to determine whether or not such faulting extended into the proposed reservoir area. Aerial photographs taken in 1958, USGS topographic maps, drilling information, and field study were used to delineate the structure.

Faulting is notable in the Bald Eagle Formation at the east end of the Bedford Narrows. A minor fault, the north side of which has moved down in relation to the south side, is present

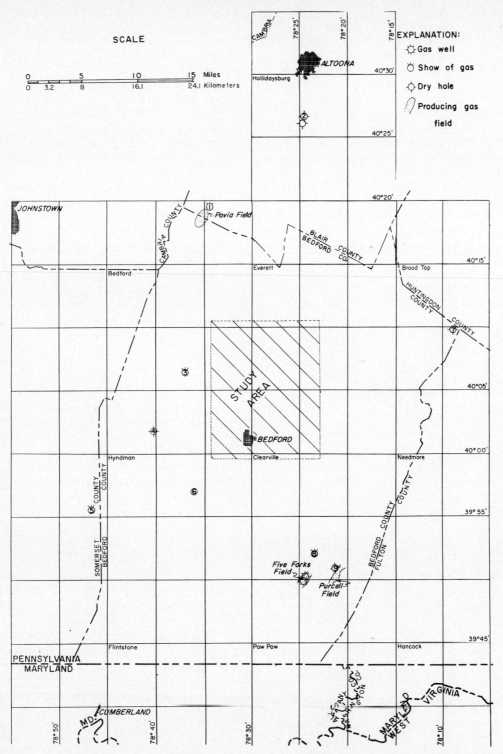

Fig. 13.—Locations of deep wells in Bedford area. Five-minute land grid shows locations of U.S. Geological Survey 15-minute quadrangle maps. Numbered wells are identified in Table I. Source: Pennsylvania Geol. Survey Bull. M45 (Lytle *et al.*, 1961).

about 4,000 ft (6.4 km) north of the Bedford Narrows. The fault severs the Tuscarora ridge, but no eastward or westward extension was found. Farther west, off the north slope of Wills Mountain, another fault is shown by Gray *et al.* (1960).

The possibility that the strata north of the town of Cessna between Dunning Mountain and Black Oak Ridge may be thinner than normal, or "squeezed," suggests the presence of another thrust fault or series of small displacements which has not been verified.

Deep wells in the vicinity of Bedford generally find faulting at considerable depth (Fig. 13, Table I). In all cases, the faulting is presumed to be either high-angle reverse or low-angle thrust similar to that postulated by Moebs and Hoy (1959; Cate, personal commun., 1963) in Blair and Huntingdon Counties, where extensive thrust faults and associated branching offsets are believed to be present. The hanging walls of these faults are theorized to have been thrust on a buried, domed surface. Subsequently the faults were exposed by folding and erosion. The faults are marked by fracturing, recementation, grooving, and polishing.

STRUCTURAL IMPLICATIONS FOR DISPOSAL OF LIQUID WASTES

The Bedford area is the westward limit of sharp surface folding. Of greatest interest in this study is the subsurface configuration of the Tuscarora Sandstone. The structure and resulting clo-

sure of this formation are determining factors in evaluating the possibility of escape of toxic wastes from the reservoir.

The top of the sandstone is about 2,500 ft (762 m) below sea level and 3,600–3,700 ft (1,097–1,128 m) below the surface at the center of the basin. None of the broad undulate synclines or anticlines locally influences the configuration of the Tuscarora. On the west flank of the syncline, the Tuscarora is about 1,000 ft (305 m) below the surface or 200 ft (61 m) above sea level. Near Bedford, at the south end of Dunning Cove, the sandstone is about 1,300 ft (396 m) beneath the surface or 100 ft (30.5 m) below sea level. If it is assumed that the liquid wastes cannot drain downward into the underlying Juniata and Bald Eagle, and that upward percolation through the overlying shale of the Clinton Group is improbable, the structural closure will give a total reservoir volume in the Tuscarora of more than 1.6 cu mi (6.5 cu km).

CLEAVAGE AND JOINTING

An evaluation of the extent and ease of fracturing and deformation is necessary in order to determine the feasibility of applying hydraulic fracturing to reservoir formations before the injection of cement slurries or the introduction of less dense liquids.

Because the formations receiving wastes in cement slurries should be thick enough to contain large quantities of wastes and perhaps to provide ion exchange sufficient to cleanse percolating

TABLE I. IDENTIFICATION OF DEEP WELLS ON FIGURE 13

Well No. on Fig. 13	Company	Name	Total Depth (ft)	Oldest Geologic Formation or Group Reached	Significant Structure and Comments
1	Phillips Petroleum Co.	Pa. Tract 26A No. 1	6,964	Helderberg-Oriskany	
2	Independent	Edward Bigley No. 1 Rankey No. 7	1,568	Juniata	Low-angle thrust superimposed Juniata over Tonoloway
3	South Penn *et al.*	Jesse B. Miller No. 1	8,979	Beekmantown (Bellefonte Dol.)	Significant faulting
4	South Penn	Hillegas		Rose Hill	Significant faulting
5	Peoples Natural Gas Co.	Mowry No. 1	9,253 (?)	Tuscarora (?)	Presumed faulting
6	Kerr-McGee	(Isabelle and Mary) Martin No. 1	6,676	Beekmantown	Low-angle thrust at 6,174 ft; Beekmantown over upside-down Martinsburg-Oswego-Juniata
7	Benedum-Trees Oil Co.	Rock Hill Coal No. 1	11,743	Tully or Hamilton	
8	N. Y. State Natural Gas	Morris		Helderberg	Significant faulting
9	N. Y. State Natural Gas	Clearville 1 (Miller No. 1) Clearville 2 (Ruie Rice No. 1) Clearville 3 (Miller No. 2)	5,300±	Oriskany	

wastes, the shale beds of the Clinton Group and the Wills Creek Shale may be worth consideration. The rest of the limestone and calcareous shale beds are not considered suitable for the disposal of acidic wastes because they are susceptible to leaching.

Both the Wills Creek and the Clinton shale beds absorb deformation and yield easily along thin bedding planes and fractures. The jointing is generally perpendicular to the bedding and both parallel with and perpendicular to the strikes of the shale beds. This orientation of fractures is common to most strata exposed along the anticlines (Wills and Evitts Mountains) of the area. Therefore it is believed that hydraulic fracturing and solution injection will lead to the easy formation of fractures in both horizontal and vertical planes away from the injection wells.

The Tuscarora is relatively more competent and fractures less easily than the shale, but there are widespread fractures perpendicular to bedding in the sandstone at the Bedford Narrows and Wolfsburg quarry sites. Both locations are in areas of folding, although no local folds are apparent in the formation.

GEOPHYSICAL INFORMATION

A. S. Cate (personal commun., 1963) reports that the following companies have conducted seismic studies in the Bedford area: South Penn Oil Co., Tidewater Oil Co., Shell Oil Co., Mobil Oil Co., Kerr-McGee Oil Industries, New York State Natural Gas Co., Peoples Natural Gas Co., Phillips Petroleum Co., and Sun Oil Co.

Geophysical well logs have been completed for wells Nos. 3, 4, 5, 6, and 9, shown on Figure 13. In well No. 3, which reached the Ordovician Beekmantown, gamma-ray logging and temperature logging were done. A gamma-ray log was run to total depth on well No. 4, which reached the Rose Hill(?) Formation. Gamma-ray and temperature logs were run on well No. 9, but it was drilled only to the Oriskany (Wagner, 1959). Well No. 5 was drilled to the Tuscarora, and gamma-ray and velocity logs were run. Gamma-ray, neutron, sonic, directional, induction, and density logs were run on well No. 6.

There are no cores or chips suitable for thin sections from any of the Bedford County deep wells.

TABLE II. DEEP PETROLEUM-PRODUCING WELLS IN PENNSYLVANIA THROUGH 1950, BY FORMATIONS[1]

Deepest Formation Tested	Total Wells	No. of Wells Producing
Onondaga	21	20
Oriskany	485	260
Helderberg	19	0
Salina	11	1
Lockport (McKenzie)	6	1
Albion (Tuscarora-Juniata)	47	3
Oswego (Bald Eagle)	1	0
Trenton	2	0
Beekmantown	1	0

[1] Source: Pennsylvania Geol. Survey Bull. M31 (Fettke, 1950a); published by permission.

The practice of waterflooding is used extensively to increase petroleum production in Pennsylvania. Waterflooding processes are similar to disposal of liquid wastes in porous formations. Therefore, experience gained in waterflooding will be of value in an appraisal of disposal conditions. Fettke (1950b) reported that in 1946 about 80 percent of the oil produced in Pennsylvania was obtained by waterflooding procedures. However, only formations of Devonian and younger ages were considered, and the only economically successful waterfloods are in the Bradford pool of northern Pennsylvania.

ECONOMIC GEOLOGY

The economic application of geology in Bedford County is limited to an active search for gas and oil, agricultural lime, and cement lime, and minor quarrying for silica-brick sand and road material. The synclinal structure of the Dunning Cove basin has ruled out the presence of gas or oil at economic depths. Therefore it is doubted that the introduction of contaminated wastes will harm future petroleum supplies.

Table II shows the number of deep petroleum-productive wells in Pennsylvania, by formation, through 1950. Intensive Tuscarora exploration was begun after 1950; thus the significance of that formation is not shown by the table.

DEPTH AND CAPACITY OF TUSCARORA RESERVOIR

If the Tuscarora Sandstone is regarded as a permeable aquifer confined by relatively impermeable formations, the structural closure as shown by the structural cross sections of Figure 14 provides an ellipsoid reservoir measuring about 4 by 8 mi (7.4 by 14.8 km) across its minor east-west and major north-south axes, respec-

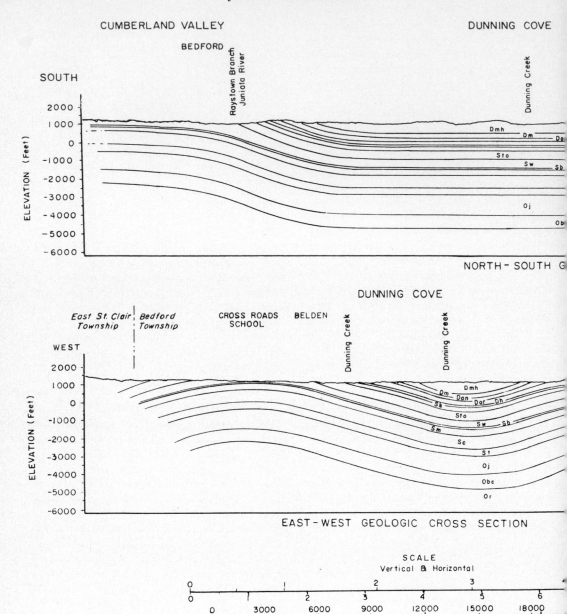

Fig. 14.—Generalized structural cross s

tively. If a relatively smooth subsurface structure is assumed, which is a reasonably accurate assumption at the map scale used, the base of the Tuscarora is 4,100 ft (1,250 m) beneath the center of the basin.

The top of the Reedsville then is estimated to

be approximately 6,000 ft (1,829 m) below the center of the basin. Around the western limit of the basin the Tuscarora is at a depth of 1,000 ft (305 m) below the exposed surfaces of the Wills Creek shale beds. South of Bedford, the Tuscarora is about 1,300 ft (396 m) beneath the sur-

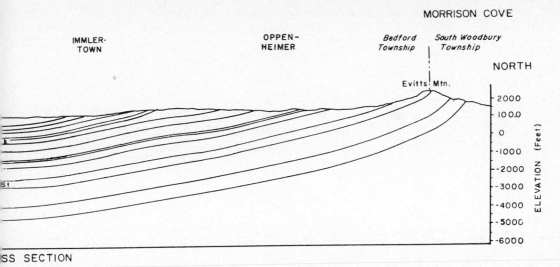

MORRISON COVE

 SS SECTION

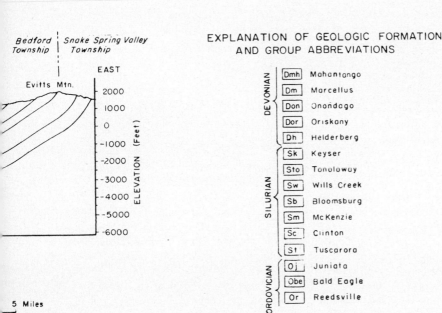

EXPLANATION OF GEOLOGIC FORMATION
AND GROUP ABBREVIATIONS

DEVONIAN	Dmh	Mahantango
	Dm	Marcellus
	Don	Onondaga
	Dor	Oriskany
	Dh	Helderberg
SILURIAN	Sk	Keyser
	Sto	Tonoloway
	Sw	Wills Creek
	Sb	Bloomsburg
	Sm	McKenzie
	Sc	Clinton
	St	Tuscarora
ORDOVICIAN	Oj	Juniata
	Obe	Bald Eagle
	Or	Reedsville

ford area. Traces of cross sections shown on Figure 5.

face. These depths are sufficient to provide protection against shallow-water contamination, and drilling costs should not be excessive.

The structural relief of the Tuscarora Sandstone for disposal purposes is thus about 2,500 ft (762 m). If a porosity of 15 percent is assumed, the available void area in the reservoir would be about 0.25 cu mi (1 cu km).

DETAILED LITHOLOGY AND POROSITY

Two sandstone units are considered—the Ridgeley Sandstone Member of the Oriskany Forma-

TABLE III. POROSITY MEASUREMENTS, TUSCARORA AND JUNIATA SANDSTONES

Sample	Specimen	Dry Weight (g)	Grain Volume (cc) P = 2.65	Volume (Mercury) (cc)	Pore Volume (cc)	Porosity (%)	Final Weight Change of Specimen (g)
Tuscarora							
1	a	56.98	21.50	25.00	3.50	14	0.0
	b	76.89	29.02	34.50	5.48	16	+0.2
	c	82.46	31.12	36.00	4.48	14	+0.2
	d	110.84	41.83	46.00	4.17	9	0.0
2	a	85.42	32.23	38.00	5.77	15	+0.05
	b	83.21	31.40	36.5	5.10	14	+0.2
	c	65.20	24.60	30.0	5.40	18	+0.05
	d	69.32	26.16	31.0	4.84	16	0.0
3	a	89.00	33.58	40.0	6.42	16	+0.1
	b	59.51	22.46	27.5	5.04	18	0.0
	c	60.61	22.87	22.87	4.63	17	+0.2
	d	40.80	15.40	19.00	3.60	19	0.0
4	a	62.15	23.45	28.00	4.55	16	+0.1
	b	80.88	30.52	35.00	4.48	13	+0.15
	c	41.76	15.76	19.00	3.24	17	+0.15
	d	39.80	15.02	18.00	2.98	17	+0.03
	e	76.69	28.94	33.00	4.06	12	+0.04
	f	34.69	13.09	(not measureable)			+0.2
5	a	72.79	27.47	31.5	4.03	13	0.0
	b	85.24	32.17	35.5	3.33	9	0.0
Juniata							
1	a	72.09	27.20	30.0	2.80	9	+0.1
	b	65.05	24.55	28.0	3.45	12	+0.1
	c	68.13	25.71	28.5	2.79	10	+0.05
	d	60.81	22.95	25.5	2.55	10	+0.05
	e	49.20	18.57	21.0	2.43	12	0.0
	f	43.49	16.41	18.5	2.09	11	0.0

tion and the Tuscarora Sandstone. They are clean sandstones of interest to oil and gas operators in the western half of Pennsylvania.

The Ridgeley contains a heavy-mineral assemblage which indicates derivation from sedimentary rocks (Stow, 1938). Microscopic examination of Ridgeley outcrops near Everett, Bedford County, shows that the light minerals in the sandstone are nearly 100 percent quartz, whereas a typical heavy-mineral assemblage contains 20 percent tourmaline, 15 percent zircon, 50 percent leucoxene, 15 percent limonite, and a trace of rutile. The heavy minerals constitute 0.1–0.2 percent by volume of the total sample as reported by Stow.

Stow also found 10–25 percent chert in the Ridgeley in Blair County, but it is likely that this high percentage is the result of the transition with the underlying Helderberg Limestone and the presence of the Shriver Chert Member of the Oriskany. South of Bedford near the Maryland state line, 21–32 percent chlorite is reported in the heavy-mineral assemblage, but no clay or chert fraction is reported (Stow, 1938). Low per-

centages of the feldspars, about 1–4 percent, have been found, but not in the samples from Everett.

The zircon and tourmaline were found to be essentially rounded grains, distributed uniformly but not distinctively. The leucoxene is present as opaque, rounded grains—an alteration product of ilmenite. Authigenic quartz, calcite, orthoclase, microcline, albite, and pyrite are reported in the Ridgeley of West Virginia (Heald, 1950) and are thought to have crystallized after burial and compaction (Krynine, 1941).

Part of the information available on the Tuscarora Sandstone has been reported in the stratigraphic description of the formation. In addition, the fact that the sand is used for silica brick indicates that the thermal conductivity of the sandstone rises appreciably with an increase in temperature. This characteristic would be beneficial to the dissipation of heat produced by decomposing wastes.

Porosity measurements as summarized in Table III were made by the writer on five specimens collected from different zones in the Tuscarora

TABLE IV. CHEMICAL ANALYSES OF TUSCARORA SANDSTONE[1]

Site Location	Type of Exposure	Composition (%)					Fusion Point (°C)		Percent of Outcrop Usable in Manufacture of Silica Brick
		SiO₂	Al₂O₃	Fe₂O₃	CaO	Total	Coarse	Fine	
J. L. Hartmann quarry St. Clairsville quarry near	Outcrop	97.40	0.98	1.17	0.14	99.69	1,725	1,725	80
St. Clairsville on road to Brumbaugh	Talus	97.82	0.85	0.90	0.10	99.67	1,746	1,745	65
Tates quarry near Cliffs, Evitts Mtn.	Outcrop	97.70	0.82	1.01	0.12	99.65	1,763	1,746	80
E. R. Baldridge quarry near Wolfsburg	Outcrop	98.11	0.85	0.80	0.09	99.85	1,772	1,760	70

[1] Adapted from Pennsylvania Geol. Survey Rept. M3 (Moore and Taylor, 1924); published by permission.

in the Wolfsburg quarry.[5] The procedure was, by necessity, approximate and simplified. Chunk specimens were dried in an oven at about 100°F (38°C), weighed, and then submerged in mercury to determine the bulk volume. A grain density of 2.65 g/cm³ was assumed to calculate the grain volume. The resulting porosity of the Tuscarora averages 15 percent; 19 measurements gave a range from 9 to 19 percent.

The specimens were not coated protectively when placed in mercury, but were weighed before and after immersion to determine whether any mercury had been adsorbed. These weighings showed that the increase in the weight of a specimen never exceeded 0.02 g and averaged less than 0.01 g. This negligible increase in weight may be attributed to adsorption of mercury and/or adsorption of atmospheric moisture.

Heald and Anderegg (1960) measured as much as 5 percent argillaceous material (sericite and probably some illite), by volume, in Tuscarora sandstone from Pendleton County, West Virginia, and Highland County, Virginia. However, the writer believes that the degree of porosity and presence of fluids at depth in the Tuscarora near Bedford make it possible to disregard as negligible the clay fraction of the sandstone. Heald and Anderegg show that the fractures in the Tuscarora specimens have been filled with quartz. The quartz was determined to have been deposited as the fractures were formed. Although fractures were found in the Tuscarora near Bedford, no healing by quartz was established. The filling of such fractures is governed by the quantity of secondary silica available. Where filling is incom-

plete at depth, secondary porosity may be formed (Heald and Anderegg, 1960).

Most Paleozoic sandstones of West Virginia contain 98 percent or more silica where a minor part of the silica is in the form of chert. The small percentage of other minerals generally includes clay, calcite, dolomite, siderite, pyrite, and limonite (Arkle and Hunter, 1957). The Tuscarora has been sampled at locations near and inside Dunning Cove, and chemical analyses have been made. These sites are former commercial sources of silica-brick sand. The locations and analyses are summarized in Table IV. It is useful to note that the Tuscarora sand is found to absorb water more readily than other sands used in the manufacture of silica brick (Moore and Taylor, 1924).

In contrast to the Tuscarora porosity of 15 percent, the average porosity of samples of a large chunk of Juniata sandstone, as determined by limited measurements, averaged 10 percent (Table III). This lower porosity is in part the basis for the writer's belief that the Juniata will act as an impermeable boundary to liquid wastes, or at least will make their velocity of travel negligible.

The shales of the area are of interest from the standpoints both of providing impermeable boundaries to the wastes and of serving as artificially fractured reservoirs for wastes. Both the Wills Creek Shale and shales of the Clinton Group are present extensively in the basin. Shale of the Rose Hill Formation, the major formation of the Clinton, deforms easily and fractures along thin bedding planes and cleavage surfaces. No evidence of "plastic flow" was observed, though small folds are common.

The Wills Creek also absorbs deformation

[5] Located 0.5 mi west of Wolfsburg on north side of Raystown Branch, south of U.S. Highway 30.

(Buckwalter, 1959) and is eroded easily because of its softness (Butts, 1945). Buckwalter describes the Wills Creek shale sequence as very incompetent. Although apparently not as easily fractured or folded as the Rose Hill, the Wills Creek is notably calcareous and thus may react unfavorably with acidic wastes. The Wills Creek shales generally contain less clay than the Clinton shales.

HYDRODYNAMICS AND PRESENCE OF BRINE

No wells have been drilled to the Tuscarora in the Dunning Cove basin. As a result, the hydrodynamic conditions at depth must be inferred. The Jesse B. Miller No. 1 well on the west is of interest because of the presence of brine in the Tuscarora at depths of 2,920, 2,938, and 3,150 ft beneath the surface. The fact that the salt water ceased flowing before operations were completed suggests that the brine is isolated from replenishable supplies.

Poth (1962) summarized the character of brine in Pennsylvania from formations of Cambrian through Pennsylvanian age. The dissolved-solids content of Pennsylvania brines was found to be as great as 100,000 ppm. In formations lower than the Middle Devonian, where equilibrium conditions are presumed to be present, the dissolved-solids content is on the order of 300,000 ppm. Two samples of brine from Upper Silurian rocks had dissolved-solids contents of 190,000 ppm (Poth, 1962).

The generally high percentage of dissolved solids and salt suggests that the waters are connate. If there are hydrologic connections with recharge or discharge areas, the presence of connate water indicates that low permeability of the rocks negates exchange of the fluids.

SITE EVALUATION AND SUGGESTED INVESTIGATIONS

From this preliminary study, it appears to the writer that the basin is favorable for the installation of waste-disposal facilities. The drilling of about six deep wells in the study area, especially along the western and southern perimeters, will provide the complementary samples and information needed for final consideration of the site.

As Roedder (1959) reports in his comprehensive study, a sandstone aquifer is better suited to receive acidic wastes than is a more reactive and soluble limestone. The writer believes that the suggested six additional wells should be used to locate the Tuscarora Sandstone and determine its thickness near Cessna and Bedford and in the center of Dunning Cove. Cores from these should be subjected to porosity, permeability, ion-exchange, fracture-orientation, thermal-conductivity, thermal-expansion, and chemical-reaction tests to determine their suitability and compatibility with the wastes. Furthermore, chemical analyses should be performed on the brines of the reservoir sandstones to determine compatibility.

A principal problem will be the retention of the wastes in the Tuscarora strata. Therefore, it will be important to determine the effectiveness of the formations adjacent to the Tuscarora in forming impermeable boundaries to the wastes.

The synclinal configuration and attendant structural closure of Dunning Cove are believed to be free of structural discontinuities, especially faults. Therefore, the possibility of leakage through poorly healed fracture zones into permeable formations is slight.

The presence of a considerable quantity of salt water in the nearby Jesse B. Miller No. 1 well, where brine found in the Tuscarora Sandstone at depths of 2,920, 2,938, and 3,150 ft below the surface was quickly depleted, suggests that the Tuscarora of the study area is hydrologically isolated.

The combination of structural closure and hydrologic isolation fulfills some of the necessary requirements for waste disposal. It is estimated that the Tuscarora has an effective porosity of about 15 percent in relatively unweathered surface outcrops. The underlying Juniata has an effective porosity of 10 percent under the same conditions; because both silt and shale are present, it probably can be assumed to be a relatively impermeable barrier to liquid wastes. Because of the normal decrease of permeability and porosity with depth, the need for tests on fresh cores is emphasized.

The writer believes that correlation of full-scale seismic-reflection studies with velocity-logged wells may show a mappable horizon throughout the study area and along its western perimeter; thus the zone of future contamination can be delineated with a minimum number of deep wells. The value of such seismic work will depend greatly on the extent to which the deep structure is reflected in the near-surface structure. It will be possible also to utilize the exploratory wells for monitoring or for injection, dilution, or removal of the wastes.

The shale beds available for fracturing and disposal, principally the Wills Creek and Rose Hill, are present in thicknesses of 450 and about 600 ft (137 and 183 m), respectively. Along the north and east sides of the basin these shales are remote from populated areas. The shale beds are relatively weak and easily fractured. The presence of calcareous material in both sequences may cause problems of neutralization, and the presence of thin, irregular "iron sandstone" beds in the Rose Hill and thin limestone beds in the Wills Creek may cause localized breaking during hydraulic fracturing. The limited knowledge of the variables of hydraulic fracturing (Cleary, 1958a, 1958b, 1959; Parkison, 1957) indicates that shales probably will fracture with ease, but the extent and direction of the breaking will be difficult to predict.

The presence of the Ridgeley Sandstone Member of the Oriskany Formation at shallow depths, and its continuous outcrop around the basin, may make it a suitable shallow test aquifer for use with tracer solutions to test theories of hydrology and monitoring. Because little drilling is necessary to reach the sandstone, a pilot project might be economical.

The accessibility of the Bedford area by road, railroad, and air should facilitate transport of men, equipment, and wastes. Land costs probably will be reasonable because the farmland is not very productive. The area does include the populated area of Bedford, but tests may prove its location to be compatible with the test requirements of safety.

The locations of all existing wells must be determined accurately, and they must be plugged in order to prevent the escape of contaminating wastes into supplies of potable water.

The single outlet for the surface drainage through the Bedford Narrows will facilitate monitoring of the surface runoff, and the use of reservoirs for local potable water will lessen the chance of contamination. The climatological data show that runoff is not excessive near the cove. Therefore, the chance of accidentally emitted wastes being carried to supplies of potable water is slight.

REFERENCES

Amsden, T. W., R. M. Overbeck, and R. U. R. Martin, 1954, Geology and water resources of Garrett County, Md.: Maryland Dept. Geology, Mines and Water Resources Bull. 13.

Anderegg, R. C., 1955, Petrology and cementation of the Tuscarora Sandstone in Pendleton County, West Virginia, and Highland County, Virginia: Unpub. M.S. thesis, Univ. West Virginia.

Arkle, T., Jr., and R. G. Hunter, 1957, Sandstones of West Virginia: West Virginia Geol. and Econ. Survey Rept. Inv. No. 16.

Arndt, H. H., et al., 1959, Structure and stratigraphy of central Pennsylvania and the anthracite region: Geol. Soc. America Guidebook, Field Trip No. 1.

Bell, A. H., 1957, Brine disposal in Illinois oil fields: Illinois Geol. Survey Circ. 244.

——— et al., 1956, Underground storage of liquid petroleum hydrocarbons in Illinois: Illinois Geol. Survey Repr. Ser. 1956-H.

Bernard, G. G., 1957, Effects of reactions between interstitial and injected waters on permeability of reservoir rocks, in Symposium on water-flooding: Illinois Geol. Survey Bull. 80.

Buckwalter, T. V., chm., 1959, Geol. Soc. America Guidebook, Field Trip No. 1.

Butts, Charles, 1905, Ebensburg (Pa.) geologic folio: U.S. Geol. Survey Geol. Atlas No. 133.

——— 1918, Geologic section of Blair and Huntingdon Counties, central Pennsylvania: Am. Jour. Sci., ser. 4, v. 46, p. 523–537.

——— 1945, Hollidaysburg-Huntingdon (Pa.) geologic folio: U.S. Geol. Survey Geol. Atlas No. 227.

Carroll, Dorothy, 1959, Ion exchange in clays and other minerals: Geol. Soc. America Bull., v. 70, no. 6, p. 749–780.

Cate, A. S., 1961, Stratigraphic studies of the Silurian rocks of Pennsylvania (pt. 1): Pennsylvania Geol. Survey, 4th ser., Spec. Bull. 10.

Cleary, J. M., 1958a, Hydraulic fracture theory, pt. 1, Mechanics of materials: Illinois Geol. Survey Circ. 251.

——— 1958b, Hydraulic fracture theory, pt. 2, Fracture orientation and possibility of fracture control: Illinois Geol. Survey Circ. 252.

——— 1959, Hydraulic fracture theory, pt. 3, Elastic properties of sandstone: Illinois Geol. Survey Circ. 281.

Cleaves, A. B., 1949, Guidebook to the geology of the Pennsylvania Turnpike, Carlisle to Irwin: Pennsylvania Geol. Survey, 4th ser., Bull. G24.

Cooper, G. A., chm., 1942, Correlation of the Devonian sedimentary formations of North America [Chart No. 4]: Geol. Soc. America Bull., v. 53, no. 12, pt. 1, p. 1729–1793.

Fettke, C. R., 1948, Subsurface Trenton and sub-Trenton rocks in Ohio, New York, Pennsylvania and West Virginia: Pennsylvania Geol. Survey, 4th ser., Bull. G21; repr. from Am. Assoc. Petroleum Geologists Bull., 1948, v. 32, no. 8, p. 1457–1492.

—— 1950a, Summarized records of deep wells in Pennsylvania: Pennsylvania Geol. Survey, 4th ser., Bull. M31.

—— 1950b, Water flooding in Pennsylvania, *in* Secondary recovery in the United States, 2d ed.: New York, Am. Petroleum Institute.

—— 1954, Structure contour maps of the Plateau region of north-central and western Pennsylvania: Pennsylvania Topog. Geol. Survey Bull. G27.

—— 1956, Summarized records of deep wells in Pennsylvania, 1950 to 1954: Pennsylvania Geol. Survey, 4th ser., Bull. M39.

—— 1960, Jesse B. Miller No. 1 well, Napier Township, Bedford County: Pennsylvania Geol. Survey, 4th ser., Well Sample Record No. 56 (Scout Log).

—— and V. Fairall, 1953, Oil and gas development in the Appalachian basin, past and present: Pennsylvania Geol. Survey, 4th ser., Bull. M37.

Fisher, D. W., 1959, Correlation of the Silurian rocks in New York state: New York State Museum and Sci. Serv., Geol. Survey Map and Chart Ser. No. 1, 1960.

—— 1962, Correlation of the Ordovician rocks in New York state: New York State Museum and Sci. Serv., Geol. Survey Map and Chart Ser. No. 3.

Foose, R. M., 1942, Manganese minerals of Pennsylvania: Pennsylvania Geol. Survey, 4th ser., Prog. Rept. No. 128.

Ganguly, A. K., 1951, Base-exchange capacity of silica and silicate minerals: Jour. Phys. Colloid Chem., v. 55, p. 1417–1428.

Gray, Carlyle, *et al.*, 1960, Geologic map of Pennsylvania: Pennsylvania Geol. Survey, 4th ser., scale 1:250,000.

Grim, R. E., *et al.*, 1947, 1. Reaction of different clay minerals with some organic cations; 2. Reaction of clays with organic cations in producing refractory insulation: Illinois Geol. Survey Rept. Inv. No. 123.

Haught, O. L., 1959, Symposium on the Sandhill deep well, Wood County, West Virginia: West Virginia Geol. Survey Rept. Inv. No. 18.

Heald, M. T., 1950, Authigenesis in West Virginia sandstones: Jour. Geology, v. 58, no. 6, p. 624–633.

—— and R. C. Anderegg, 1960, Differential cementation in the Tuscarora Sandstone: Jour. Sed. Petrology, v. 30, no. 4, p. 568–597.

Hoskins, D. M., 1961, Stratigraphy and paleontology of the Bloomsburg Formation of Pennsylvania and adjacent states: Pennsylvania Geol. Survey, 4th ser., Bull. G36.

Jones, T. H., and A. S. Cate, 1957, Preliminary report on a regional stratigraphic study of Devonian rocks of Pennsylvania: Pennsylvania Geol. Survey, 4th ser., Spec. Bull. 8.

Kauffman, N. M., 1960, Climates of the states; Pennsylvania: U.S. Dept. Commerce, Weather Bur. Climatography of U.S., No. 60–36.

Kay, G. M., 1942, Development of the northern Allegheny synclinorium and adjoining regions: Geol. Soc. America Bull., v. 53, no. 11, p. 1601–1658.

—— 1943, Chemical lime in central Pennsylvania: Econ. Geology, v. 38, no. 3, p. 188–203.

—— 1944, Middle Ordovician of central Pennsylvania, pts. 1, 2: Jour. Geology, v. 52, no. 1, p. 1–23; v. 52, no. 2, p. 97–116.

Keroher, G. C., *et al.*, 1966, Lexicon of geologic names of the United States for 1936–1960: U.S. Geol. Survey Bull. 1200, 4341 p. (*see* p. 452, 1684).

Krynine, P. D., 1941, Petrographic studies of variations in cement material in the Oriskany Sandstone, *in* Proc. 10th Pennsylvania mining industries conf.: Pennsylvania State Coll. Bull. No. 33, p. 108–116.

Le Grand, H. E., 1961, Geology and groundwater hydrology of the Atlantic and Gulf Coastal Plain as related to disposal of atomic wastes: U.S. Geol. Survey Rept. TEI-805.

Leighton, H., 1934, The white clays of Pennsylvania: Pennsylvania Topog. Geol. Survey Bull. No. 112.

Lesley, J. P., 1873, St. Clairsville and Bedford Railroad and Dunning's Creek fossil iron ore: Am. Philos. Soc. Proc., v. 13, p. 156.

Lohman, S. W., 1938, Ground water in south-central Pennsylvania: Pennsylvania Topog. Geol. Survey Bull. W5.

Lynn, R. D., 1962, Deep well construction for the disposal of uranium mill tailing water by the Anaconda Company at Grants, N.M.: Am. Inst. Min. Mech. Engineers, Repr. 62855.

Lytle, W. S., *et al.*, 1961, A summary of oil and gas developments in Pennsylvania—1955 to 1959: Pennsylvania Geol. Survey, 4th ser., Bull. M45.

—— *et al.*, 1962, Oil and gas developments in Pennsylvania in 1961: Pennsylvania Geol. Survey, 4th ser., Prog. Rept. 160.

Manger, E. G., 1962, Porosity and bulk density, dry and saturated, of sedimentary rocks: U.S. Geol. Survey Rept. TEI-820.

Mann, C. J., and W. E. Gross, 1911, Soil survey of Bedford County, Pennsylvania: U.S. Dept. Agriculture, Field Operations Bur. Soils, Rept. 13, p. 175–267.

Mehlich, A., 1942, Adsorption of barium and hydroxyl ions by soils and minerals in relation to pH: Soil Sci., v. 53, no. 2, p. 115–124.

Miller, J. T., 1961, Geology and mineral resources of the Loysville quadrangle: Pennsylvania Geol. Survey, 4th ser., Geol. Atlas Pennsylvania No. 127.

Moebs, H. N., and R. B. Hoy, 1959, Thrust faulting in Sinking Valley, Blair and Huntingdon Counties, Pennsylvania: Geol. Soc. America Bull., v. 70, no. 8, p. 1079–1088.

Moore, E. S., and T. G. Taylor, 1924, Silica refractories of Pennsylvania mineral resource: Pennsylvania Geol. Survey, 4th ser., Rept. M3.

Parkison, H. R., 1957, Water injection–well fracture treatments, Benton field, Franklin County, Illinois, *in* Symposium on water-flooding: Illinois Geol. Survey Bull. 80.

Pennsylvania Department of Forests and Waters, 1940–1941, Stream flow records of Pennsylvania: Div. Hydrography.

Poth, C. W., 1962, The occurrence of brine in western Pennsylvania: Pennsylvania Topog. Geol. Survey Bull. M47.

Price, P. H., *et al.*, 1937, Salt brines of West Virginia: West Virginia Geol. Survey, v. 8.

Rodgers, John, 1950, Mechanics of Appalachian folding as illustrated by Sequatchie anticline, Tennessee and Alabama: Am. Assoc. Petroleum Geologists Bull., v. 34, no. 4, p. 672–681.

Roedder, Edwin, 1959, Problems in the disposal of acid aluminum nitrate high-level radioactive waste solutions by injection into deep-lying permeable formations: U.S. Geol. Survey Bull. 1088.

Rose, Walter, 1957, Fluid flow in petroleum reservoirs, pt. 2, Predicted effects of sand consolidation: Illinois Geol. Survey Circ. 242.

―――― 1960, Fluid flow in petroleum reservoirs, pt. 3, Effects of flu'd-fluid interfacial boundary condition: Illinois Geol. Survey Circ. 291.

Slaughter, T. H., and J. M. Darling, 1962, The water resources of Allegheny and Washington Counties: Maryland Dept. Geology, Mines and Water Resources Bull. 24.

Smoot, T. W., 1960, Clay mineralogy of pre-Pennsylvanian sandstones and shales of the Illinois basin, pt. 1, Relation of permeability to clay mineral suites: Illinois Geol. Survey Circ. 286.

―――― and K. Narain, 1960, Clay mineralogy of pre-Pennsylvanian sandstones and shales of the Illinois basin, pt. 2, Clay mineral variations between oil-bearing and non-oil-bearing sandstones: Illinois Geol. Survey Circ. 287.

South Pennsylvania Oil Co., 1952, South Pennsylvania Oil Co. et al. Jesse B. Miller (well), Napier Township, Bedford County, Pa.: Eng. Dept. (mimeo. descr.)

Stevenson, J. J., 1882, The geology of Bedford and Fulton Counties: Pennsylvania Geol. Survey, 2d ser., Prog. Rept. T 2.

Stose, G. W., 1909, Mercerburg-Chambersburg, Pennsylvania, folio: U.S. Geol. Survey Geol. Atlas No. 170.

―――― and F. M. Swartz, 1912, Paw-Paw–Hancock folio, Md.-W.Va.-Pa.: U.S Geol. Survey Geol. Atlas No. 179.

Stow, M. H., 1938, Conditions of sedimentation and sources of the Oriskany Sandstone as indicated by petrology: Am. Assoc. Petroleum Geologists Bull., v. 22, no. 5, p. 541–564.

Straub, C. P., 1956, Fundamentals of underground waste disposal: Paper presented at Natl. Conf. Am. Soc. Civil Engineers, Dallas, Texas, 1956.

Swartz, F. M., 1926, The Helderberg Group from central Pennsylvania to southwest Virginia: Pennsylvania Acad. Sci. Proc., v. 1, p. 1924–1926.

―――― 1935, Relations of the Silurian Rochester and McKenzie Formations near Cumberland, Md. and Lakemont, Pa.: Geol. Soc. America Bull., v. 46, no. 8, p. 1165–1194.

―――― 1948, Trenton and sub-Trenton of outcrop areas in New York, Pennsylvania, and Maryland: Am. Assoc. Petroleum Geologists Bull., v. 32, no. 8, p. 1493–1595; Pennsylvania Geol. Survey, 4th ser., Bull. G22.

―――― 1950, Subsurface projection of Cambro-Ordovician sediments in the Pennsylvania-New York region: Pennsylvania Geol. Survey, 4th ser., Bull. G25.

―――― and F. M. Swain, 1941, Ostracodes of the Middle Devonian Onondaga beds of central Pennsylvania: Geol. Soc. America Bull., v. 52, no. 3, p. 381–458.

Theis, C. V., 1954, Geologic and hydrologic factors in ground disposal of waste: Sanitary Eng. Conf., Baltimore, Md., 1954, p. 261–283.

Thompson, H. D., 1939, Drainage evolution in the southern Appalachians: Geol. Soc. America Bull., v. 50, no. 8, p. 1323–1356.

Tucker, R. C., 1943, Summarized records of deep wells: West Virginia Geol. Survey, v. 16.

U.S. Department of Commerce, 1940–1961, United States earthquakes, 1938 through 1960 (separate volumes): Washington, D.C., Coast and Geodetic Survey.

―――― 1959–1960, Sectional aeronautical charts: Washington, D.C., Coast and Geodetic Survey (Cleveland 50th ed., July 12, 1960; Huntingdon 44th ed., July 1, 1960; Washington 50th ed., July 27, 1959; New York 51st ed., Sept. 8, 1959).

Visher, S. S., 1954, Climatic atlas of the United States: Cambridge, Mass., Harvard Univ. Press.

Wagner, W. R., 1959, Catalogue of deep well samples and geophysical logs to January 1, 1959: Pennsylvania Geol. Survey, 4th ser., Inf. Circ. 16.

White, A. W., 1958, Water-sorption properties of homoionic clay minerals: Illinois Geol. Survey Rept. Inv. No. 208.

―――― and E. Pichler, 1959, Water-sorption characteristics of clay minerals: Illinois Geol. Survey Circ. 266.

Willard, Bradford, 1934, A Tully Limestone outcrop in Pennsylvania: Pennsylvania Acad. Sci. Proc., v. 8.

―――― 1935a, Hamilton Group along the Allegheny Front, Pennsylvania: Geol. Soc. America Bull., v. 46, no. 8, p. 1275–1290.

―――― 1935b, Portage Group in Pennsylvania: Geol. Soc. America Bull., v. 46, no. 8, p. 1195–1218.

―――― 1935c, Hypothyridina venustula (Hall) in Pennsylvania: Am. Soc. Sci., 5th ser., v. 29, p. 93–97.

―――― 1938, A Paleozoic section in south-central Pennsylvania: Pennsylvania Topog. Geol. Survey Bull. G8.

―――― and A. B. Cleaves, 1939, Ordovician-Silurian relations in Pennsylvania: Geol. Soc. America Bull., v. 50, no. 7, p. 1165–1198.

―――― F. M. Swartz, and A. B. Cleaves, 1939, The Devonian of Pennsylvania: Pennsylvania Topog. Geol. Survey, 4th ser., Bull. G19, no. 12, 481 p., maps.

Wilmarth, M. G., 1928, Tentative correlation of the named geologic units of Pennsylvania: U.S. Geol. Survey, unnumbered.

―――― 1938, Lexicon of geologic names in the United States: U.S. Geol. Survey Bull. 896, 2396 p.

Woodward, H. P., 1941, The Silurian System of West Virginia: West Virginia Geol. and Economic Survey Repts., v. 14.

―――― 1943, The Devonian System of West Virginia: West Virginia Geol. and Economic Survey Repts., v. 15.

―――― 1961, Reappraisal of Appalachian geology: Am. Assoc. Petroleum Geologists Bull., v. 45, no. 10, p. 1625–1633.

Yeakel, L. S., 1962, Tuscarora, Juniata, and Bald Eagle paleocurrents and paleogeography in the central Appalachians: Geol. Soc. America Bull., v. 73, no. 12, p. 1515–1540.

GEOLOGY OF SUBSURFACE WASTE DISPOSAL IN MICHIGAN BASIN[1]

LOUIS I. BRIGGS, JR.[2]
Ann Arbor, Michigan 48104

ABSTRACT

The Michigan basin, an almost circular and symmetrical structural basin, contains in the deepest part approximately 14,000 ft of Paleozoic sedimentary rocks. The autogeosyncline developed as a tectonic element in Late Silurian time, during which the middle third of the sedimentary section was deposited. The strata dip generally less than 1° toward the center of the basin, although locally there are gentle open folds and a few high-angle faults. The sedimentary formations can be class-fied into four generalized sequences—(1) the sandstone sequence of the Cambrian, (2) the carbonate-evaporite sequence of the Ordovician to Middle Devonian, (3) the shale-sandstone sequence of the Late Devonian to Mississippian, and (4) the coal-bearing sequence of the Pennsylvanian.

The Cambrian sandstones (Mount Simon) have the most favorable properties for high-volume liquid-waste disposal. They are suitably thick and reasonably shallow principally in southeastern Michigan near Detroit. The Mount Simon is a typical blanket feldspathic, quartzose sandstone; it is characterized by quartz and feldspar cement, present as grain overgrowths, and detrital and matrix carbonate minerals. Where measured, the porosity averages about 10 percent and the permeability about 30 md. The Cambrian sandstone beds are overlain by a thick, extensive shale layer (Utica) and salt beds (Salina), which are of secondary importance to liquid- and solid-waste disposal.

INTRODUCTION

The Michigan basin was selected as one of six geologic provinces in which studies of waste-disposal potentials might be rewarding. As with the studies of other geologic provinces, it became evident that a considerable amount of information relative to the evaluation of waste disposal in terms of geology and geography had not been published, but could be made available. The committee for the study of the Michigan basin undertook the collection and synthesis of these data into suitable form.

During the study, new information became available as a result of additional drilling and testing of subsurface strata. The petroleum indus-try, which provides almost all of the subsurface information, became aware of the needs of the committee and cooperated in providing information that otherwise might have been lost or not gathered. This cooperation ultimately led to bottomhole support for coring and analysis of a well being drilled into the Cambrian sandstones, the most suitable formation for disposal of hazardous liquid waste. The importance of this help cannot be overemphasized. It provided the committee with the only core of this formation, from which were obtained porosity, permeability, mineralogic, petrologic, and detailed fluid and pressure data.

The suitability of an area for any type of waste disposal must be based first on geologic factors and second on geographic and economic factors. The geologic factors, in order of importance for radioactive wastes, are: (1) the presence of a deep porous and permeable sandstone with sufficient fluid capacity and receptivity for long-term, high-volume fluid disposal; (2) the presence of thick salt beds at shallow depth for storage of solid materials in artificial solution cavities or mined cavities; and (3) the presence of a thick shale for possible injection of grout into hydraulically produced fractures.

The proper geologic conditions are present in much of Michigan north of the lowest tier of

[1] Manuscript received, June 7, 1965.

[2] The University of Michigan.

This report was prepared by a committee composed of Steven H. Howell, K. K. Landes, G. D. Lindberg, Garland Ells, R. D. Matthews, and John Shea, and L. I. Briggs, chairman. Other persons advised the committee, particularly members of the Geologic Survey Division, Department of Conservation, Michigan, and the geologists of petroleum companies operating in the state. Particular thanks are due Donald Deskins for preparation of the geographic data and maps used in this report. The committee also thanks John Galley for his patience and perseverance in bringing this project on the Michigan basin to completion.

counties and south of the Mackinac Straits—in the thick quartzose Cambrian sandstone beds of the Munising Formation, the salt beds of the Silurian Salina Formation, and the shale beds of the intermediate Ordovician Cincinnati Series. These strata are at reasonable depths primarily in southeastern Michigan near Detroit. Thus, this study is directed toward an evaluation of the geologic and geographic potential of southeastern Michigan for liquid-waste disposal.

The formation most suitable for the disposal of liquid waste products in deep porous reservoirs in the Michigan basin is the Cambrian Mount Simon Sandstone Member of the Munising Formation. It is below the important drilling targets of the petroleum and other mineral industries, and it overlies the Precambrian crystalline basement. The Mount Simon Member underlies rocks of secondary interest for radioactive-waste disposal—the Cincinnatian Utica Shale and the Salina salt beds. Geologic, geographic, and economic factors prescribe the location of any prospective injection test site to the southeasternmost corner of Michigan. Near Chicago, Illinois, adjacent to southwestern Michigan, Mount Simon sandstone is a principal source of potable groundwater, a resource which must be protected from contamination.

The nine deep tests through the Mount Simon to the basement in this part of Michigan, and significantly more deep tests in neighboring Ontario, Ohio, and Indiana, provide a good subsurface record of formation depths, thickness, and petrologic characteristics. The Utica and Salina strata are known accurately from records of hundreds of wells in southeastern Michigan and data from the bordering states and provinces.

Geology of Michigan Basin

Regional stratigraphy and structure.—The Michigan basin is an almost circular and symmetrical structural and sedimentary basin in the Central Interior platform of the United States (Cohee, 1962). It is on the southern edge of the Canadian Shield, and is separated from the Appalachian basin by the Cincinnati-Findlay Algonquin arches on the southeast and from the Illinois basin by the Kankakee-Wisconsin arches on the southwest.

The circular basin, or autogeosyncline, was developed as a structural element in Late Silurian time, during which the middle third of the total sedimentary section was deposited. The lithology of the Cambrian through Pennsylvanian strata (Fig. 1), which have a maximum thickness of about 14,000 ft, gives a general idea of the Paleozoic structural and sedimentary history.

The sedimentary rocks in the Michigan basin can be classified into four generalized sequences (De Witt, 1960)—(1) the sandstone sequence of the Cambrian, (2) the carbonate-evaporite sequence of the Lower Ordovician to Middle Devonian, (3) the shale-sandstone sequence of the Upper Devonian to Mississippian, and (4) the coal-bearing sequence of the Pennsylvanian.

Throughout its history, the Michigan basin has been the site of predominantly carbonate deposition; almost half of the entire section is limestone and dolomite. Sandstone and siltstone make up an additional one-fourth of the section; shale, one-sixth; and gypsum, anhydrite, and halite, one-eighth (Fig. 1).

The sedimentary strata in the Michigan basin dip very gently (0.5–1°) toward the center of the basin, which is a few miles west of Saginaw Bay. Locally, broad, open anticlinal folds trend northwest-southeast. They are associated in a few places with high-angle normal faults of small displacement (De Witt, 1960, Fig. 12), features which should cause little difficulty in the disposal of waste products into a deep porous reservoir. There are two known faults in southeastern Michigan. One, associated with the Howell anticline (Fig. 2), trends southeastward across Livingston County[3] into the northwest corner of Wayne County at N50°W; another, associated with the Lucas-Monroe structure, trends north-south from Lucas County, Ohio, along the Lenawee-Monroe County border. Faults of this type are difficult to find in the subsurface unless they have large displacement, because most of the area is mantled by glacial drift which hides the bedrock structure.

Physiography.—Most of the Michigan basin is within Lower Michigan, an inland peninsula bounded on three sides by Lakes Michigan,

[3] Livingston County adjoins Oakland County on the west. Counties are labeled on Figs. 11-18.

GENERALIZED COLUMNAR SECTION OF MICHIGAN

SYSTEM	SERIES	GROUP or FORMATION	LITHOLOGY	MAXIMUM THICKNESS
QUATERNARY	PLEISTOCENE	Glacial drift	Boulder clay, gravels	850 (feet)
JURASSIC	KIMERIDGIAN	"Redbeds"	Sand, clay	200
PENNSYLVANIAN	CONEMAUGH	Grand River	Sandstone	200
	POTTSVILLE	Saginaw	Shale, limestone, coal, sandstone	550
MISSISSIPPIAN	MERAMECIAN	Bayport	Limestone, dolomite	150
		Michigan	Shale, gypsum, dolomite	600
	OSAGIAN	Marshall	Sandstone	350
	KINDERHOOKIAN	Coldwater	Shale, sandstone	1300
MISSISSIPPIAN – DEVONIAN	BRADFORDIAN	Ellsworth	Shale	600
	CHAUTAUQUAN	Antrim	Shale, limestone	600
DEVONIAN	SENECAN	Traverse	Shale, limestone	800
	ERIAN	Rogers City– Dundee	Limestone	450
		Detroit River	Dolomite, anhydrite, salt, sandstone	1700
	ULSTERIAN	Bois Blanc	Dolomite, limestone, chert	1100
		Garden Island	Dolomite, shale, sand	100
SILURIAN	CAYUGAN	Bass Islands	Dolomite, anhydrite	700
		Salina	Salt, anhydrite, dolomite	3150
	NIAGARAN	Niagara – Clinton	Dolomite, shale	1000
	ALEXANDRIAN	Cataract	Dolomite, shale	200
ORDOVICIAN	CINCINNATIAN	Richmond – Maysville	Shale, limestone	450
		Utica	Shale	500
	MOHAWKIAN	Trenton	Limestone, dolomite	500
		Black River	Limestone, dolomite	600
	CHAZYAN	St. Peter	Sandstone	200
	CANADIAN	Prairie du Chien	Dolomite, sandstone	400
CAMBRIAN	ST. CROIXAN	Trempealeau	Dolomite	750
		Munising — Franconia/Dresbach	Sandstone	90
		Munising — Eau Claire	Sandstone, limestone	100
		Munising — Mt. Simon	Sandstone	1100
		Jacobsville	Sandstone	1100
PRE–CAMBRIAN			Lavas, conglomerate, iron formation, schist, gneiss, granites	

FIG. 1.—Generalized columnar section of Michigan.

Huron, and Erie. The low, rolling topography is typical of glacial morainal regions throughout that section of North America. Flat, featureless plains border the edge of Lake Michigan, Saginaw Bay, Lake Huron, and Lake Erie as remnants of the muddy bottoms of swollen proglacial lakes which occupied the present basins of the Great Lakes. Inland from the lake plains, moraines roughly outline the lake borders in successive ridges which formed along the edge of ice fronts. The differential relief is low, generally no more than a few hundred feet.

In places the sequence of outwash gravel, morainal tills, and lake-bottom clay is almost 1,000 ft thick, but the glacial sediments in most of southeastern Michigan are less than 250 ft thick. The sequence of gravel and till in a region of moderate precipitation provides abundant groundwater supplies for most community and individual needs. This water eventually flows to the Great Lakes.

Climate.—Contrary to popular belief, the climate in the Lower Peninsula of Michigan is not extreme, mainly because of the thermal reservoir in the water mass of the Great Lakes. Temperatures rarely range higher than 100°F or lower than −25°F. In Detroit, temperatures higher than 100°F occur on the average of once every 4 years. In one year in six there are no readings below 0°F. During the winter months, snow showers are accompanied by strong northwestern winds, tempered by the thermal storage in Lake

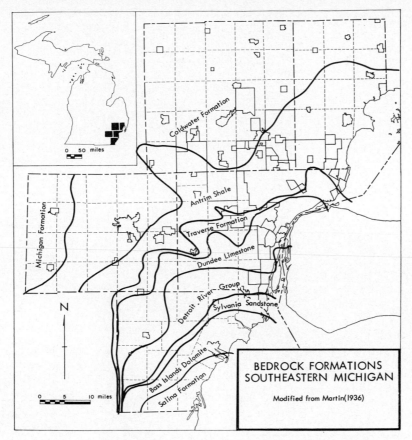

Fig. 2.—Map showing bedrock formations, southeastern Michigan.

Michigan. Tempering effects of the lakes also delay seasonal changes to spring and winter because of lag in the change of water temperature. In Detroit the average rainfall of 39.83 in. is spread throughout most of the year; the average snowfall of 40.3 in. occurs mainly in December, January, and February. The mean annual temperature is 49.3°F.

Barometric storms move over Michigan predominantly from west to east; hence almost all major winds come from the western sector. In addition, most storm centers moving eastward across the United States and Canada pass close enough to southeastern Michigan to create frequent changes in the weather pattern.

GEOGRAPHY OF SOUTHEASTERN MICHIGAN

Physical geography.—The topography of south-

eastern Michigan results primarily from the deposits left during the retreat of the last Wisconsin glaciers less than 25,000 years ago. Ice lobes from the continental ice sheets which amassed in the basins of Lake Erie and Lake Huron, along the eastern side of the Lower Peninsula of Michigan, flowed westward and southward across the entire region during the height of the glacial stages. Coevally with their retreat near the end of the Wisconsin Stage, the melting glaciers left a series of subparallel morainal ridges which follow the general shape of the lake borders, each successive one in general being closer to the lakes. Along the former edges of the ice sheets (Fig. 3), the morainal ridges make a rolling, hummocky topography of several hundred feet of relief.

When the glaciers had retreated into the lake basins, melt water from the ice accumulated in

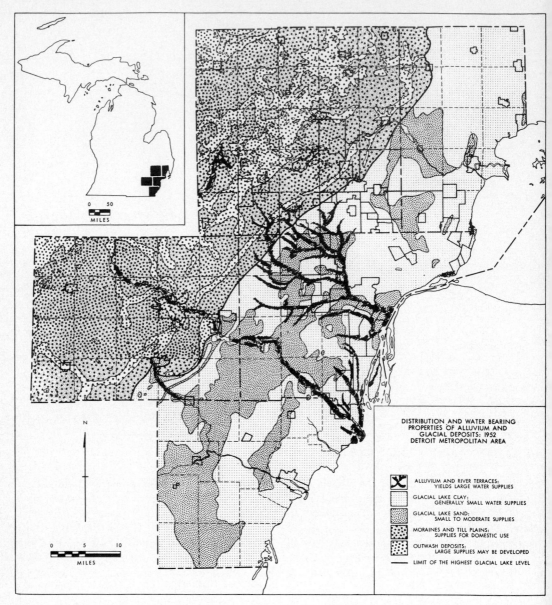

DISTRIBUTION AND WATER BEARING
PROPERTIES OF ALLUVIUM AND
GLACIAL DEPOSITS: 1952
DETROIT METROPOLITAN AREA

ALLUVIUM AND RIVER TERRACES:
YIELDS LARGE WATER SUPPLIES

GLACIAL LAKE CLAY:
GENERALLY SMALL WATER SUPPLIES

GLACIAL LAKE SAND:
SMALL TO MODERATE SUPPLIES

MORAINES AND TILL PLAINS:
SUPPLIES FOR DOMESTIC USE

OUTWASH DEPOSITS:
LARGE SUPPLIES MAY BE DEVELOPED

LIMIT OF THE HIGHEST GLACIAL LAKE LEVEL

FIG. 3.—Distribution and water-bearing properties of alluvium and glacial deposits, 1952,
Detroit metropolitan area.

the basins in front of the ice masses. These swollen proglacial lakes drained through outwash
channels higher in elevation than the present lake
outlets. Fine-grained debris from the melting glaciers accumulated as lake mud and silt, and today
underlies a featureless topography which slopes
gently toward the lake shores. Detroit is within

such an area. The line separating the morainal
hills from the lake-bottom plains is shown clearly
on the map depicting groundwater resources (Fig.
3).

Much of the morainal region is poorly drained.
The glacial ice retreated too recently for the
streams to have developed well-defined drainage

systems. The low gradients of most of the streams and the coarseness of the bed material also slow this process. Similarly, the lake plains drain poorly because of their flatness. Many are drained artificially by means of drainage tile and ditches in the farming region that covers much of the lake plain outside of the metropolitan areas. The well-drained, broad, flat, gravel-coated outwash plains which spread from the front of the ice sheets during pauses in their retreats contain the most abundant groundwater supplies (Fig. 4).

Water and sewerage facilities.—Many communities in the Detroit metropolitan area are served by efficient water-supply and sewerage systems. Water is obtained from the Detroit River, which connects Lakes St. Clair and Erie, to serve a population of more than 3 million persons (1960), one-half of whom are residents of the city of Detroit. Outside of Detroit, the system supplies water to other cities and townships in Wayne County, as well as to neighboring Macomb and Oakland Counties (Fig. 5). Other communities and individuals obtain water from wells sunk into glacial deposits or into the bedrock formations where the till is relatively barren of water. Waters from the bedrock characteristically contain

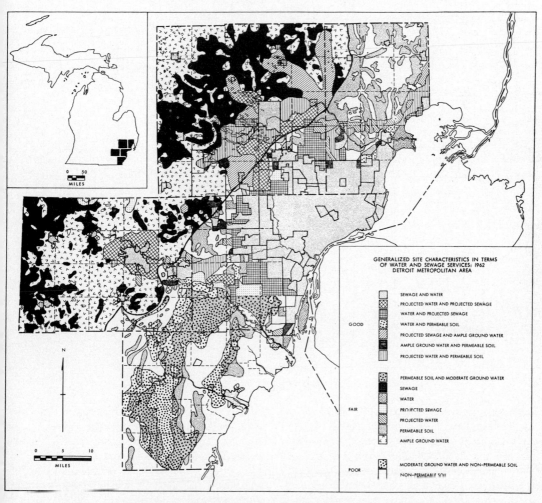

Fig. 4.—Generalized site characteristics in terms of water and sewage services, 1962, Detroit metropolitan area.

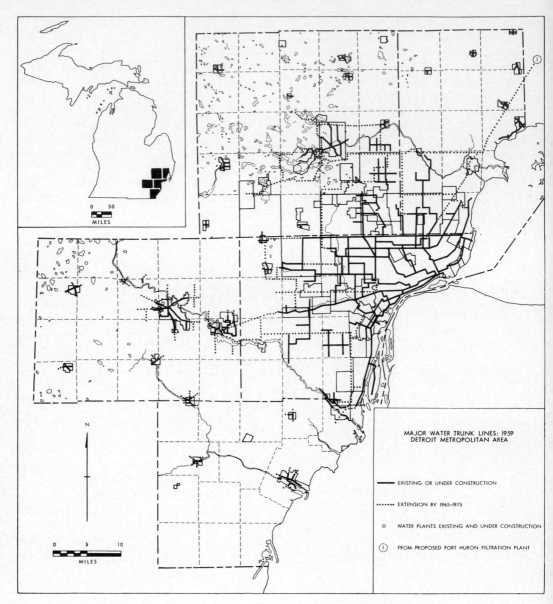

Fig. 5.—Major water trunk lines, 1959, Detroit metropolitan area.

large quantities of dissolved solids, as illustrated by those at Petersburg (Table I). Some water is obtained from small lakes (Adrian, Table I) or rivers (Ann Arbor, Dundee, Table I). Michigan municipal water supplies have been described by the Michigan Department of Health (1961). Some of the data from this source are summarized in Table I.

The quality of water-supply and sewer facilities (Fig. 4) is related to the drainage properties and groundwater-supply potential of the surface glacial deposit. These are integrated with characteristics of the sewer and water-supply pipeline systems into a classification scheme (Deskins, 1963). The map (Fig. 4) has particular value in the appraisal of water-supply and sewerage features

TABLE I. ANALYSES OF MUNICIPAL WATER SUPPLIES

Municipality and Source	Total	Chemical Analysis (ppm)								
		SiO₂	Fe	Ca	Mg	Alk.	Cl	SO₄	HCO₃	CaCO₃
Wayne County										
Detroit										
Detroit River[1]	126	2	0.0	29	7	2	8	17	75	100
Washtenaw County										
Ypsilanti										
Wells in drift[2]	210	8	0.0	20	9	34	21	85	17	86
Ann Arbor										
Wells in drift										
Huron River[2,5]	140	8	0.0	17	8	14	12	54	34	76
Chelsea										
Wells in drift[3]	458	13	2.2	100	26	17	22	60	363	255
Milan										
Wells in drift	334	11	0.7	50	18	63	49	0	318	200
Saline										
Wells in drift	366	12	1.0	82	24	21	27	23	370	305
Oakland County										
Pontiac										
Wells in drift[4]	408	17	1.1	76	29	32	39	30	350	310
Bloomfield Twp.										
Wells in drift[4]	320	16	1.3	60	24	17	11	3	332	250
Monroe County										
Dundee										
Raisin River[2]	276	3	0.0	30	1	59	24	115	10	78
Monroe										
Lake Erie[1,5]	176	4	0.0	40	8	11	21	34	107	132
Petersburg										
Wells in rock[4,6]	474	12	0.0	90	24	20	6	155	244	325
Lenawee County										
Adrian										
Lake Adrian[2,5]	160	6	0.0	20	15	12	15	57	0	113
Hudson										
Wells in drift	418	16	1.5	77	31	27	22	45	359	320
Tecumseh										
Wells in drift[5]	406	9	0.1	94	26	10	8	85	303	344

[1] Treated by filtration.
[2] Treated by lime softening.
[3] Treated for iron removal.
[4] Treated by chloridation.
[5] Treated by fluoridation.
[6] Treated for H₂S removal.

that might affect the location of an industrial plant or waste-disposal plant where these factors are of considerable importance.

Wisler et al. (1952) summarized the water-supply potential of the Detroit area as being restricted only by the possible shortage of proper transmission facilities. No serious shortage of water supplies at their source is foreseen. Approximately 50 percent of the area (Fig. 4) has an adequate groundwater supply; the rest probably will have to depend on resources in the nearby Great Lakes for future large supplies. In all probability the Detroit metropolitan system will grow to encompass all of southeastern Michigan, and most of the water will come from Lake Huron and the Detroit River (Fig. 5).

Transportation facilities.—Michigan has one of the finest highway systems in the nation. The intrastate expressway system and the railroads form adequate access to almost all parts of southeastern Michigan (Fig. 6). Outside of the metropolitan areas, the state highway system forms an intricate network of high-grade surfaced roads; however, many county roads are unsurfaced and difficult to travel during the spring thaws, generally during March and early April. Restricted load limits are maintained during that period.

The Detroit area is about 50 mi north of the major east-west railroad trunklines, and rail transportation is less adequate than in some other cities of comparable size. This deficiency is offset by the availability to water transportation on the Great Lakes and connection with marine ports by means of the St. Lawrence Seaway.

Electricity is available to all communities in southeastern Michigan, and natural gas to most. Telephone and other communication services are available throughout the area.

Population distribution and prediction of future growth.—Outside of the major metropolitan areas, Michigan has a relatively low population density. This factor, combined with the beauty of

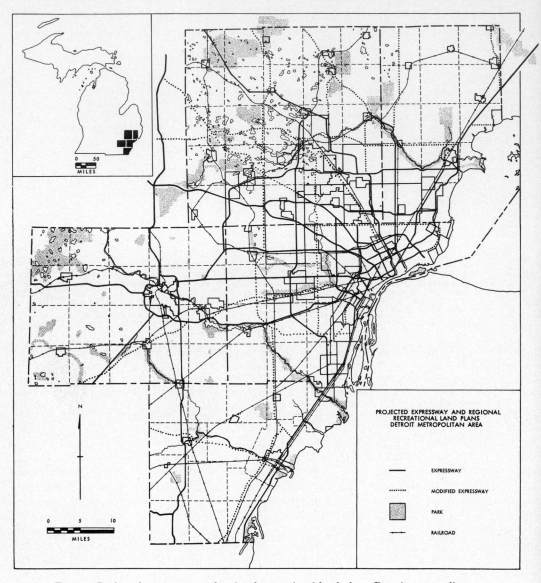

FIG. 6.—Projected expressway and regional recreational land plans, Detroit metropolitan area.

the glacial terrain, hardwood forests, and many lakes, makes the suburban regions attractive sites for parks and other recreational uses (Fig. 6).

The five counties in southeastern Michigan, elsewhere referred to as the "Detroit metropolitan area," contain only 5.8 percent of the land area of the state, but 51.5 percent of the population (Deskins, 1963, p. 2). The population was distributed in 1960 (Fig. 7) mainly in the city of Detroit and on projections to the nearby cities of Pontiac (northwest), Ann Arbor-Ypsilanti (west), and Monroe (southwest). The predicted population distribution for 1970 (Fig. 8) was made by Deskins (1963) following the model proposed by Borchert (1961), modified on the basis of local characteristics of the terrain, water supply, and drainage (Fig. 4). Deskin's model very accurately predicted the 1960 population distribution on the basis of the 1930, 1940, and 1950 census data, and the 1970 prediction should be equally valid.

Although there is a high concentration of population in about 50 percent of the area of southeastern Michigan (Figs. 7, 8), the high population density is restricted mostly to the city of Detroit and the regions adjoining other large communities nearby. Elsewhere, population density is less than 100 persons per square mile. Most of the area is farmland, and most farms are not large and not very productive. The writer estimates the average rural tract to be less than 100 acres.

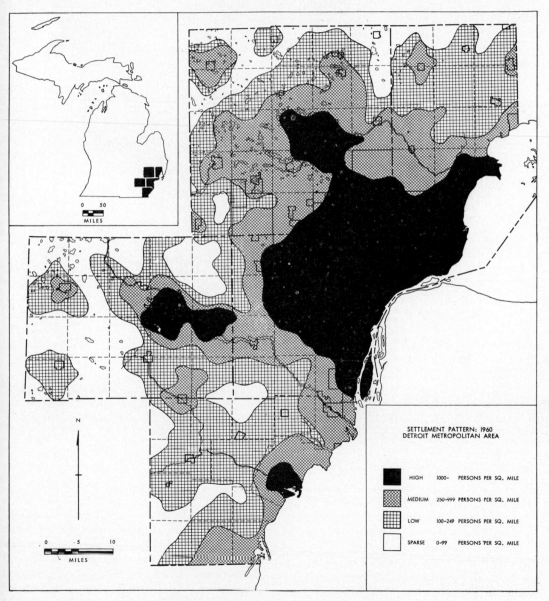

FIG. 7.—Settlement pattern, 1960, Detroit metropolitan area.

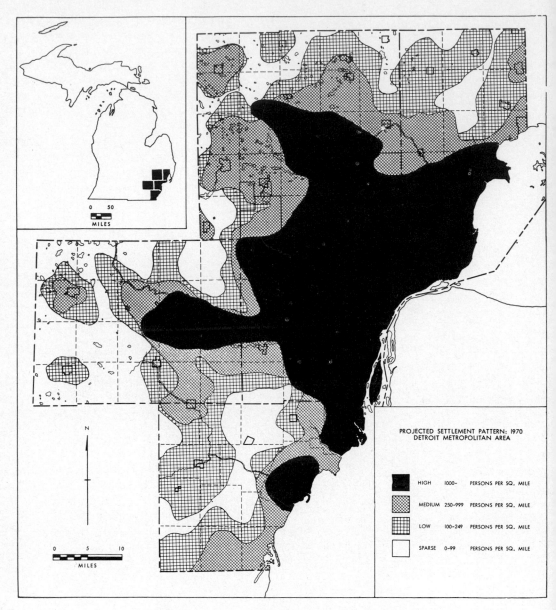

FIG. 8.—Projected settlement pattern, 1970, Detroit metropolitan area

RECOMMENDED DISPOSAL RESERVOIRS IN SOUTHEASTERN MICHIGAN

PERMEABLE SANDSTONES

Permeable sandstone beds suitable for injection of fluids are present in rocks representing the Cambrian System in the Michigan basin. They make up about 27 percent of the stratigraphic column (De Witt, 1960, p. 13), and are composed almost entirely of quartzose sandstone, siltstone, and arenaceous dolomite. Near the bottom of the stratigraphic section, the sandstone beds overlying the Precambrian rocks are commonly feldspathic, as typified by the Munising sandstone in the core taken north of Detroit. Outcrops of Cambrian rocks (Jacobsville, Munising, and Hermansville) are present in Michigan only in the Upper Peninsula (Fig. 1). Rocks of equivalent age crop out or directly underlie glacial drift in Wisconsin along a narrow belt extending from Upper Michigan almost to the Illinois line; they crop out locally in Illinois along the Sandwich fault. East of Michigan the nearest outcrop of Cambrian rocks is along the St. Lawrence River in northern New York and Ontario, Canada, where the Potsdam Sandstone is exposed.

In the subsurface of the Michigan basin, the Munising Formation is subdivided into the Mount Simon Sandstone, Eau Claire Sandstone, Dresbach Sandstone, and Franconia Sandstone Members, in ascending order (Fig. 1). These are overlain by dolomite of the Trempealeau Formation. In general the upper beds of the Cambrian

sequence in the southern part of the Michigan basin contain more dolomite cement and interbedded dolomite than those in the northern part of the basin. This facies change can be seen even in the small region of southeastern Michigan and northern Ohio in the Eau Claire Member (Fig. 9). As the proportions of limestone, dolomite, and carbonate-mineral cement increase toward the south and east in the Michigan basin, the porosity and permeability of the sandstone should decrease proportionally.

The Cambrian formations are thickest in southwestern Michigan and northern Illinois; the axis of greatest thickness is along the west-central part of Michigan in a troughlike extension of the Illinois basin. The Cambrian clastic rocks range in thickness from 500 ft in eastern Wisconsin to more than 3,500 ft in northern Illinois (De Witt,

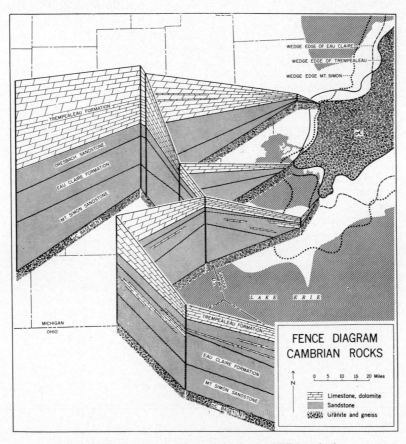

FIG. 9.—Fence diagram of Cambrian rocks, Michigan basin.

1960, p. 16). Eastward the beds wedge out in the subsurface against the Algonquin arch in the southern peninsula of Ontario (Fig. 9; Sanford and Quillian, 1959); this region apparently was a peninsular landmass in the Late Cambrian seas. The truncation of older beds beneath younger in this sequence may effectively seal the edges of the truncated formations, but this is hypothetical without supporting evidence from the character of the fluids in the formations.

The geological information most pertinent to determination of the suitability of Mount Simon sandstone for the injection of liquid wastes includes the petrology and mineralogy, hydrodynamic properties, thickness, depth, and geologic structure of the sandstone, and the nature of adjacent formations.

Porosity and permeability measurements.—A core was cut from the Mount Simon or other Cambrian rocks in southern Michigan in the Consumers Power Co. Brine-Disposal Well No. 139, Sec. 31, T. 4 N., R. 15 E., St. Clair County. The few other cores previously taken by petroleum-exploration companies now have been discarded.

The core taken from the Consumers Power Co. boring penetrated the following rocks.

Unit	Interval (ft)	Length (ft)
Black River	4,468–4,486	18
Glenwood	4,486–4,488	2
Eau Claire and Mount Simon	4,488–4,605	117
Precambrian	4,605–4,628	23
	Total	160

Samples of the core were taken at 1-ft intervals between 4,521 and 4,612 ft, and measurements were made of porosity and permeability. In general, the results show that the porosity ranges from 4 to 20 percent; three samples have porosity values of less than 3.0 percent. For comparison, a loosely packed sandstone may have a porosity as high as 40 percent, but rarely does sandstone have porosity greater than 25 percent. The average sandstone has a porosity of 15–20 percent (Pettijohn, 1949, p. 69). Slightly more than half (47) of the samples in the core have porosities greater than 10 percent; of these, 32 have permeabilities greater than 20 md, the greatest being 193 md.

The most porous and permeable intervals more than 2 ft thick are the following.

Interval (ft)	Average Porosity (%)	Average Permeability (md)
4,517–4,520	15.8	117.0
4,539–4,555	13.5	38.1
4,574–4,592	13.1	57.4
4,601–4,604	13.5	29.5

Permeability in the interval 4,574–4,592 ft ranges widely and irregularly from less than 0.1 to 182.7 md, and in the interval 4,601–4,604 ft, only the upper two samples have significant permeability. The average permeability in the Cambrian sandstone is 32 md. There is no demonstrable relationship between depth in the sandstone interval and porosity or permeability. The correlation coefficient between porosity and depth is only 0.19, not demonstratively different from random; the correlation coefficient between log permeability and depth is even less. In contrast, correlation is fairly high (0.86) between porosity and log permeability, as it is in most rock formations. It is important to stress, however, that there is no consistent trend of either porosity or permeability with depth in the Cambrian sandstone.

Receptivity measurements.—The Consumers well was drilled for brine disposal, and tests of injection rate *versus* surface pump pressure were made at the time of initial drilling and later after additional treatment of the formation.

After drilling was completed, the hole was cleaned out and the formations treated with 3,000 gal of acid. Injection tests indicated the following receptivity of the formation in the lower 128 ft of the hole (4,500–4,628 ft).

Pump Pressure (psig surface)	Receptivity/Time (bbl/min)	Receptivity/Day (bbl/24 hr)
600	6/21	410
800	6/13	660
1,020	12/18	960

At a pump pressure of 1,000 psig, the injection rate was about 930 bbl per day. To increase receptivity, the Consumers Power Co. re-treated the well by fracturing the rock and injecting 20,000 lb of sand in about 535 bbl of water at 2,600 lb average pressure to hold the fractures open (hydraulic-fracturing technique). After fracturing, the receptivity of the formation increased to 1,600 bbl per day at surface discharge pressure of 825 psi. In approximately 1 month, a cumulative total of 46,670 bbl (1 bbl = 42 gal) of brine had been injected into the formation.

Summary of porosity, permeability, and injection tests.—The total thickness of Cambrian quartz sandstone in the Consumers Power Co. brine-disposal well north of Detroit is 89 ft. The sandstone is overlain by dolomite and underlain by granite gneiss and granite of Precambrian age. The average permeability is 32 md and the average porosity is 10.6 percent. Both permeability and porosity are extremely varied in the formation, and have no consistent trend with depth. In general, rocks of low porosity and low permeability have a dolomitic cement.

Receptivity of the sandstone is moderately high if the rock is treated with acid and by hydraulic-fracturing techniques. The Consumers Power Co. well accepted almost 2 million gal of salt water a month at pump pressure of 825 psi after such treatment.

It would be presumptuous to generalize these data without other tests on additional holes. One sample could be misleading. Furthermore, data from additional wells would make it possible to determine other very important properties of the formations, especially regional permeability, receptivity, and hydrodynamic gradients, which govern fluid migration and flow. At present, no estimates can be made regarding the movement through the formation of the brine injected into the Consumers Power Co. Brine-Disposal Well No. 139. The drill-stem tests taken in this well give only one point on a potentiometric surface. Similar data from at least two other localities, judiciously selected to provide three points to define the potentiometric surface, will be needed before the desired results can be computed.

Mineralogy and petrography.—Wherever observations have been made of cores and cuttings taken from Mount Simon sandstone in the subsurface of Michigan and from outcrops in adjacent areas, the rock is a feldspathic, quartzose sandstone. In most rocks, crystalline overgrowths of quartz and feldspar partially cement the sand grains. Locally, the overgrowths interlock into a relatively nonporous texture; in other rocks, especially those high in the section, calcite and dolomite form a tight cement.

The mineralogy and petrography of the Cambrian rocks in the core from the Consumers Power Co. brine-disposal well are summarized in Table II. The sandstone is very feldspathic; most is arkose. Many of the quartz and feldspar grains have authigenic overgrowths of secondary-mineral cement, the feldspar having a surprising amount. The rocks containing high percentages of dolomite were originally detrital sands of quartz and calcite grains, as is evident from the original outlines of the carbonate grains that are still visible. The average grain size is that of medium sand (0.32 mm); the standard deviation (sorting) is only fair. Most of the grains have moderate sphericity (0.73 in comparison to that of the average sand, 0.07). Roundness is relatively low (0.44).

Stepwise regression of permeability (K) against the petrographic measurements at the 10-percent level of significance (90-percent confidence level) shows that the only properties that significantly affect permeability are dolomite percentage and grain roundness. Dolomite accounts for 23 percent of the variation in permeability, and grain roundness accounts for 10 percent. Porosity is significantly related to dolomite percentage at the 10-percent level; however, dolomite percentage accounts for only 18 percent of the variation in porosity.

At the 25-percent significance level (75-percent confidence level), 42 percent of the variation in permeability can be accounted for by quartz percentage, dolomite percentage, grain sorting, and grain roundness. The predicted permeability for each sample is:

$$\log_{10}(100K) = -0.20 + 0.03 \text{ qtz. } \% - 0.02 \text{ dol. } \%$$
$$- 2.24\sigma + 5.13 \text{ rnd.}$$

Dolomite percentage accounts for 23 percent of the permeability variation; grain roundess, 10 percent; quartz percentage, 4 percent; and sorting coefficient (standard deviation), 5 percent. At the 25-percent level, porosity is significantly related only to dolomite percentage.

The analysis shows, therefore, that the petro-

TABLE II. MINERALOGY AND PETROGRAPHY OF CAMBRIAN SANDSTONE, CONSUMERS POWER CO. BRINE-DISPOSAL WELL 139

Depth (ft)	Porosity (%)	Permeability (md)	Quartz[1] (%)		Feldspar[1] (%)		Dolomite (%)	Grain Measurements			
			Grain	Cement	Grain	Cement		M.D.[2] (mm)	St.D.[3] (mm)	Roundness[4]	Sphericity[4]
4,519.5	18.0	158.0	33.8	2.4	45.0	5.0	13.7	0.24	0.32	0.4	0.80
4,522.5	3.9	0.1	37.0	0.0	46.6	2.4	13.9	0.16	0.18	0.3	0.75
4,524.4	5.2	0.1	65.4	0.2	17.3	1.8	15.6	0.20	0.25	0.3	0.80
4,525.4	6.2	0.1	27.6	1.0	23.0	3.8	45.5[5]	0.30	0.49	0.3	0.75
4,533.5	4.9	<0.1	35.8	0.1	21.1	0.3	35.5	0.15	0.20	0.3	0.70
4,529.8	16.2	34.8	57.6	0.5	30.7	7.8	3.3	0.16	0.19	0.3	0.75
4,539.2	6.5	4.6	91.8	1.2	5.2	0.0	1.7	0.58	0.30	0.5	0.80
4,534.5	12.2	115.7	92.5	0.7	4.5	2.3	0.0	0 34	0 17	0 3	0.80
4,535.3	15.1	174.0	81.0	1.6	14.5	2.4	0.6	0.23	0.21	0.4	0.80
4,536.5	5.0	2.2	46.5	0.0	16.7	1.3	35.6[5]	0.34	0.43	0.6	0.80
4,537.4	5.5	0.4	26.4	0.0	22.8	0.2	50.6[5]	0.50	0.50	0.5	0.80
4,548.2	20.0	193.0	50.2	0.0	44.5	0.0	5.3	0.38	0.22	0.5	0.70
4,549.2	13.4	42.3	31.1	0.0	57.4	1.1	10.5	0.27	0.17	0.5	0.70
4,551.2	17.0	51.1	25.5	1.3	21.5	0.0	51.7	0.19	0.25	0.7	0.80
4,546.3	9.5	14.3	17.4	0.0	48.0	0.7	34.1[5]	0.19	0.22	0.5	0.75
4,547.1	14.7	28.5	31.2	0.4	38.3	1.5	28.5[5]	0.24	0.28	0.5	0.75
4,548.7	10.3	0.2	48.5	0.5	7.8	0.5	42.8[5]	0.60	0.80	0.4	0.80
4,550.2	9.0	35.4	70.7	1.0	12.3	2.7	13.4	0.34	0.33	0.5	0.80
4,556.1	4.4	0.1	14.8	0.7	65.3	2.0	17.2	0.11	0.12	0.5	0.70
4,564.2	4.6	1.9	18.5	1.3	55.6	0.6	23.6	0.13	0.15	0.5	0.70
4,566.1	7.3	<0.1	24.5	0.0	45.9	0.0	29.7	0.11	0.13	0.4	0.70
4,561.2	6.5	0.1	13.5	0.0	27.0	0.4	59.4[5]	0.50	0.23	0.5	0.80
4,570.0	9.0	5.6	42.5	0.3	4.7	0.6	51.2	0.18	0.20	0.3	0.70
4,577.4	12.1	0.3	62.4	7.7	20.6	2.1	7.1	0.32	0.30	0.4	0.70
4,589.4	10.0	3.0	32.4	0.7	15.7	0.0	50.5	0.23	0.15	0.3	0.50
4,584.3	12.6	174.0	88.5	1.1	7.7	0.9	1.8	0.45	0.40	0.5	0.80
4,596.2	14.8	116.0	64.4	2.2	30.6	0.0	3.6	0.62	0.35	0.7	0.60
4,590.3	15.4	26.1	63.8	0.7	29.9	0.4	0.4	0.34	0.33	0.4	0.75
4,600.3	6.6	3.9	24.3	1.0	18.7	0.0	56.0	0.23	0.10	0.6	0.60
4,595.4	14.2	96.5	79.7	0.0	17.5	1.7	1.0	0.60	0.60	0.3	0.80
4,599.2	8.0	1.1	46.0	0.0	4.6	0.0	39.4[5]	0.63	0.75	0.5	0.65
4,602.2	14.3	72.3	70.5	7.8	17.1	4.1	0.4	0.48	0.55	0.7	0.75
Average	10.3	43.72	46.6	0.9	26.5	1.4	24.0	0.32	0.30	0.44	0.73

[1] Percentages of grains and cement based on point counts of 400-600 points; potash feldspars were stained before counting.
[2] Median diameter.
[3] Standard deviation.
[4] Standard charts.
[5] Primary detrital grains.

graphic properties of the Mount Simon sandstone which most greatly affect reservoir characteristics are primarily dolomite (and calcite) percentage and secondarily grain roundness, sorting, and percentage of quartz. This analysis strengthens the idea expressed elsewhere in this report that, where the sandstone grades laterally into carbonate facies, the reservoir properties should become much less favorable for the storage of waste liquids. If more cores become available, it would be of interest to make a regional evaluation of reservoir characteristics based on petrographic properties, and of regional gradients based on discriminant analyses of the petrographic and reservoir data (Griffiths, 1964, p. 646).

In summary, the general lithology and mineralogy of the Mount Simon and Jacobsville(?) sandstones (Fig. 1) are reasonably consistent and predictable in southeastern Michigan. The Mount Simon is a feldspathic, quartzose sandstone, in most places cemented moderately by quartz and

feldspar overgrowths, and locally by dolomite and calcite. A feldspathic sandstone similar to the Jacobsville of the Upper Peninsula commonly lies at the base of the sedimentary section in contact with the Precambrian basement. It is quartz-rich, and contains hematite, clay, and glauconite. Glauconite is sufficiently widespread and abundant in the entire Cambrian sandstone section to make it potentially important for the adsorption of radioactive cations from atomic wastes.

In all of southeastern Michigan and adjacent Ontario and Ohio, the Mount Simon Sandstone Member of the Munising Formation directly overlies gneiss, schist, and granite of the Precambrian basement (Summerson, 1962). Elevation of the Precambrian surface ranges from −2,500 ft in the southeastern corner of Wayne County to about −5,500 ft in central Washtenaw County, across the region of principal interest in southeastern Michigan (Fig. 10).

Across this region the Mount Simon Member

ranges in thickness from about 200 to 500 ft (Fig. 11), and would constitute a reservoir of immense capacity for fluids. However, it should be stressed that the points of control from drill cuttings in the Mount Simon sandstone in this region are sparse, and the thicknesses shown (Fig. 11) in areas where there are no nearby wells should be accepted with reservation. Prediction of the exact thickness at any one point on the map would be difficult, although the representation of regional variation in thickness over the area is probably fairly accurate.

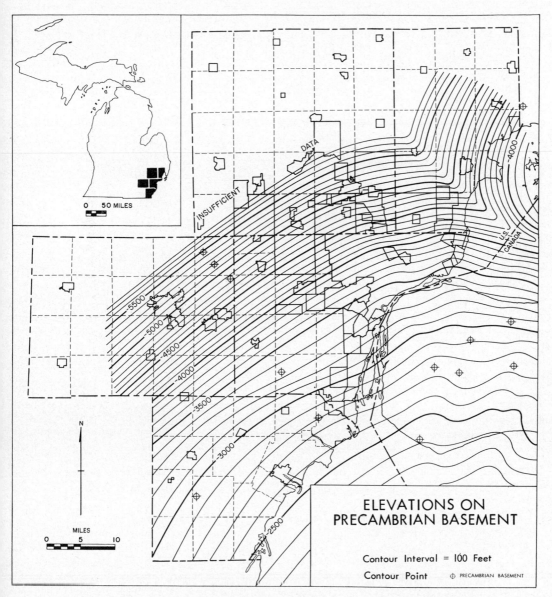

Fig. 10.—Map showing elevations on the Precambrian basement. Canadian data from Sanford and Quillian (1959).

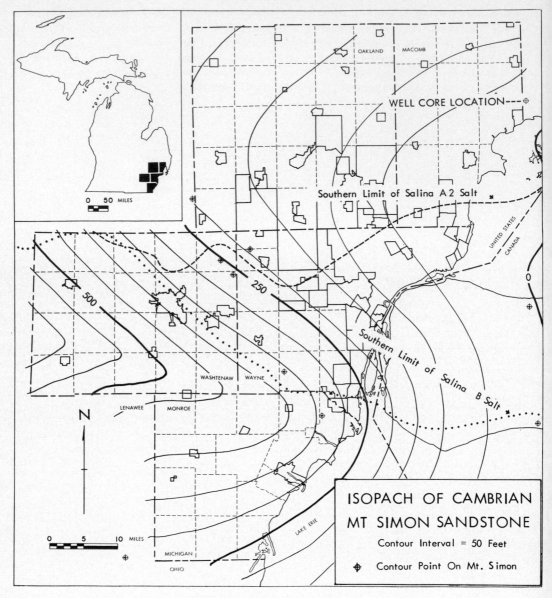

Fig. 11.—Isopach map of Cambrian Mount Simon sandstone.

In the five counties of southeastern Michigan, the drilling depth from the surface to the top of the Mount Simon sandstone ranges from less than 2,500 ft to more than 7,500 ft (Fig. 12), and is between 3,000 and 5,500 ft in the area of principal interest. This drilling depth is adequate to assure lithologic separation of the potential reservoir rock and its enclosed fluids from fluids of the near-surface formations.

Formation fluids.—Measurements of fluid properties and bottomhole pressures in the Cambrian rocks are very scarce. Most of the data of this type in Michigan have been recorded from the Trenton–Black River beds of Ordovician age, and most of these are from the so-called "Albion-Scipio trend" in southern Michigan (Hillsdale, Jackson, and Calhoun Counties). A summary of these data can be obtained from the Petroleum Section, Geological Survey Division, Michigan Department of Conservation, Lansing, Michigan.

The available data for the Cambrian formations are summarized in Table III from the driller's logs collected by the Michigan Geological Survey and from chemical analyses made by the Dow Chemical Company. The records of fluids in the Cambrian formations suggest the type of information desired for studies of hydrodynamic gradients in the subsurface formations where waste liquids may be disposed. The information now available is an entirely inadequate basis for conclusions regarding the hydrodynamic pressure

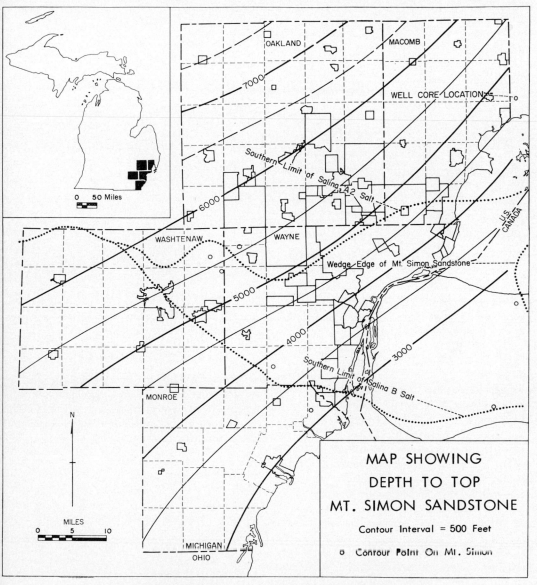

FIG. 12.—Map showing depth to top of Mount Simon sandstone.

TABLE III. FLUID RECORDS, CAMBRIAN FORMATIONS, SOUTHEASTERN MICHIGAN

Unit and Location	Depth (ft)	Description of Fluid Properties
Trempealeau Lenawee Co., Sec.		
36, T5S, R5E	3,133	1 bbl water/hr
	3,285	Hole full water, 3,210–3,250 ft
	3,339	1/2 bbl water/hr, 3,335–3,340 ft
Dresbach Monroe Co., Sec.		
29, T5S, R10E	2,912	400 ft water/hr at 2,900 ft
Monroe Co., Sec.		
29, T6S, R9E	2,681	Hole full water, 2,675–2,681 ft
Eau Claire Lenawee Co., Sec.		
32, T8S, R5E;	3,455	Hole full water at 3,420 ft
Jackson Co., Sec.		
29, T3S, R1W	5,880	DST 5,836–6,055 ft, 2 hr, rec. 65 ft salty mud, pressure zero
Macomb Co., Sec.		
34, T3N, R13E	4,678	200 ft/hr at 4,695 ft; at 4,678 ft chemical analysis: S.G. 1.190, $CaCl_2$ 9.31%, $MgCl_2$ 1.99%, ratio Ca/Mg 4.68, NaCl 10.73%, KCl 0.39%
St. Clair Co., Sec.		
31, T4N, R15E	4,487	DST chemical analysis: S.G. 1.191, $CaCl_2$ 10.31%, $MgCl_2$ 2.95%, ratio Ca/Mg 4.35, NaCl 14.33%, KCl 0.34%, Na_2SO_4 0.37%, total dissolved solids 267, 412 ppm, pH 5.9
Wayne Co., Sec.		
17, T1S, R8E	5,469	At 5,469 ft chemical analysis: S.G. 1.211, $CaCl_2$ 10.81%, $MgCl_2$ 1.85%, ratio Ca/Mg 5.84%, NaCl 11.20%, KCl 0.47%
	5,453	DST chemical analysis: S.G. 1.211, $CaCl_2$
	5,483	10.72%, $MgCl_2$ 1.83%, ratio Ca/Mg 5.85,% NaCl 11.50%, KCl 0.47%
Wayne Co., Sec.	4,398	DST chemical analysis: S.G. 1.204, $CaCl_2$
17, T1S, R8E	4,419	9.30%, $MgCl_2$ 1.84%, ratio Ca/Mg 5.05%, NaCl 12.34%, KCl 0.46%
Mount Simon Lenawee Co., Sec.		
32, T8S, R5E	3,865	Hole full water at 3,615 ft
St. Clair Co., Sec.		
11, T5N, R16E	4,785	2,000 ft water fill-up/1 hr
	4,789	3,460 ft water fill-up/12 1/2 hr

gradients and the direction of fluid migration in the subsurface formations. This situation emphasizes the need for additional data.

SHALE FORMATIONS

The Ordovician Utica Shale is a continuous, relatively thick sheet throughout this part of the Michigan basin. It ranges in thickness from about 200 to more than 400 ft (Fig. 13), and in depth from 1,000 to 5,000 ft (Fig. 14).

A core taken from the Utica Shale in southeastern Michigan is composed primarily of hard, brittle, dark-gray to greenish-black, calcareous shale that is fairly homogeneous throughout. The X-ray patterns show the presence of illite, quartz, and calcite. On four samples, porosity ranges from 1.5 to 4.2 percent and permeability from less than 0.05 to 2.5 md. The values for the permeability should be regarded with considerable caution, because fractures created during the cor-

ing could greatly increase the permeability. No analyses of fluids or fluid-pressure measurements are recorded from the Utica Shale.

SALT FORMATIONS

Within the Silurian Salina Formation (Fig. 1) are numerous beds of almost pure halite, some of which extend into southeastern Michigan. The terminology of units within the Salina Formation in the subsurface, in descending order, is as follows.

G Argillaceous dolomite
F Salt
E Dolomite
D Salt
C Argillaceous dolomite
B Salt
A Units
   A-2 Dolomite
   A-2 Salt
   A-1 Dolomite
   A-1 Salt

Niagara (Lockport-Guelph) Dolomite underlies the Salina strata. Generally, the salt beds within the Salina Formation are continuous sheets except near the edge, where disjoint lenses of salt are present in structural lows in the Niagara Dolomite (Evans, 1950). The A salts are essentially single beds where they are present in southeastern Michigan, the vertical continuity being interrupted only by thin layers of anhydrite and dolomite. The B salt, the thickest in this region, is less homogeneous and contains numerous layers of anhydrite and dolomite. The higher salts (D and F), part of a sequence of dolomite and salt, contain up to seven salt beds in certain areas.

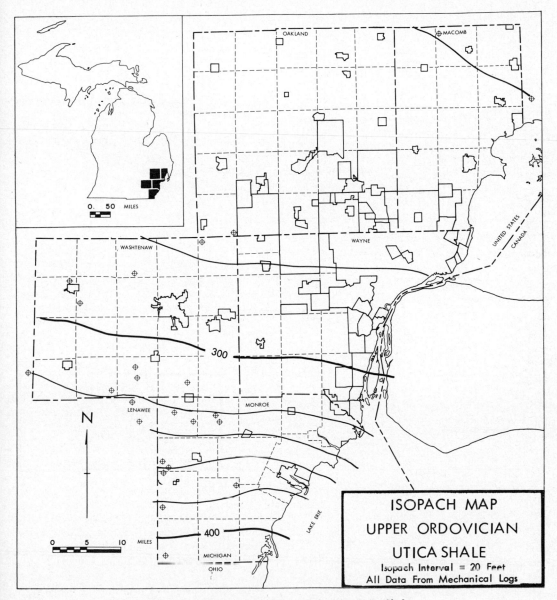

FIG. 13.—Isopach map of Upper Ordovician Utica Shale.

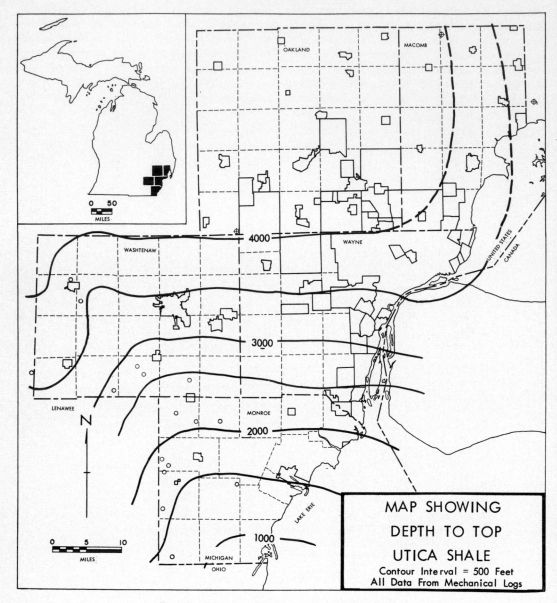

Fig. 14.—Map showing depth to top of Utica Shale.

The F salt is mined in southwestern Detroit by the International Salt Company at a depth of about 1,300 ft.

The distribution of the anhydrite and halite facies within the evaporite units of A-1 salt, A-2 salt, and B evaporite (Figs. 15–17) shows that the B salt is the most extensive of the lower halite beds. Depth to the top of the B salt (Fig. 18)

ranges from 1,000 to 3,000 ft in most of the area. The D salt and F salt are distributed over much of the same area at a shallower depth, but their exact position and distribution are not well known.

Like most bedded salt deposits, the Salina salts contain individual layers of salt ranging from several millimeters to a little more than 1 ft in thickness. The halite beds are separated by thin, dark layers of anhydritic dolomite; locally the thicker dark dolomite beds are called "shale" by the salt miners. The Salina evaporites contain much less anhydrite and gypsum than most other similarly laminated salt deposits, the principal anhydrites being marginal to the salt around the edges of the basin (Figs. 15, 16). The salt is prin-

cipally halite, containing 2–10 percent anhydrite and dolomite, and traces of barite, celestite, pyrite, quartz, and other more rare minerals. The halite is relatively free of clay minerals and formation fluids.

CONCLUSIONS

Operators interested in porous sandstone reser-

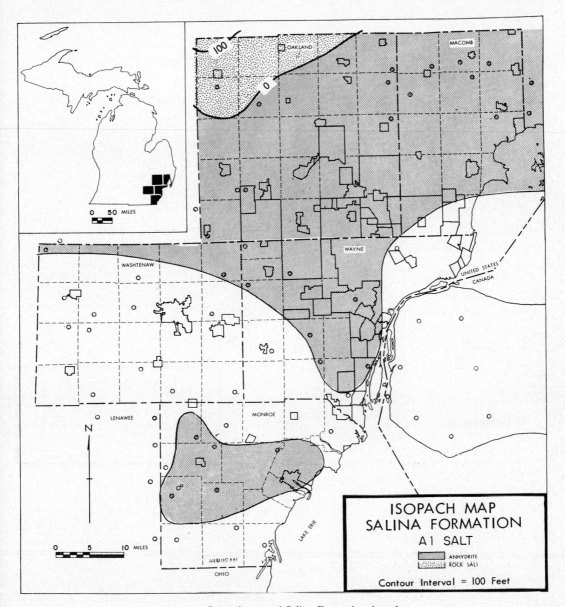

FIG. 15.—Isopach map of Salina Formation A1 salt.

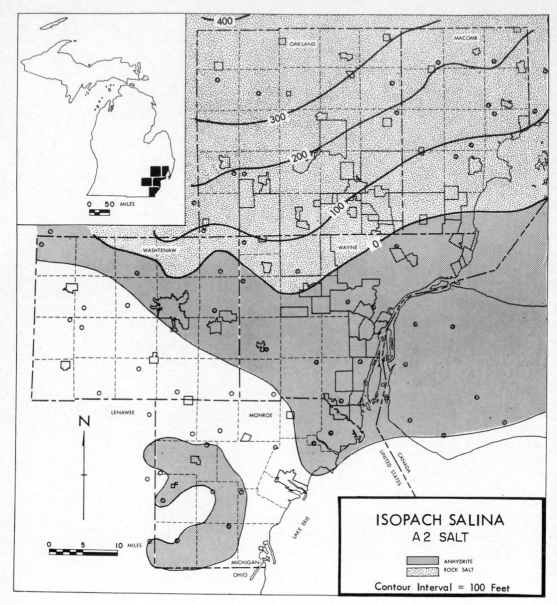

FIG. 16.—Isopach map of Salina Formation A2 salt.

voirs in the Michigan basin for the disposal of large volumes of liquid wastes should consider the Cambrian Mount Simon sandstone in southeastern Michigan. They can be reasonably certain that the disposed wastes will not reach fresh-water supplies or otherwise contaminate the biosphere. In most of the state, the Mount Simon is too deep for economic disposal of high-volume liquids; near southwestern Michigan, it is exploited for fresh-water supplies. Underlying the five counties which make up the Detroit metropolitan area, the Mount Simon sandstone ranges from about 200 to 500 ft in thickness and can be reached by drilling 2,500–7,500 ft.

The lithology and mineralogy are reasonably consistent in the region. The Mount Simon is a feldspathic, quartzose sandstone, in most places cemented moderately by quartz and feldspar, and locally by dolomite and calcite. In the one core extensively studied, porosity averages 10.7 percent and permeability averages 32 md. These res-ervoir characteristics are affected most by the percentage of dolomite and calcite in the rock, both as detrital carbonate grains and as intergranular cement. Receptivity is relatively high. After acid and hydraulic-fracturing treatment, the cored well received 46,670 bbl of brine in the first month of operation at a pump-discharge pressure

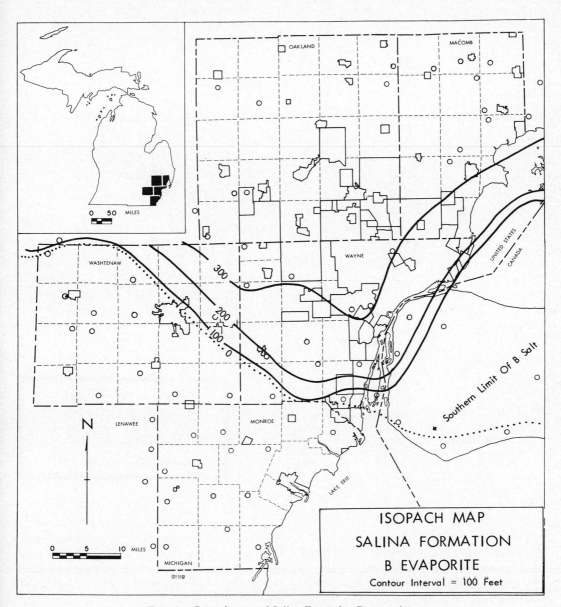

FIG. 17.—Isopach map of Salina Formation B evaporite.

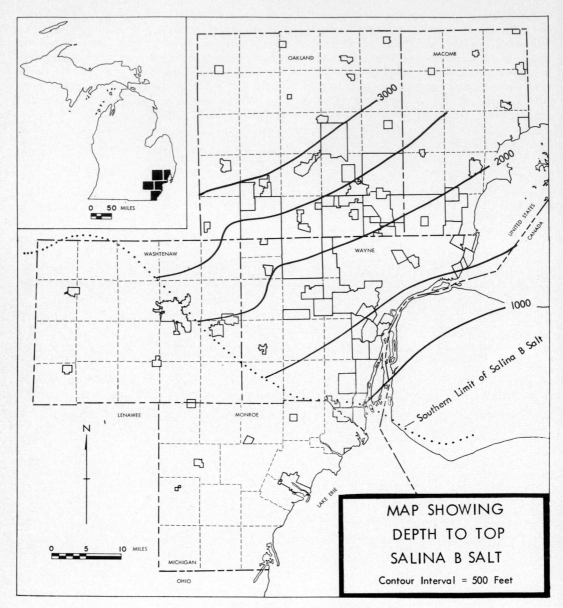

FIG. 18.—Map showing depth to top of Salina B salt.

of 825 psi.

Other types of wastes may be disposed of in southeastern Michigan in formations that overlie the Mount Simon Sandstone Member. Low-volume radioactive liquids with high cation concentrations can be injected as grout into fractures developed in the Utica Shale by hydraulic-fracturing techniques; the clay minerals in the shale are particularly important for cation exchange and trapping of offensive waste cations. Wastes which have been converted into relatively stable solids can be stored safely for long periods of time in caverns excavated or dissolved in the Salina salt beds, which are free of formation waters.

Waste disposal of any of the types mentioned should pose no problems if appropriate geological information is used and adequate precautions are taken. Where a large-volume, long-term program is anticipated for disposal of noxious liquid wastes into Mount Simon sandstone, it would be wise to drill sufficient test borings to determine the hydrodynamic properties of the formation waters, especially the direction of fluid movement. Such knowledge is imperative to insure that the waste liquids will be trapped indefinitely within the subsurface reservoir.

REFERENCES

Borchert, J. R., 1961, The Twin Cities urbanized area: past, present, future: Geog. Rev., v. 51, p. 47–70.

Cohee, G. V., et al., 1962, Tectonic map of the United States: U.S. Geol. Survey and Am. Assoc. Petroleum Geologists.

Deskins, D. R., 1963, Settlement patterns for the Detroit metropolitan community research project: Inst. Human Adjustment, Univ. Michigan.

De Witt, Wallace, 1960, Geology of the Michigan basin with reference to subsurface disposal of radioactive wastes: U.S. Geol. Survey Trace Elements Inv. Rept. 771.

Evans, C. S., 1950, Underground hunting in the Silurian of southwestern Ontario: Proc. Geol. Assoc. Canada, v. 3, p. 55–85.

Griffiths, J. C., 1964, Statistical approach to the study of potential oil reservoir sandstones, in Computers in the mineral industries, pt. 2: Stanford Univ. Pub. Geol. Sci., v. 9, no. 2, p. 637–668.

Martin, H. M., 1936, The centennial geological map of Michigan: Michigan Geol. Survey Pub. 39.

Michigan Department of Health, 1961, (Title unavailable): Eng. Bull. 4.

Pettijohn, F. J., 1949, Sedimentary rocks: New York, Harper and Brothers, 526 p.

Sanford, B. V., and R. G. Quillian, 1959, Subsurface stratigraphy of Upper Cambrian rocks in southwestern Ontario: Geol. Survey Canada Paper 58, 12 p.

Summerson, C. H., 1962, Precambrian in Ohio and adjoining areas: Ohio Geol. Survey Rept. Inv. No. 44, 16 p.

Wisler, C. O., G. J. Stramel, and L. B. Laird, 1952, Water resources of the Detroit area, Michigan: U.S. Geol. Survey Circ. 183, 36 p.

SUBSURFACE WASTE-DISPOSAL POTENTIAL
IN SALINA BASIN OF KANSAS[1]

R. W. EDMUND[2] AND EDWIN D. GOEBEL[3]
Rock Island, Illinois 61201, and Lawrence, Kansas 66044

ABSTRACT

Study of the geology of the Salina basin in Kansas shows good potential storage reservoirs for industrial waste in a Cambrian sandstone, in Pennsylvanian shale beds, and in Permian salt beds. The natural flow of fluids in the basin is thought to be from north to south at a slow rate.

GEOGRAPHY

The Salina basin includes all or parts of 22 counties in north-central Kansas and 45 counties in eastern Nebraska (Fig. 1). The geographic center of the continental United States is within the Salina basin. Physiographically, the Salina basin is in the Great Plains province. The land surface is maturely dissected, and flat to rolling; maximum topographic relief is generally less than 1,000 ft (305 m). Elevation of the surface is from 1,000 to 2,000 ft (305 to 610 m) above sea level, and the area is relatively well drained. The topography was produced by erosion of gently dipping layers of sedimentary rock, which resulted in low ridges with eastward-facing escarpments and long backslopes. These ridges are separated by relatively flat lowlands. The streams and rivers of the area have low gradients and flow southeastward, transverse to the regional strike of the formations.

The mean annual temperature of the Salina basin area is about 54°F (12°C), and extremes range from −25° to +117°F (−32° to +47°C). The average July temperature is about 80°F (27°C). The average annual precipitation is nearly 24 in. (61 cm), and about three-fourths of it occurs in the warm season from April through

September. Prevailing winds are southerly, but northerly winds are frequent in the winter.

Salina, Kansas, is the largest city in the area, having a population of nearly 43,000. McPherson Kansas, is at the southern edge of the Salina basin and has a population of about 10,000. Two cities with about 7,000 population and four cities with populations ranging from 2,500 to 5,000 are within the Salina basin. Other communities in the area are classed properly as rural rather than urban.

The Salina basin region is predominantly rural; county seats are of modest size. The main occupations are raising small grain and cattle. Most of the land is owned privately and generally is farmed by the owner. The sizes of individual holdings range from small farms of about 20–40 acres to ranches of several hundred or a few thousand acres. It is estimated that less than 5 percent of the land in the Salina basin in Kansas is leased to oil companies for exploratory purposes.

All parts of the Salina basin are accessible by farm-to-market roads connected with major highways that trend north-south. All county seats are connected by paved highways. Several important railroads cross the area, mainly in an east-west pattern. None of the waterways are navigable. There are few airports in the area, but Salina is served by commercial airline and most of the county seats have facilities for small planes.

The supply of surface water in the Salina basin area is limited. The water quality is commonly poor because of high mineral content. The Dakota Formation (Cretaceous) is the principal aquifer, and the water in the sandstone beds of the Dakota

---

[1] Manuscript received, November 2, 1963; revised, June 13, 1966.

[2] Augustana College.

[3] Kansas State Geological Survey.

This paper is based on work with the Kansas Geological Society Study Committee: E. E. Pugh, Jr., chairman, National Cooperative Refinery Association; M. F. Bear, independent oil producer; E. D. Goebel, Kansas State Geological Survey; R. P. Lehman, Phillips Petroleum Company; and D. J. Malone, Pickrell Drilling Company.

154

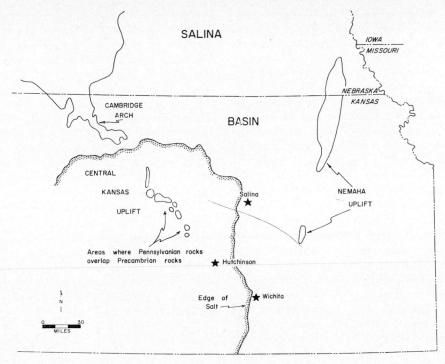

FIG. 1.—Index map of Salina basin in Kansas and part of Nebraska.

is highly mineralized. Alluvial deposits along major streams generally yield more potable water than the Dakota Formation. Volumes of water are adequate for stock and domestic use; well outputs range up to 100 gal/min or more.

Utilities are generally available. Electric power is available in all counties, and many communities are supplied with natural gas from the several pipelines that cross the area.

Wilson Reservoir is in the southwestern part of the Salina basin, on the Saline River a short distance west of Sylvan Grove, Kansas, near the western edge of Lincoln County; it was built primarily for flood control. This reservoir is a potential source of water for industrial use. Wilson Reservoir was constructed to provide storage of 510,000 acre-ft for flood control and 225,080 acre-ft for conservation of water and collection of sediment. Water in conservation storage, not dedicated, will supplement the supply for downstream users. Milford Reservoir at Fort Riley, Kansas, on the eastern edge of the Salina

basin area, and Kanopolis Reservoir in Ellsworth County, Kansas, are other potential sources of water. Surface storage of large quantities of water is planned for the Woodbine area in Dickinson County, the Lovewell area in Jewell County, and the Glen Elder Reservoir in Mitchell County, Kansas.

Ceramic clay, volcanic ash, lignite, salt, oil and gas, and construction materials—such as limestone, quartzite, sand, and gravel—are the principal mineral resources recovered from the study area. Except for the southern flank of the Salina basin, few oil and gas exploratory holes have been drilled in the area. Several major interstate gas and oil transmission lines cross the area.

BOUNDARIES AND GEOLOGIC SETTING

The Salina basin first was defined by Barwick (1928, p. 179) as ". . . the pre-Pennsylvanian syncline bounded on the east by the Nemaha granite ridge [now Nemaha anticline], on the southwest by the Barton arch [now Central Kansas uplift], and on the south by the saddle between the Chautauqua arch and the Barton arch. The basin continues northward into Nebraska, where its exact termination is not known."

The Salina basin is on the margin of an older structural basin referred to by Rich (1933) as the "North Kansas basin." The uplifting of the Nemaha anticline divided the North Kansas basin into the Salina basin on the west and the Forest City basin on the east. In the early stages of development these were structural basins, as shown by the beveling of pre-Pennsylvanian rocks. During Pennsylvanian time the basins were subsiding areas in which deposits accumulated in greater thicknesses than at the margins.

The Salina basin is elongate north to south (Fig. 1); the western margin is marked by Pennsylvanian strata overlying north-south-trending truncated edges of older Paleozoic strata (Fig. 2). The basin terminates on the southwest against the Central Kansas uplift, where a large part of the stratigraphic section was removed by pre-Pennsylvanian erosion. At the northern end of the basin the older beds terminate against the south flank of the Sioux arch in southeastern South Dakota. The eastern flank of the Salina basin is bounded by the prominent Nemaha anticline, which extends from southeastern Nebraska to central Kansas. The south end of the Salina basin is partially open into the Sedgwick basin in south-central Kansas, and southward the Sedgwick basin joins the Anadarko basin of Oklahoma.

STRUCTURE

The Salina basin is a relatively simple asymmetric syncline, with a fairly uniform and gentle axial tilt from north to south. The basin is deepest along the southwestern flank adjacent to the Central Kansas uplift, as shown by the configuration of the top of the Precambrian rocks (Fig. 3). Anticlinal folds within the basin are few, simple in form, and of low structural relief. Some of these features, delineated by seismic surveys, have been tested unsuccessfully for oil and gas.

In the Salina basin, three principal periods of folding are indicated by thickness maps, and two secondary periods of folding are indicated by structural maps (Lee, 1956, p. 133). The first period of folding affected rocks between the top

of the Precambrian strata and the base of the St. Peter Sandstone. The second episode of folding occurred during the deposition of the rocks that lie between the St. Peter Sandstone and the base of the Mississippian System. The third period of folding began early in Mississippian time, but was of maximum intensity during Late Mississippian and Early Pennsylvanian times. This movement continued with decreasing intensity throughout most of the Permian Period. The fourth period of folding was during Late Permian and Cretaceous times, and the fifth was between Cretaceous time and the present.

The present attitude of the rocks in the Salina basin is a result of the conflicting structural movements that occurred at several different times during geologic history. The deformation which produced the folds occurred mainly in a series of mild orogenic pulses.

There is faulting of the southwestern and southern flanks of the Salina basin, but there is very little, if any, faulting within the Salina basin proper. No intense folding or faulting has occurred since early in Pennsylvanian time.

STRATIGRAPHY

The stratigraphy of the Salina basin in Kansas is well known from a study by Lee (1956). In most of the basin, Permian and Pennsylvanian rocks are at the surface; Tertiary rocks cover a very small area of the westernmost part of the basin, and a thin veneer of Cretaceous rocks covers the rest of the western part of the basin. Paleozoic sedimentary rocks range in age from Permian to Cambrian. They are underlain by Precambrian rocks which are at a maximum depth of 4,500 ft (1,372 m) below the surface (Fig. 2). Precambrian rocks in the southern part of the Salina basin consist of granite, syenite, quartzite, gneiss, and diabase. Figure 4 shows the locations and penetrations of boreholes known to have drilled Precambrian igneous and metamorphic rocks. Thicknesses and lithologies of pre-Arbuckle detrital sedimentary and metasedimentary rocks, including the Reagan (Lamotte) Sandstone (Upper Cambrian), also are indicated. A section of more than 1,000 ft (305 m) of pre-Upper Cambrian feldspathic sandstone and shale, the Rice Formation (Scott, 1966), is found in a

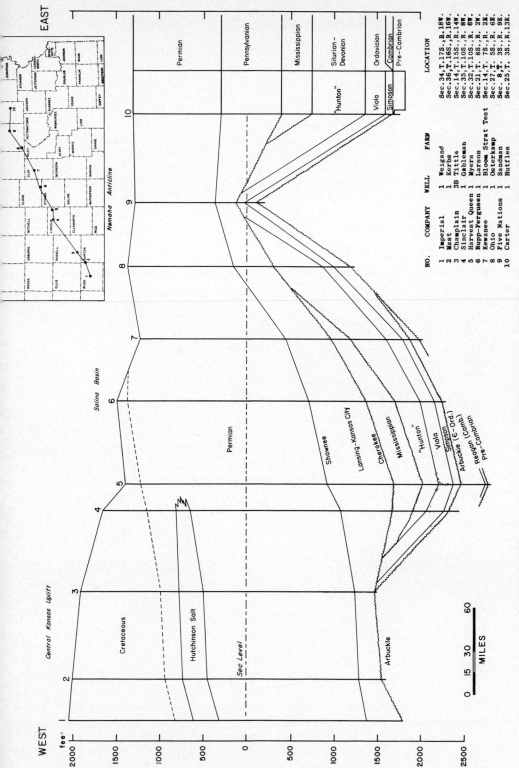

Fig. 2.—Cross section from Rush County to Nemaha County, Kansas, showing stratigraphic units and thicknesses from southwest (Central Kansas uplift) across the Salina basin to northeast (Nemaha anticline). Insert shows line of section.

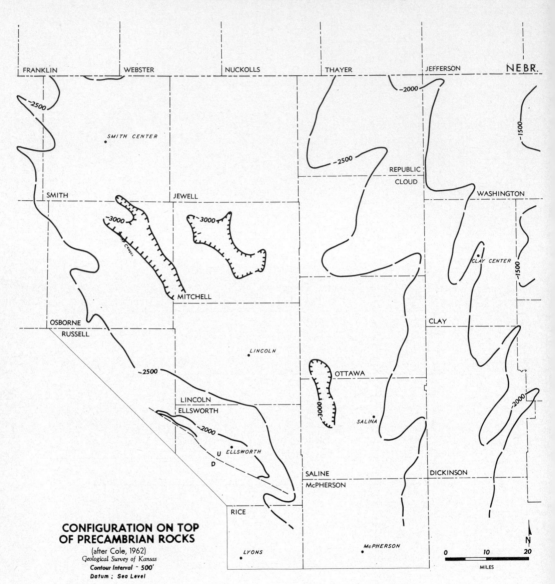

FIG. 3.—Configuration on top of Precambrian rocks.

roughly triangular area extending from Republic and Washington Counties on the north to Osborne County on the west and Reno County on the south.

The Reagan (Lamotte) Sandstone, of Late Cambrian age, overlies the Rice Formation. The Reagan was deposited on an irregular erosion surface of low relief cut into the Rice Formation and into Precambrian rocks. The overlying Ar-

buckle rocks, of Late Cambrian and Early Ordovician ages, thicken southwestward across the basin to a maximum thickness of approximately 500 ft (152 m) (Fig. 5). The term "Arbuckle dolomite" is used in this report to refer to all rocks between the top of the Reagan (Lamotte) Sandstone and the base of the Simpson Group. Truncated Arbuckle strata provide important oil-productive zones on the Central Kansas uplift

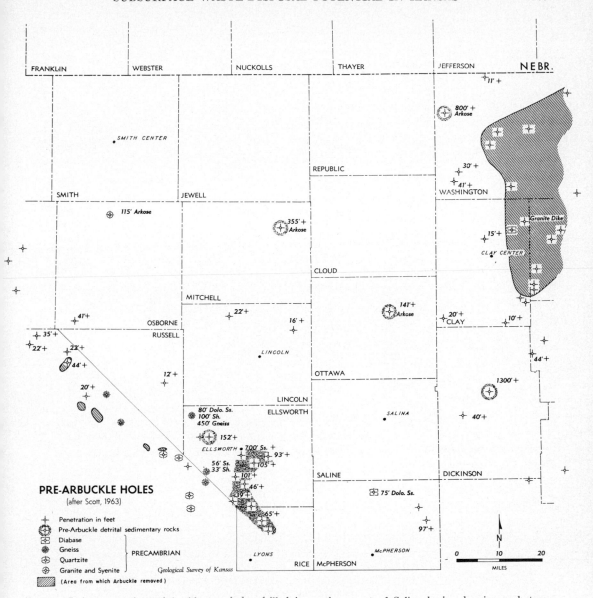

Fig. 4.—Index map of pre-Arbuckle test holes drilled in southern part of Salina basin, showing rock types and penetration in feet.

(Fig. 2). Thin but persistent beds of sandstone, shale, and dolomite of the Simpson Group overlie the Arbuckle. These Middle Ordovician rocks are overlain by the Viola Limestone, also of Middle Ordovician age. The Viola Limestone contains limestone beds that grade upward into cherty limestone. The Viola is fairly uniform in character and is about 200 ft (61 m) thick throughout the southern part of the Salina basin. The Maquoketa Shale (Upper Ordovician) is generally less than 100 ft (30 m) thick and constitutes the uppermost part of the Ordovician section. Silurian and Devonian carbonate rocks were truncated and removed from the southwestern part of the basin

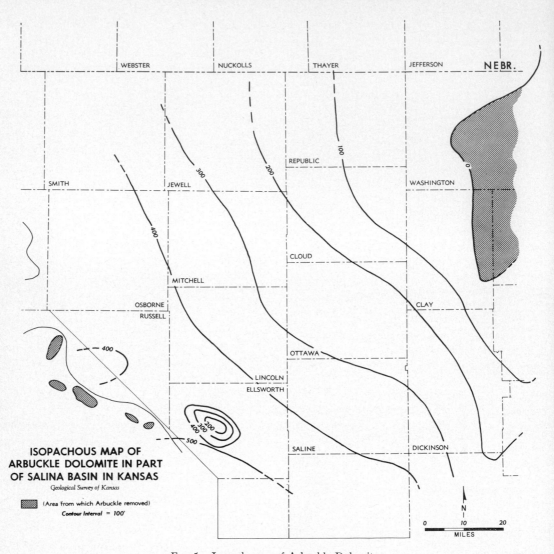

FIG. 5.—Isopach map of Arbuckle Dolomite.

by pre-Mississippian erosion. The Silurian and Devonian rocks have a maximum thickness of approximately 600 ft (183 m) along the eastern margin of the basin, adjacent to the Nemaha anticline.

In the Salina basin, a sequence of black and gray shale beds, of undetermined age in part, separates limestone that is definitely of Mississippian age from limestone and dolomite beds that are definitely of Devonian age. This shale sequence comprises the Boice Shale, above, and the Chattanooga Shale, below. The use of the term "Kinderhook" has become standard among oil-company geologists in reference to this shale section. The Misener sandstone member at the base of the Chattanooga Shale is distributed erratically in the Salina basin. The thickness of the Chattanooga Shale ranges from zero to at least 260 ft (79 m). The Boice Shale, of Early Mississippian age, overlies the Chattanooga Shale in the eastern part of the Salina basin. Maximum thickness of the Boice is 110 ft (33.5 m). The overlying Mississippian limestone beds are thickest in the structurally deepest part of the Salina basin where they were affected least by pre-Pennsylvanian erosion. Chert constitutes a major part of the older Mississippian rocks, but becomes less important in the upper part of the Mississippian section.

In the Kansas part of the Salina basin, the Lower Pennsylvanian formations range in thickness from approximately 50 ft (15 m) to more than 300 ft (91 m) (Fig. 2). Pennsylvanian rocks of Desmoinesian age are thickest in the structurally deepest part of the basin and thin by overlap onto the Central Kansas uplift and the Nemaha anticline. These strata are predominantly shale or thin, lenticular sandstone beds. The Missourian and Virgilian rocks of Late Pennsylvanian age and the Wolfcampian rocks of Early Permian age are made up of a succession of thin limestone beds and intervening thin shale beds. In the aggregate, these units are approximately 2,000 ft (610 m) thick. Lower Permian beds of Leonardian age are redbeds interspersed with gypsum, limestone, and salt. The most significant salt beds compose the Hutchinson Salt Member of the Wellington Formation. The Hutchinson is present locally in the southwest part of the Salina basin (Fig. 6) and has maximum thickness in the basin of about 300 ft (91 m).

The most important bed of the overlying Cretaceous section is the Dakota Formation, which is an aquifer.

UNCONFORMITIES

There is a major unconformity at the base of the Reagan Sandstone of Late Cambrian age. A minor unconformity is present at the base of the Simpson Group. Either Mississippian carbonate strata or Chattanooga shale beds overlap onto topographic highs that were caused by the truncation of Ordovician, Silurian, and Devonian strata in the southern part of the Salina basin. Significant unconformities are present within the Mississippian section. The most important unconformity of the Salina basin area is at the base of the Pennsylvanian System where Pennsylvanian rocks overlap onto prominent areas of uplift and erosion which delineate the basin. Residuals of Mississippian chert and other rock materials were

reworked by the Early Pennsylvanian seas. It is not everywhere possible to differentiate between residual and detrital material, but residual material at the unconformity is referred to as "Mississippi chat," and detrital material is called "Pennsylvanian basal conglomerate." Across the Central Kansas uplift and the Nemaha anticline, Pennsylvanian beds lie on the truncated edges of successively older formations that range in age from Mississippian to Precambrian. Since Early Pennsylvanian time the Salina basin area has been relatively stable, except for minor eastward tilting of the region in post-Cretaceous time.

SELECTED RESERVOIRS

The preferred permeable reservoir for injection of liquid industrial waste in the Kansas part of the Salina basin is the basal Cambrian sandstone —where it lies on the Precambrian basement or where it is in contact with the thick section of pre-Upper Cambrian metasediments. The Reagan Sandstone ranges from a few feet of detrital sand to relatively pure quartzite more than 100 ft (30 m) thick with only a few shale breaks, and to detrital arkosic sandstone that grades into metasediments or weathered Precambrian rock. The contact of the Reagan with the overlying Arbuckle dolomite is not distinct everywhere. In places where the Arbuckle dolomite is porous at its contact with the Reagan, the two units could serve as a common reservoir for reception of liquid industrial waste. The impermeable seal above these units is shale of the Simpson Group of Middle Ordovician age.

The Reagan Sandstone, although varied in composition and texture, is believed to be capable of receiving large volumes of fluids. Because of its low stratigraphic position and its vertical separation from the potential oil-productive rocks that are higher in the section, the Reagan Sandstone is recommended as the best unit in the Salina basin for injection of waste liquids. A history of brine-disposal operations in oil fields along the Central Kansas uplift indicates that both the Reagan and Arbuckle have transmissibility characteristics that would make these rocks suitable for injection of liquid industrial waste.

Shale of Desmoinesian age (Middle Pennsyl-

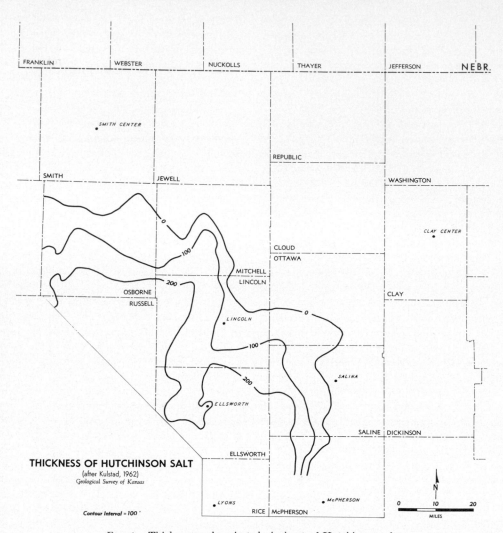

FIG. 6.—Thickness and projected pinchout of Hutchinson salt.

vanian) has been selected as being suitable for storage by injection of liquid industrial waste in slurry form into artificially produced fractures. The shale is soft, laminated, and locally contains interbeds of thin, lenticular sandstone. The thickness of the shale units ranges from 100 to 300 ft (30 to 91 m). These rocks are about 3,000 ft (914 m) below the surface.

Salt of Late Permian age is present at depths ranging from 500 to 1,500 ft (152 to 457 m) below the surface in the Salina basin; from a maximum of about 300 ft (91 m), it thins north-

eastward into the deeper parts of the basin and pinches out in Mitchell, Saline, and McPherson Counties. Salt is mined from the Central Kansas uplift area in Ellsworth, Rice, and Reno Counties. The Hutchinson Salt Member is within 1,000 ft (305 m) of the surface in the southwestern part of the Salina basin, and the salt beds range in thickness from zero to more than 200 ft (610 m). The salt is believed to have good potential for the storage of solid or liquid industrial wastes. The thickness of the overburden on the Hutchinson salt is shown in Figure 7.

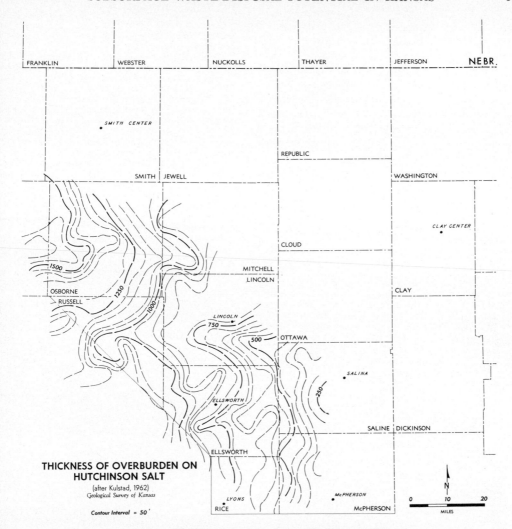

THICKNESS OF OVERBURDEN ON
HUTCHINSON SALT
(after Kulstad, 1962)
Geological Survey of Kansas

Contour Interval = 50'

FIG. 7.—Thickness of overburden on Hutchinson salt.

FLUIDS

Salt water has been found in all deep porous strata penetrated in exploratory drilling in the Salina basin. The interval drill-stem-test data from the few deep holes that have been drilled in the Kansas part of the Salina basin have been examined, but are too meager to permit construction of a map showing the attitude of the potentiometric surfaces. However, the available evidence allows the conclusion that the flow of water through permeable strata conforms to the structural configuration of stratigraphic units within the basin. The flow is generally from north to south, and probable discharge is into the Sedgwick and Anadarko basins. The southward flow along the margin of the Central Kansas uplift is modified by the movement off the flank of the uplift eastward into the basin, producing a southeastward component of flow. There is some indication of flow southwestward from the flanks of the Nemaha anticline into the Salina basin.

It is assumed that fluids in porous zones from the surface to the Precambrian rocks in this area nearly have reached a state of equilibrium, because the area has been relatively stable since Early Pennsylvanian time. It is likely that the Arbuckle dolomite and the Reagan Sandstone, as well as the metasediments of the Rice Formation, constitute a common reservoir. Much salt water is being produced from the Arbuckle dolomite and other formations on the Central Kansas uplift, and these waters are being returned to the Arbuckle dolomite by means of salt-water disposal systems.

Flow rates of fluids in the Salina basin cannot be determined from the available data, but they are presumed to be slow.

REFERENCES

Barwick, J. S., 1928, The Salina basin of north-central Kansas: Am. Assoc. Petroleum Geologists Bull., v. 12, p. 177–199.

Cole, V. B., 1962, Configuration on top of Precambrian basement rocks in Kansas: Kansas Geol. Survey Oil and Gas Inv. No. 26, map.

Eikleberry, R. W., 1950, Physical land conditions affecting use, conservation, and management of land resources, Lincoln County, Kansas: U.S. Dept. Agriculture Soil Conserv. Service and Kansas Agricultural Expt. Sta., p. 1–23.

Hambleton, W. W., et al., 1962, Economic development for Kansas, mineral and water resources: Governor's Econ. Devel. Comm., Center for Research in Kansas, Univ. Kansas, p. 1–148.

Kansas Water Resources Board, 1961, State water plan studies, pt. A, Preliminary appraisal of Kansas water problems. Sec. 8, Solomon-Saline Unit: p. 1–154.

Kulstad, R. O., 1962, Map of Hutchinson salt in Kansas: Kansas Geol. Survey, unpub. ms.

Lee, Wallace, 1956, Stratigraphy and structural development of the Salina basin area: Kansas Geol. Survey Bull. 121, p. 1–167.

Rich, J. L., 1933, Distribution of oil pools in Kansas in relation to pre-Mississippian structure and areal geology: Am. Assoc. Petroleum Geologists Bull., v. 17, p. 793–815.

Schoewe, W. H., 1949, The geography of Kansas, pt. 2, Physical geography: Kansas Acad. Sci. Trans., v. 52, no. 3, p. 261–333.

Scott, R. W., 1963, Map of distribution of Precambrian rock types in Kansas: Kansas Geol. Survey, unpub. ms.

——— 1966, New Precambrian(?) Formation in Kansas: Am. Assoc. Petroleum Geologists Bull., v. 50, no. 2, p. 380–384.

POTENTIAL OF DENVER BASIN FOR DISPOSAL OF LIQUID WASTES[1]

GEORGE S. GARBARINI[2] AND HARRY K. VEAL[3]
Denver, Colorado 80201, and Dallas, Texas

ABSTRACT

A reconnaissance subsurface geologic study has shown that three types of reservoirs are available for liquid-waste disposal in the Denver basin—fractured Precambrian rocks, porous sandstone reservoirs, and thick shale suitable for disposal by the hydraulic-fracturing technique.

From early 1962 through early 1966, fractured Precambrian rocks at a depth of 12,000 ft were used as a disposal reservoir for toxic effluent produced at the Rocky Mountain Arsenal near Denver. The disposal well is now shut in pending investigation of the possible relationship of waste injection to Denver-area earthquakes, which increased in frequency and magnitude during the injection period.

Data on the Precambrian of the Denver basin are sparse because only a few test wells penetrated it in search for oil and gas. Two borings on the Apishapa uplift indicate a good fractured Precambrian reservoir.

Porous sandstone reservoirs considered most favorable for waste disposal are the Permian Lyons Sandstone, the Triassic Dockum sandstone, the Triassic-Jurassic Jelm-Entrada sandstone, and sandstones in the Cretaceous Dakota Group and the "Hygiene zone" of the Pierre Shale. The Lyons, Dockum, and Dakota are best suited for waste disposal in the southern part of the basin. Exploration for oil and gas in this part of the basin has been very slow in recent years, whereas activity is moderate to brisk in the central part of the basin where the Lyons and Dakota are prime drilling objectives. The Dockum sandstone, potentially the best disposal reservoir volumetrically, is limited to the southeast part of the basin. The Jelm-Entrada and Hygiene-zone sandstones are potential disposal reservoirs along the heavily populated strip between Denver and Cheyenne.

Cretaceous marine black shale suitable for disposal by the hydraulic-fracturing technique is present everywhere in the basin. The shale crops out over large areas. Beneath the populous strip along the Front Range, the shale is covered locally by as much as 2,000 ft of Upper Cretaceous and Tertiary transitional to continental strata.

INTRODUCTION

It is the twofold purpose of this report (1) to provide an outline of the regional stratigraphy and structure of the Denver basin, and (2) to specify and describe the formations or units which appear most favorable for disposal of liquid waste through well bores.

In the preparation of this report, all available surface and subsurface geological information was used, including published maps and reports; per-

[1] Manuscript received, May 24, 1966.

[2] Sun Oil Company.

[3] Wolf Exploration Company.

The writers thank the following persons who were very helpful in providing data for this report: James H. Irwin, U.S. Geological Survey, Ground Water Branch; James G. Mitchell and John Greene, American Stratigraphic Company; George R. Downs; and Louis Scopel. Sun Oil Company and Wolf Exploration Company gave permission to publish this paper. John E. Galley reviewed the manuscript and aided the project in many ways. Funds from the U.S. Atomic Energy Commission were made available through the Atomic Waste Disposal Subcommittee of the Research Committee, AAPG, to cover drafting, reproduction, and typing costs.

sonal communications; and sample logs, mechanical logs, and miscellaneous information on about 1,000 selected borings. Twelve illustrations, including three cross sections, show the general geology of the Denver basin. The bibliography lists many of the important contributions to the geologic knowledge of the Denver basin.

GEOGRAPHY

The area of the Denver basin, part of the Great Plains province of North America, is characterized by relatively undisturbed sedimentary rocks. Water, or the lack of it, has an important influence on the distribution of population. Major cities and industry are located along the North Platte, South Platte, and Arkansas Rivers, and in a narrow strip along the Front Range of the Colorado Rockies. Most of the population is in and around the cities of Pueblo, Colorado Springs, and Denver, Colorado, and Cheyenne, Wyoming. Between the major drainages, the semiarid plains area is used mainly for grazing and dry-land wheat farming.

The High Plains slope eastward away from the

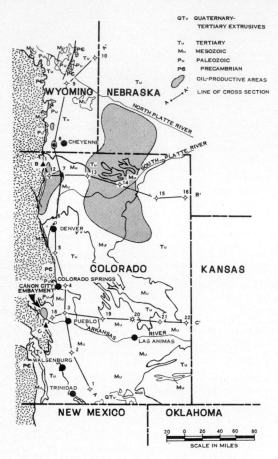

FIG. 1.—Generalized geologic map of Denver basin showing lines of cross section (Figs. 4, 5) and major oil-productive areas, which contain many small fields productive principally from sandstone beds in upper part of Dakota Group.

Front Range across the Denver basin from elevations of 5,000–7,000 ft near the mountains to 3,500–4,000 ft along the Kansas border. Main river valleys are as much as 1,000 ft below the elevation level of the High Plains.

GENERAL GEOLOGY

STRUCTURE

The Denver basin is a broad, oval, asymmetric structural basin extending over parts of Colorado, Nebraska, and Wyoming for a distance of about 300 mi north-south and about 170 mi east-west. Figure 1 is a generalized geologic map of the basin. Along the basin axis, which is very close to

the western margin of the basin (Fig. 2), two "deeps"—one in the Denver area and one in the Cheyenne area—contain sedimentary sections about 13,000 ft thick. The eastern flank has a west dip of about 30–50 ft/mi, and small anticlinal features have closure measurable in tens of feet at the top of the Dakota Group. The western flank is typified by steep east dip interrupted by larger anticlinal features, some with closure measurable in hundreds of feet. Faulting is scarce in

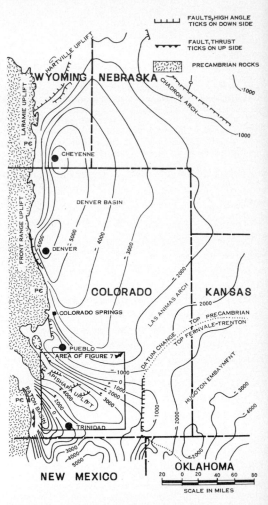

FIG. 2.—Generalized tectonic map of Denver basin and surrounding uplifts, after Tectonic Map of the United States (Cohee, 1962). Note location of Figure 7. Structure contours in southeast part of map are of top of Ordovician Fernvale-Trenton; elsewhere, top of Precambrian.

the basin except at the west margin, where a major fault system marks the border between the basin and the Front Range uplift. Structural relief on the top of Precambrian rocks across this fault system west of Denver is at least 21,000 ft.

Other smaller uplifts limit the basin on the south, east, and north. Of primary importance to this study are the Las Animas arch and the Apishapa uplift, which border the basin on the southeast and south. The area with the thickest potential disposal reservoirs encompasses the southern part of the Denver basin and the flanks of these uplifts.

STRATIGRAPHY

The Denver basin contains sedimentary rocks ranging in age from Cambrian to Recent. With the possible exception of the Silurian, all systems are represented in some part of the basin. Figure 3 is a generalized stratigraphic column. Three cross sections, one north-south (Fig. 4) and two east-west (Fig. 5), depict the stratigraphic section from the Precambrian through the Cretaceous Dakota Group. The cross sections are diagrammatic and are presented to show the correlation of major stratigraphic units and to identify the several possible disposal reservoirs.

Rocks of Cambrian through Mississippian age are present in the northern and southern parts of the basin; they are absent in the central part on the early and middle Paleozoic positive feature, Siouxia (Martin, 1965). Devonian rocks probably are limited to a small area around Colorado Springs (Rothrock, 1960, p. 20). Lower and middle Paleozoic strata have a maximum thickness in the basin of about 900 ft on the southeast margin

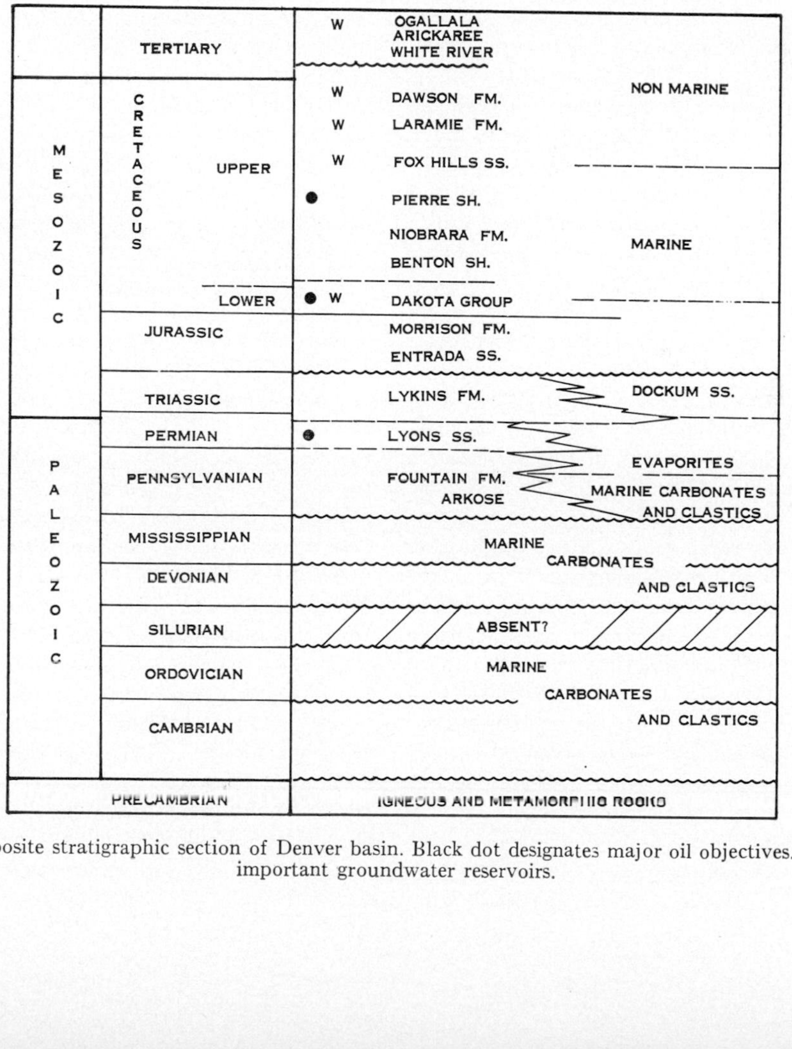

	TERTIARY		W	OGALLALA ARICKAREE WHITE RIVER
MESOZOIC	CRETACEOUS	UPPER	W	DAWSON FM. — NON MARINE
			W	LARAMIE FM.
			W	FOX HILLS SS.
			●	PIERRE SH.
				NIOBRARA FM. — MARINE
				BENTON SH.
		LOWER	● W	DAKOTA GROUP
	JURASSIC			MORRISON FM.
				ENTRADA SS.
	TRIASSIC			LYKINS FM. — DOCKUM SS.
PALEOZOIC	PERMIAN		●	LYONS SS.
	PENNSYLVANIAN			FOUNTAIN FM. ARKOSE — EVAPORITES / MARINE CARBONATES AND CLASTICS
	MISSISSIPPIAN			MARINE CARBONATES
	DEVONIAN			AND CLASTICS
	SILURIAN			ABSENT?
	ORDOVICIAN			MARINE CARBONATES
	CAMBRIAN			AND CLASTICS
PRECAMBRIAN				IGNEOUS AND METAMORPHIC ROCKS

FIG. 3.—Composite stratigraphic section of Denver basin. Black dot designates major oil objectives. *W* designates important groundwater reservoirs.

TABLE I. IDENTIFICATION OF POINTS ON CROSS SECTIONS (FIGS. 4, 5)

No.	Operator and Well	Loc.	Sec.	T.	R.	County	State
1	Baker and Taylor Drlg. No. 1 LeSage	SE SE	2	33S	60W	Las Animas	Colo.
2	Skelly No. 1 Busch	NE NE	30	26S	63W	Huerfano	Colo.
3	Continental No. 1 Young	SW SE	11	19S	65W	Pueblo	Colo.
4	Milton Peterson No. 1 Lewis	NW NW	23	14S	65W	El Paso	Colo.
5	J. S. Abercrombie No. 1 State	NW SW	16	8S	67W	Douglas	Colo.
6	U. S. Army Corps of Engineers No. 1 Rocky Mountain Arsenal	NW NE	26	2S	67W	Adams	Colo.
7	California Co. No. 1 UPRR-Ferch	SE NE	27	8N	66W	Weld	Colo.
8	California Co. No. 1 King	NW SW	13	13N	68W	Laramie	Wyo.
9	Seabord Oil No. 1 Wilson	SE SW	29	25N	65W	Platte	Wyo.
10	General Petroleum No. 45-32-P Van Tassel	NE NE SW	32	30N	60W	Goshen	Wyo.
11	Outcrop section, Owl Canyon (McKee, 1957)		11	9N	70W	Larimer	Colo.
12	California Co. No. 1 Meyer	SW SE SW	19	8N	68W	Larimer	Colo.
13	British American No. 1 Wise	SW NW	19	8N	61W	Weld	Colo.
14	Anderson–Pritchard No. 1 Blanchard	SE NE	11	6N	55W	Morgan	Colo.
15	Shell Oil No. 1 Olsen	SE NE	21	4N	48W	Yuma	Colo.
16	Shell Oil No. 1 Kinnie	SW NE	1	4N	43W	Yuma	Colo.
17	Outcrop section near Buelah (McKee, 1957)		2	23S	68W	Pueblo	Colo.
18	Pan American No. 1 Ingham	NE SE	4	20S	67W	Pueblo	Colo.
19	Stoddard No. 1 Wright	SE NE	11	20S	58W	Crowley	Colo.
20	Stanolind No. 1 Lamberson	SE SE	7	20S	52W	Kiowa	Colo.
21	Harrington No. 1-A Baughman Farms	NW SE	19	20S	47W	Kiowa	Colo.
22	Snee and Eberly No. 1 Bothwell	SW SW	31	20S	42W	Kiowa	Colo.

(Rold, 1961, p. 148) and thicken southeastward across the Las Animas arch into the Anadarko basin of southwest Kansas and Oklahoma. The rocks are mainly carbonate, locally porous, and include some beds of sandstone and shale.

The Pennsylvanian System lies on a profound erosion surface which truncates all older rocks. In large areas of the basin Pennsylvanian rocks lie directly on the Precambrian. Along the west margin of the basin, Pennsylvanian and Permian rocks are composed mainly of red clastic material (Fountain Formation, Lyons Sandstone and equivalents). In the southern part of the basin, near Colorado Springs, this redbed section has a maximum thickness of about 5,000 ft (Wilson, 1958, p. 72; Martin, 1965, p. 1919). The redbeds grade northeastward into a carbonate section generally about 2,000 ft thick in the northeastern corner of Colorado (Taylor, 1958, p. 65; Martin, 1965, p. 1919). At the top of this carbonate section is a Permian evaporitic sequence that reaches a maximum thickness of about 1,500 ft in the western part of the Nebraska Panhandle and the northeastern corner of Colorado. This evaporite sequence contains the only significant salt deposit in the basin. The salt is locally 500 ft thick at depths of 5,000–8,000 ft. In the western part of the basin, Permian and Triassic redbeds constitute a conformable sequence, whereas in the southeastern part the Permian-Triassic contact is unconformable.

The Fountain Formation was investigated carefully because it has been suggested as a possible disposal reservoir. Few exploratory wells penetrate the entire Fountain section except in the southern part of the basin, where pre-Fountain carbonate reservoirs are present. Analysis of drill cuttings and electric logs indicates that sandstone and conglomerate beds in the Fountain are generally poorly sorted and have low porosity. Relatively thin (20 ft or less), lenticular, porous sandstone beds with an aggregate thickness of as much as 100 ft have been penetrated in a few wells, but sparse control causes difficulty in projecting these data. Abundant clay matrix in these porous beds implies that permeability is low.

Triassic rocks, mostly redbeds, have a maximum thickness of about 700 ft in the northwest part and 600 ft in the southeast part of the basin (McKee et al., 1959). Triassic rocks are absent from most of the east flank of the basin because of Late Triassic and Early Jurassic erosion. The Jelm Formation is at the top of the system along the northwest edge of the basin. Because the Jelm is difficult to differentiate in the subsurface from the overlying Entrada Sandstone, the two are treated as one unit and identified as "Entrada" on the cross sections. In the southern part of the basin the Triassic section is called the "Dockum Group." The thick sandstone which constitutes most of the group is herein referred to as the "Dockum sandstone" (informal name) and is essentially equivalent to the "unnamed unit" of Oriel and Mudge (1956, p. 20).

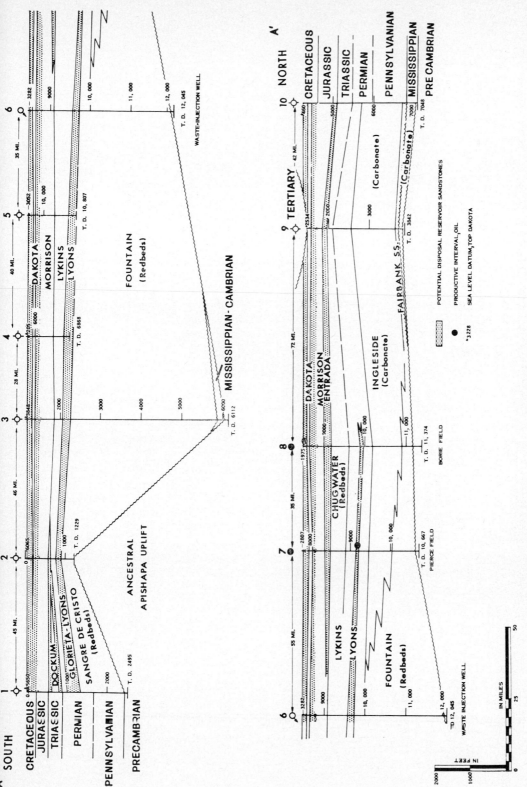

FIG. 4.—South-north cross section *A-A'*, showing major stratigraphic units from Precambrian to top of Dakota Group. See Figure 1 for location of cross section. Points on cross section are identified in Table I.

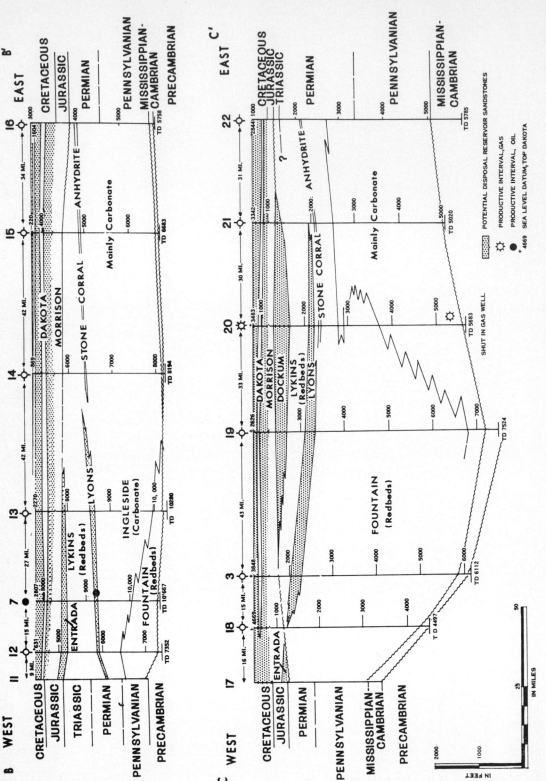

Fig. 5.—West-east cross sections *B-B'* and *C-C'*, showing major stratigraphic units from Precambrian to top of Dakota Group. See Figure 1 for location of cross sections. Points on cross section are identified in Table 1.

Jurassic rocks, 200–500 ft thick in the basin, are generally divisible into a basal sandstone unit, the Entrada Sandstone, and an upper shale unit, the Morrison Formation (McKee *et al.*, 1956). The Entrada Sandstone is present at the southern edge and in the northern part of the basin. In the latter area the Entrada Sandstone and sandstone of the Jelm Formation together make up a sandstone unit averaging about 75 ft in thickness. At the southern edge of the basin the Entrada is thin, generally about 50 ft or less, and lies directly on the Dockum sandstone; differentiation is difficult.

The Morrison Formation is principally shale and claystone but includes thin, lenticular sandstone and carbonate beds. The formation is present throughout the basin and has a maximum thickness of about 500 ft. The Morrison of the Denver basin contains a much lower percentage of sandstone than the Morrison of the San Juan basin. The sandstone beds are lenticular and generally thin, and are unsuitable for use as disposal reservoirs.

The Cretaceous System comprises most of the sedimentary rocks in the basin and has a maximum thickness of about 10,000 ft along the basin axis (Haun and Weimer, 1960, p. 61). The Cretaceous rocks are predominantly marine shale, but there is an oil-productive sandstone sequence at the base. In this paper the term "Dakota Group" is used to refer to the entire basal sandstone sequence. The Dakota Group, composed of three or more sandstone units separated by shale units, is 200–600 ft thick within the basin and thickens eastward to about 800 ft in Kansas and central Nebraska. The uppermost sandstone units of the Dakota Group ("D" and "J") are the objectives for most wells drilled for oil and gas in the Denver basin. Reservoir properties and stratigraphic variations which account for oil entrapment also make this unit attractive for waste disposal.

The overlying marine shale section, which has a maximum thickness of about 8,500 ft, is made up of the Benton Shale, Niobrara Formation (calcareous shale and thin beds of limestone), and Pierre Shale. The Pierre contains several sandstone members, collectively called the "Hygiene zone" (Nolte, 1963; Scott and Cobban, 1959).

Overlying the Pierre Shale are the Fox Hills Sandstone and the Laramie, Arapahoe, and Den-

ver Formations, remnants of which are preserved mainly along the axis of the basin. The Fox Hills Sandstone, 100–200 ft thick, has fair to good porosity and is generally at a rather shallow depth (less than 2,000 ft). It is present only in the more heavily populated part of the basin, where it is a source of groundwater. For this reason it is not considered as a potential disposal reservoir.

The Laramie Formation, 700–1,000 ft thick near Denver, is composed of sandstone and claystone, and has commercially important coal seams in the lower part. The Arapahoe Formation is pebble conglomerate and sandstone, about 400 ft thick. The Denver Formation, about 100 ft thick, is principally claystone, mudstone, and arkosic sandstone, but includes some beds of conglomerate. Both the Arapahoe and Denver Formations of the Denver area grade southward into the Dawson Arkose, which is 500–3,000 ft thick in the area of Castle Rock about midway between Denver and Colorado Springs. The Cretaceous-Tertiary boundary is within the Denver and Dawson strata. The Paleocene Green Mountain Conglomerate, at least 600 ft thick, lies on the Denver Formation in the area west of Denver.

Oligocene, Miocene, and Pliocene sedimentary rocks are widespread in the northern and eastern parts of the basin, and unconformably onlap all older rocks. These middle to late Tertiary rocks are principally claystone, mudstone, and sandstone, but include some conglomerate and volcanic debris. In the Nebraska Panhandle these rocks are about 1,800 ft thick. In the area east of Denver they are about 500 ft thick.

OIL AND GAS

Oil first was discovered in the Denver basin in 1862 in a shallow well drilled near an oil seep on Oil Creek (T.17S., R.70W.) about 6 mi north of Canon City, Fremont County, Colorado (Brainerd and Van Tuyl, 1954). In 1876 oil was discovered in fractured zones in the Pierre Shale at a depth of 1,187 ft in a well drilled near the present site of Florence (T.19S., R.69W.), several miles southeast of the Oil Creek discovery. These wells marked the discovery of the Florence–Canon City field, which is still on production and had produced about 14.5 million bbl of oil at the end of 1964.

Oil and gas fields of the Denver basin had

yielded a cumulative total of about 458 million bbl of oil and about 506 billion cu ft of gas by the end of 1963. About 97 percent of the oil came from sandstone beds in the Dakota Group, and 3 percent came from the Lyons Sandstone and other reservoirs. During 1963 oil production from Denver basin fields was about 39 million bbl.

Oil and gas pools at the east margin of the Denver basin (Figs. 1, 2) are localized in stratigraphic traps in sandstone beds in the upper part of the Dakota Group. These stratigraphic traps consist of porous lenticular bodies of sandstone which pinch out laterally into shale or sandy shale. Many fields have been discovered and developed in the last 15 years.

Oil and gas fields on the west flank of the basin are concentrated in a relatively narrow band. The fields are on distinct north- or northeast-trending anticlines, many of which can be mapped by surface geologic methods. The main reservoirs are the Dakota Group sandstone beds and the Lyons Sandstone.

OTHER MINERAL RESOURCES

Sand and gravel deposits along the larger drainage systems are major sources of building material and groundwater. Shale suitable as raw material for lightweight aggregate is present in Cretaceous rocks. Limy units within this section are quarried for cement rock. Along the west margin of the basin, several units in the section are sources of subbituminous coal, fireclay, gypsum, dimension stone, and limestone for sugar refining and metallurgical uses.

Coal is third in value among the mineral resources in Colorado, and in this resource the state ranks eleventh nationally. The principal sources of coal are the Upper Cretaceous Laramie Formation, which is present in outcrop or at shallow depth along the axis of the basin, and the Upper Cretaceous Vermejo Formation, which is present in a relatively small area in the Canon City embayment. Mining operations, mainly underground, are conducted in the Canon City area and in the Boulder-Weld County coal field north of Denver.

WATER RESOURCES

Surface water.—In the central and northern part of the Denver basin, surface-water resources are derived mainly from the watersheds of the North and South Platte Rivers. Both of these streams originate in the mountainous area west of Denver, where average annual runoff is approximately 5 in., compared to the 0.25–0.5 in. on the High Plains of the Denver basin. The Arkansas River watershed furnishes most of the surface-water resources in the southern part of the Denver basin. Its headwaters are in the mountainous area west of Pueblo.

Much of the water contained in these major streams is committed to use by other states by interstate compacts. Most of the rest is committed to local irrigation and municipal uses. Water is being added to the Arkansas and South Platte River drainage systems from Colorado's Western Slope by a series of dams which divert waters, originally flowing westward, through tunnels beneath the Continental Divide and into the drainage systems of the Denver basin area.

Groundwater.—The principal aquifers in the Denver basin are the Pliocene Ogallala Formation and Recent unconsolidated alluvial sand and gravel in the North Platte, South Platte, and Arkansas River drainages. Primarily on the basis of age of aquifers, the Colorado part of the Denver basin is divisible into five groundwater areas (Odell and Coffin, 1964)—the South Platte River basin, the Arkansas River basin, the High Plains area, the Arkansas Valley artesian area, and the Denver artesian basin. In the first two areas, the aquifers are valley-fill deposits; in the latter three, the aquifers are in bedrock.

In the Arkansas and South Platte River basins, the chief aquifer is the valley-fill deposits along these rivers and their principal tributaries. Utilization of groundwater has reached a high level in these areas, principally for irrigation but also for municipal and industrial needs. In the High Plains area, between these two drainage basins, the main aquifer is the Ogallala Formation. Precipitation is the only source of water recharge into the Ogallala, because the South Platte and Arkansas Rivers have eroded below the base of the formation. Thus the Ogallala, potentially a vast water-storage reservoir, is only partly filled.

The Arkansas Valley artesian area covers most of the region south of the Arkansas River, overlapping the southern part of the Arkansas River basin. The principal artesian aquifers are sandstone beds in the Dakota Group. Because of regional dip and topography, sandstone beds of the Dakota Group are generally at a depth of 1,000 ft or more (Fig. 6) north of the Arkansas River (Fig. 1), and probably contain saline water (Odell and Coffin, 1964, p. 269). The river marks the approximate northern limit of drilling to this aquifer. Water is used primarily for municipal and irrigation purposes.

The Denver artesian basin centers about the structurally low area around Denver. The basin extends about 50 mi north and east of Denver and about 75 mi south of Denver, and overlaps parts of the South Platte River basin and High Plains areas. The principal aquifers are sandstone and conglomerate beds in the Fox Hills Sandstone, the Arapahoe and Denver Formations, and the Dawson Arkose. Water is used for rural domestic, stock, and municipal purposes. These aquifers have been pumped for more than 80 years, and local depression of the piezometric surface of as much as 600 ft has been recorded.

POTENTIAL DISPOSAL RESERVOIRS

The main consideration in evaluating the disposal potential of several Denver basin sandstone reservoirs is isolation of the waste to prevent contamination of natural resources such as coal, gas and oil, and potable groundwater. A secondary consideration is economic—drilling depths and costs must be within a reasonable range. Drilling depths considered are between 1,000 and 5,000 ft, the former the maximum depth to which water wells now are drilled and the latter a tentative maximum disposal depth based on economic factors. Any porous reservoir at a depth of 1,000 ft or less is considered a potential groundwater source. Figure 6 is a drilling-depth map showing depth from the ground surface to the top of the Dakota Group.

In the large central part of the basin, all potential disposal reservoirs are at depths much greater than 1,000 ft. On the east flank of the basin a large area is eliminated from consideration for waste disposal because of active exploration for oil and gas (Fig. 1). The northern and southern parts of the basin are not explored actively for oil and gas,[4] and they contain reservoirs at desir-

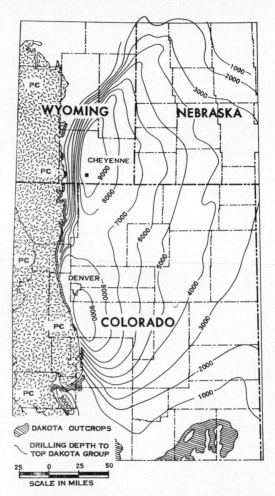

FIG. 6.—Drilling-depth map, showing depth from ground surface to top of Dakota Group.

able depths. Emphasis is placed on the southern part because of the presence there of more potential disposal reservoirs.

Consideration is given to three types of subsurface-disposal reservoirs—fractured Precambrian rock, porous sandstone, and hydraulically fractured shale.

---

[4] Although the Mississippian oil reservoir at Brandon field (T. 19 S., R. 45 W., Kiowa County, Colorado) was found in 1965, the full impact of this discovery was not apparent until after this paper was submitted. Because oil exploratory activity has since increased markedly along the Las Animas arch, statements in the text regarding the low level of activity in this area are no longer true. G.S.G. (April 25, 1968).

FRACTURED PRECAMBRIAN ROCKS

Rocky Mountain Arsenal disposal well.—At the Rocky Mountain Arsenal near Denver, fractured Precambrian gneiss at a depth of about 12,000 ft has been used as a disposal reservoir for toxic chemical wastes. Beginning in 1942, toxic effluent from chemical plants at the arsenal was collected in surface evaporating ponds, but the effluent seeped into shallow aquifers and contaminated groundwater supplies of the surrounding area (Scopel, 1964). The problem became acute in 1960, and a large, sealed, earthen reservoir for collection and evaporation of the effluent was constructed. However, accumulation exceeded evaporation to the extent that the reservoir would have been filled to capacity by late 1961. It was decided to attempt to dispose of the toxic waste in a deep porous reservoir (Mechem and Garrett, 1963).

In 1961 an injection well was drilled to a depth of 12,045 ft (well No. 6 on Figs. 1, 4, 8, 9). Sandstone beds in the Dakota Group were penetrated between 8,485 and 8,786 ft; they have very low porosity and permeability and therefore no merit for waste injection.

The Lyons Sandstone and the upper part of the Fountain Formation (from 9,582 to 10,402) have very low matrix porosity but fair to good fracture porosity. Lost circulation during drilling operations indicated that the rock in this interval probably would be a good injection reservoir; however, no injection tests were made. The several other porous sandstone reservoirs discussed in a succeeding section of this paper are not developed in the arsenal well.

Fractured Precambrian gneiss was penetrated from 11,990 ft to the total depth of 12,045 ft. Drill-stem testing indicated that this was the most favorable disposal reservoir. An injection test developed an injection rate of 400 gal/min at less than 2,000 psi surface pressure.

From the start of injection in March 1962 through June 1965, about 130 million gal of waste was injected. The injection rate has ranged from 26.5 to 300 gal/min, and injection pressure has ranged from 50 to 1,000 psig, both depending on demands put on the system. During the period from October 1963 to mid-September 1964 (11½ months), evaporation from the sealed surface reservoir handled effluent output, and the injection well was not in use. The effluent contains a very minor amount of toxic constituent and is essentially similar to water in physical characteristics.

Waste injection at the arsenal well has been stopped pending investigation of the theory proposed by Evans (1966) that there may be a direct relationship between Denver-area earthquakes and the injection of waste. After several decades of quiescence, earthquake activity was renewed shortly after injection was begun at the arsenal well. Evans noted the close correlation between frequency and magnitude of quakes and the volume of fluid and injection pressure at the well during the period from early 1962 through late 1965.

Other areas of fractured Precambrian rocks.—Relatively few wells in the Denver basin have penetrated Precambrian rocks, and these have provided little data regarding lithology of the Precambrian rocks (Edwards, 1963). It is possible that suitable fractured reservoirs are more widespread than can be deduced from available data.

Two exploratory borings on the Apishapa uplift penetrated extremely fractured Precambrian rocks. In the J. N. Champlin No. 1 U.S.A. boring (Fig. 7, well B), this zone was penetrated from a depth of 2,045 ft to the total depth of 6,210 ft. The rocks are primarily schist and argillite but include some quartzite. In the Pure Oil No. 1 Warren (Fig. 7, well A), weathered and fractured granitic and metamorphic rocks were penetrated from a depth of 2,594 ft to the total depth of 4,263 ft. Extensive fracturing has produced fair to excellent secondary porosity in the Precambrian in well B, as indicated by drill-stem tests. Two drill-stem tests in this well, at approximate depths of 5,200 and 6,000 ft, each recovered more than 2,000 ft of water. No drill-stem tests were run on well A. The areal extent of fracturing is impossible to determine because no other nearby well penetrated deeply enough into the Precambrian. The fractured zone found by these borings may be part of a major fault zone bordering the ancestral Apishapa uplift, a positive feature during deposition of the Fountain Formation and equivalents in adjacent basins.

Containment of liquid waste in the fractured

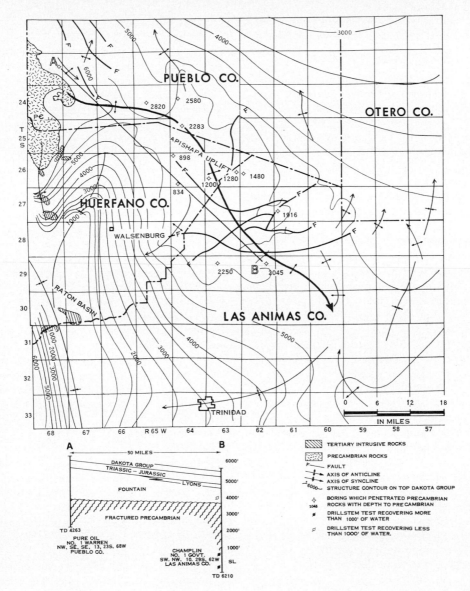

FIG. 7.—Structural contour map, Apishapa uplift; contours of top of Dakota Group (from Doeringsfeld, Amuedo, and Ivey, 1956). Cross section shows two wells that penetrated fractured Precambrian rocks. See Figure 2 for location of map area.

Precambrian reservoir would be afforded by impervious beds in the overlying Fountain Formation. The Fountain is red sandstone, siltstone, and mudstone with generally low porosity and permeability. Porous sandstone beds are present in places at or near the base of the formation, but

impervious mudstone and siltstone beds should be an effective barrier to vertical migration of fluids.

POROUS SANDSTONE

Lyons Sandstone.—The Lyons Sandstone of Permian age extends as a broad, elongate sheet from southeastern Wyoming and the southwestern part of the Nebraska Panhandle on the north, southward along the axial part of the Denver basin into northern New Mexico. Along the Colorado–New Mexico border the equivalent formation is called the "Glorieta Sandstone," and is traceable throughout northern New Mexico.

The Lyons crops out along the Front Range uplift from the Colorado-Wyoming border southward to the north end of the Canon City embayment just west of Pueblo. From that point southward to the southern end of the Raton basin in northern New Mexico, the Lyons-Glorieta does not reach as far west as the outcrop area of Permian rocks.

The Lyons lies conformably on the Fountain Formation. In places the lower part of the Lyons Sandstone intertongues with the Fountain Formation. Toward its eastern periphery the Lyons thins, becomes finer grained, and grades into a siltstone, shale, and evaporite section. On the west it appears to grade into the Fountain Formation (Fig. 5). The Lyons is overlain conformably by the Permian-Triassic Lykins Formation, 300–500 ft thick, composed of red shale and siltstone, evaporite, and carbonate.

The Lyons is a generally quartzose sandstone ranging from red to white, with fine to coarse, well-sorted grains. Cements include silica, anhydrite, and calcite; silica is the most common. Hubert (1960) gives a detailed discussion of the petrology of the Lyons in its outcrop area. Sedimentary features characteristic of beach deposition are prevalent in the Lyons in its outcrop area (Thompson, 1949) and are known in the subsurface from cores. Along and close to the outcrop, porous beds are generally discontinuous. Eastward in the subsurface the Lyons becomes more porous, having as much as 20 percent porosity in places.

Figure 8 shows the thickness and extent of the Lyons and the net thickness of porous sandstone in the Lyons in the southern half of the Denver basin. More than 200 ft of porous sandstone is present in a band extending southeastward from Colorado Springs to the New Mexico border. Individual porous sandstone units are as much as 100 ft thick. The Lyons thins gradually eastward, but thins abruptly westward as it merges with the Fountain Formation.

Lyons oil production is obtained from closed anticlinal features on the west flank of the basin between Denver and Cheyenne. Shows of oil in the Lyons are rare outside of this area.

Limited data indicate that the Lyons Sandstone reservoir has abnormally low pressure at least locally on the Apishapa uplift. Pressures of less than 50 psi have been recorded at a depth of 1,100 ft in wells at Model dome (T. 29 S., R. 60 W.) and in the vicinity. This pressure is about 10 percent of normal for the depth. The low reservoir pressure is apparently due to lack of recharge area, because the Lyons does not crop out west of the Apishapa uplift (Fig. 8). The Lyons reservoir in this large, structurally high area should be an excellent disposal reservoir, especially if abnormally low pressure proves to be of wide extent.

Except in a narrow band along the outcrop area and in places on the Apishapa uplift, the Lyons Sandstone is at a depth greater than 1,000 ft. Depth to the Lyons can be estimated from Figure 6 by adding amounts ranging from approximately 700 ft (Apishapa uplift) to 1,000 ft (central basin area) to Dakota depths. There is no record of use of the Lyons as a source of groundwater, except possibly locally along the outcrop belt.

Dockum sandstone.—The Dockum sandstone (Late Triassic) extends northward into the southeastern part of the Denver basin. It forms the northern lobe of a much larger body of clastic rocks present in eastern New Mexico and the Oklahoma and Texas Panhandles (McKee *et al,* 1959, Pl. 4). Strata of the Dockum Group crop out in places on the Apishapa uplift in southeastern Colorado (Fig. 9).

The grains of the Dockum sandstone range from silt to conglomerate size. The sandstone grades from buff to light orange to red. Clay is the principal cement, but there is some silica. Porosity, as estimated from visual examination of drill cuttings, ranges locally up to 20 percent. No cores or drill-stem tests and no shows of oil are recorded in any of the borings drilled for oil and gas.

The Dockum has a maximum thickness of about 600 ft in southeast Colorado. Net sandstone thickness ranges up to 500 ft (Fig. 9). Indi-

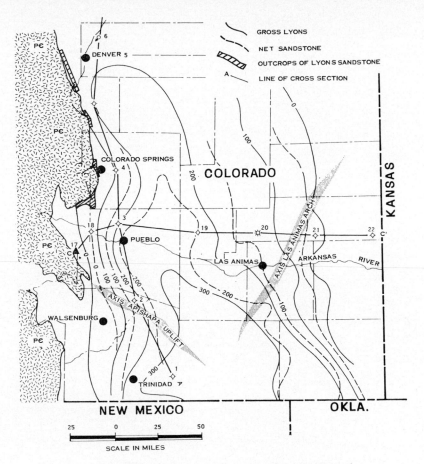

FIG. 8.—Isopach map, Lyons Sandstone, southeastern Colorado.
Dashed lines denote thickness of porous sandstone.

vidual sandstone beds are commonly more than 100 ft thick. Shale and silty beds are more common near the base of the Dockum.

The Dockum lies conformably on a Permian redbed and evaporite unit about 300 ft thick. Northward, the Dockum thins and this subjacent unit thickens and becomes recognizable as the Permian-Triassic Lykins Formation (Fig. 4). The Dockum is overlain unconformably by varicolored shale of the Morrison Formation, 150–300 ft thick. The east margin of the Dockum sandstone was formed by erosional truncation during pre-Morrison uplift. Thin (less than 50 ft) irregular patches of Entrada sandstone, difficult to distinguish lithologically from the Dockum, lie directly on it in places and are included with the Dockum in this report.[5]

The only hydrologic data on the Dockum are those collected by the U.S. Geological Survey at a boring in Sec. 27, T. 23 S., R. 52 W., 3 mi south of Las Animas, Colorado (Fig. 9), which was drilled specifically to test the water-bearing capacity of the Dockum reservoir (Koopman, Irwin, and Jenkins, 1962). Pump tests yielded at best only 7 gal/min of brackish water (5,200 ppm total solids), and indicated low porosity and per-

[5] Thin remnants of the Entrada Sandstone in the southern part of the basin are included in the "Dockum sandstone" as mapped on Figure 9.

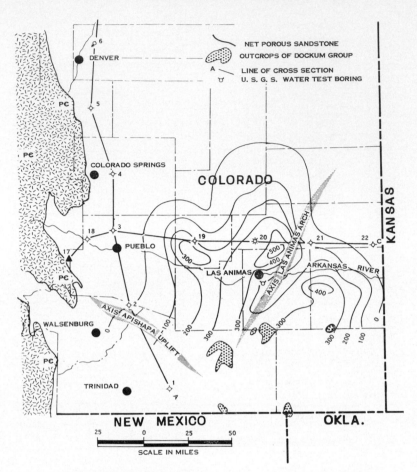

FIG. 9.—Isopach map of net Dockum sandstone, southeastern Colorado.

meability. The reservoir is thicker and has better porosity a few miles farther north (Fig. 9).

There is no record of use of the Dockum as a source of groundwater in the Denver basin part of southeast Colorado. However, the Dockum is tapped for groundwater in the southeasternmost corner of the state in the Anadarko basin. Depth to the Dockum can be estimated from Figure 6 by adding approximately 500 ft to the Dakota depths.

At its deepest northwest extremity, the Dockum sandstone is slightly less than 4,000 ft below ground surface. Shallow depth and great reservoir volume make it an attractive potential disposal reservoir.

Jelm-Entrada sandstone.—A clastic unit which may be partly Late Triassic and partly Late Jurassic in age is present in the northwestern part of the Denver basin along the Front Range and Laramie uplifts. The lower part of this unit has been called the "Jelm Formation" and the upper part has been called the "Entrada Sandstone." Both are predominantly sandstone in this area. The unconformity between the two is difficult to recognize, particularly in the subsurface. The separation of the two is based necessarily on subtle lithologic differences, because no fossils of Late Triassic age have been reported from the basal part of the unit in this area (McKee *et al.,* 1959, p. 16). For the purpose of this report, the two are treated as one stratigraphic unit and identified as the "Entrada Sandstone" on Figures 4 and 5.

The Jelm-Entrada unit is composed of sandstone and some siltstone grading from buff to orange to red. The finer grained rocks and darker hues are more typical of the lower or Jelm part of the unit. Porosity generally is higher in the upper or Entrada part of the unit.

The Jelm-Entrada sandstone lies disconformably on the Late Permian and Early Triassic Lykins Formation and equivalents, which are principally red siltstone and shale. Because the Jelm is more restricted in areal distribution than the Entrada (McKee et al., 1959, Pl. 4), the latter is in direct contact with the Lykins in a large area; the Jelm-Entrada unit is overlain with apparent conformity by the Morrison Formation and equivalents. On the north the Entrada grades into siltstone and shale of the Sundance Formation (Curtis, 1963, p. 114).

Figure 10 is an isopach map of net Jelm-Entrada sandstone. In the area along the Colorado-Wyoming border, most of the sandstone is the lower or Jelm part of the unit. In the northern and southern areas, most of the sandstone is the upper or Entrada part.

Shows of oil have been reported from the Entrada Sandstone in a few wells. Most of the shows are in a narrow belt close to the Front Range and Hartville uplifts. The Lyons Sandstone and Dakota Group sandstone units are oil-productive from several structural traps in the area, but there is no record of commercial production from the Entrada. Exploratory activity is low to moderate in the area.

Figure 10 shows that sandstone in the Jelm-Entrada unit is generally thickest near the outcrop, where the unit would be at a shallow depth. Depth to the Jelm-Entrada can be estimated from Figure 6 by adding approximately 600 ft to the Dakota Group depths. There is no record of use of the Jelm-Entrada as a groundwater source, except possibly locally along the outcrop belt.

The Jelm-Entrada unit is considered to be a potential disposal reservoir because it is not a prime target for oil exploration. There is some exploratory interest in the Lyons in the area between Denver and Cheyenne, and wells drilled to that objective will pass through the Jelm-Entrada. This factor must be considered carefully in the selection of sites for disposal in the Jelm-En-

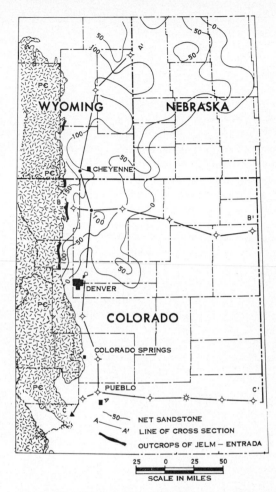

Fig. 10.—Isopach map of net Jelm-Entrada sandstone.

trada reservoir. A disadvantage of this reservoir in this area is drilling depth—more than 5,000 ft except in a rather narrow band close to the outcrop. In northwestern Nebraska, the Jelm-Entrada is at depths of less than 5,000 ft. In that area, it offers a good disposal reservoir below zones generally penetrated in oil and gas exploration.

Dakota Group.—Within the Denver basin the Dakota Group (Early Cretaceous and early Late Cretaceous) is composed of three or more sandstone units separated by shale. In general the sequence of lithologic units is: a basal nonmarine sandstone overlain disconformably by a marine to transitional sandstone, which is overlain by at least one, and in parts of the basin three, marine to transitional sandstone units and intervening marine shale beds. Because of intensive exploration for oil and gas in the upper sandstone units, several systems of terminology have been used for the Dakota strata; usage of some terms was extended from surrounding regions. Haun (1963) and MacKenzie (1963) provide a more complete discussion of terminology.

The Dakota Group averages about 400 ft in thickness in the basin and thickens gradually eastward to a maximum of about 800 ft in parts of Kansas and central Nebraska. Associated with this eastward thickening is an increase in sandstone in the group from 40–50 percent in the basin to almost 100 percent in the latter area. The increase in sandstone percentage clearly indicates an eastern source of clastic material, although a western source is recognized for parts of the Dakota Group in the southwestern part of the basin (Haun, 1963, p. 122).

Dakota Group sandstone is quartzose, buff to gray, very fine to coarse grained, and locally conglomeratic. Clay and silica are predominant cements. Crossbedding and ripple marks are common. Coal and lignitic beds are present, and animal tracks and burrows are the most common fossils. Individual sandstone beds are generally lenticular and grade abruptly, both vertically and laterally, into siltstone and shale. The sandstone lentils have excellent reservoir characteristics.

The basal nonmarine sandstone unit lies conformably on, and in places interfingers with, the Morrison Formation. This unit is characterized by channel and floodplain sandstone bodies, commonly conglomeratic and having good porosity and permeability. The sandstone bodies are more than 100 ft thick in places, but probably are of limited areal extent. The disconformity at the top of the basal unit marks the surface over which Early Cretaceous seas transgressed, depositing the overlying marine to transitional sandstone unit (MacKenzie, 1963, p. 146). The upper sandstone units interfinger with the overlying Benton Shale and its equivalents. These upper units are tongues of sandstone which project westward from the main body of Dakota Group sandstone into the marine embayment which trends northward through the Denver basin area.

Most of the Denver basin oil and gas is produced from stratigraphic traps in these upper sandstone units. Abrupt lateral and vertical facies changes, good reservoir beds, and proximity to source rocks create an excellent habitat for oil and gas. Oil and gas fields productive from the upper sandstone units are concentrated in a broad area in the central part of the east flank of the basin (Fig. 1). Many exploratory wells in the southern part of the basin have recorded shows of oil but no production from equivalent rocks. Exploratory drilling now is being done only sporadically in this southern area and primarily for sub-Dakota objectives, most commonly Pennsylvanian and lower Paleozoic carbonate reservoirs.

Figure 11 is an isopach map of net porous sandstone in the Dakota Group in the southern part of the Denver basin and surrounding uplifts. The contour pattern outlines a series of irregular "thicks" and "thins." A maximum of more than 200 ft of porous sandstone is present in certain areas. The average thickness of individual sandstone beds is 10–20 ft, but beds more than 100 ft thick are present in places.

The Dakota Group crops out in a narrow band along the west margin of the basin and in broad areas on the Apishapa uplift (Fig. 11). In and adjacent to these outcrop areas, the Dakota is an important source of groundwater, especially on the north flank of the Apishapa uplift—the Arkansas Valley artesian area. Because 1,000 ft is the maximum depth to which water wells now are drilled and the depth below which Dakota water becomes increasingly saline, the line on Figure 6 showing a depth of 1,000 ft is considered to mark the southern limit of the area in which the Dakota Group is a potential disposal reservoir.

The Dakota Group in the southern part of the basin is very attractive as a disposal reservoir because it is in an area of little oil-industry activity, it is at moderate to shallow depth, and it offers thick, porous reservoir beds.

Hygiene zone of Pierre Shale.—The middle part of the Pierre Shale in the western part of the Denver basin contains several sandstone units (Campanian age) which are equivalent to parts

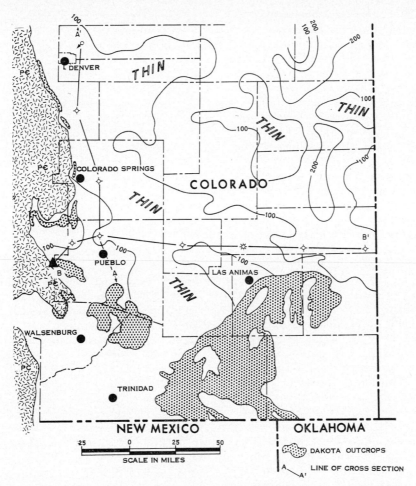

FIG. 11.—Isopach map of net porous sandstone in Dakota Group, southeastern Colorado.

of the Mesaverde Group of northwestern Colorado. These sandstone units crop out in a narrow band along the Front Range from Denver north to the Colorado-Wyoming boundary. Five sandstone units in this outcrop area have been named formally, in ascending order, the Hygiene, Terry, Rocky Ridge, Larimer, and Richard Sandstone Members of the Pierre Shale. In informal subsurface nomenclature, these sandstone beds and the intervening shale beds are called collectively the "Hygiene zone of the Pierre Shale" (Nolte, 1963, p. 156). Scott and Cobban (1959) give a more complete discussion of terminology.

Along the west flank of the basin the Hygiene

zone is best developed and has a maximum thickness of about 1,700 ft. Eastward in the subsurface the sandstone members become silty and shaly, and eventually grade into the main body of the Pierre Shale. A marine environment of deposition is indicated by both microfossils and megafossils in the sandstone (Dunn, 1959). The distribution of the sandstone units indicates that they are probably tongues of the Mesaverde Group extending into the Denver basin from the west and northwest.

All of the sandstone members are present only in a small area at the west margin of the basin. Over a broad area only one of the members is present. The Hygiene and Richard Sandstone Members extend barely as far east as the axis of the basin.

The Terry Sandstone Member is a narrow, thick sandstone lobe extending southeastward past Denver. The Rocky Ridge and Larimer Sandstone Members combine in the subsurface to make one unit, which is the thickest, most extensive tongue. Both the Terry and Rocky Ridge–Larimer tongues extend about halfway up the east flank of the basin.

The sandstone members are composed of buff to olive-gray, mainly fine-grained sandstone interbedded with gray silty shale. Sorting in the sandstone generally is poor to fair because of abundant clay matrix. Cements are clay and carbonate. Crossbedding is common in some thin beds. Individual sandstone bodies are markedly lenticular.

Shows of oil have been reported from widely scattered wells (Nolte, 1963, p. 158), and a minor quantity of oil has been produced from two small fields on the west flank of the basin (Fig. 12). Very little exploratory drilling is directed specifically toward the Hygiene zone, because generally it is not considered to be a good oil and gas objective. Therefore, there are few quantitative data on this reservoir, although thousands of wells have penetrated it. Good reservoir properties are present at least locally, as evidenced by core analyses and drill-stem tests on a few wells (Nolte, 1963, p. 160).

Figure 12 shows the distribution and net thickness of sandstone in the Hygiene zone. Most of the sandstone is present in the Terry and Rocky Ridge–Larimer Sandstone Members. Individual sandstone beds as thick as 80 ft are known in the Hygiene Sandstone Member, and as thick as 60 ft in the Terry and Rocky Ridge–Larimer Sandstone Members.

Depth to the top of the Hygiene zone can be estimated from Figure 6 by subtracting amounts ranging from 3,700 ft (Cheyenne area) to 4,400 ft (Denver area) from Dakota depths. Except in small areas around Cheyenne and Denver, the Hygiene zone is at depths of less than 5,000 ft.

The Hygiene is the best potential disposal reservoir beneath the heavily populated strip between Denver and Cheyenne. It offers a thick sandstone reservoir at a reasonable depth. There is some oil and gas exploratory activity in the area, and because all oil and gas objectives are beneath the Hygiene zone, exploratory wells will penetrate through it. Thus, the possibility of contamination from the Hygiene in producing areas will be an important factor in the selection of sites for liquid-waste disposal in this reservoir.

HYDRAULICALLY FRACTURED SHALE

A special technique is being developed for use of artificially fractured shale as a host for toxic waste. The waste is mixed in liquid form with a hardening agent such as cement. The mixture is pumped under high pressure down a well bore which is perforated opposite a shale formation that has been prepared in advance by hydraulic fracturing. After the waste mixture is dispersed into the fractures, the mixture hardens and is immobilized in the shale host rock. Thick shale sections at shallow depths are thought to be most desirable for this technique.

Cretaceous shale has a maximum thickness of about 8,500 ft near the axis of the Denver basin. The shale designated "Mu" on Figure 1 crops out in much of the basin and elsewhere is at shallow depth beneath Tertiary rocks. At Denver and Cheyenne the shale is at approximate depths of 1,000 and 2,000 ft, respectively.

The hydraulic-fracturing technique would be a very suitable subsurface waste-disposal method along the heavily populated strip just east of the Front Range, where porous sandstone reservoirs are (1) absent, (2) objectives for oil and gas exploration, (3) at too great a depth, or (4) used as a groundwater source.

CONCLUSIONS

From this reconnaissance study it is apparent that the Denver basin and surrounding uplifts have great potential for disposal of liquid wastes through well bores. Thick shale sections suitable for waste disposal by the hydraulic-fracturing technique are present throughout the basin area at shallow depth. Precambrian rocks with extensive fractured zones are present at reasonable depth on the Apishapa uplift.

For use of porous sandstone reservoirs, the southern part of the Denver basin is emphasized

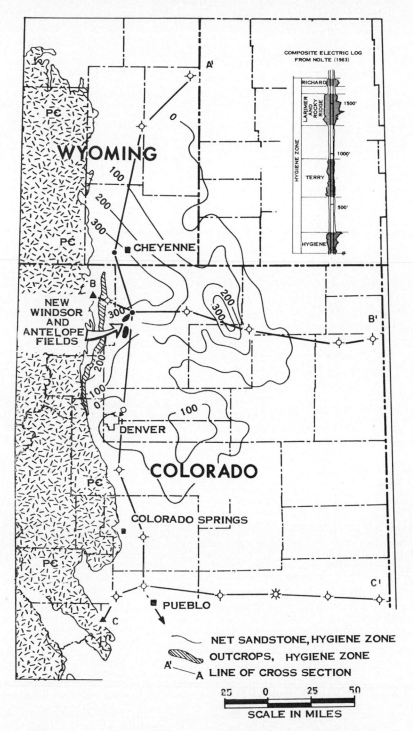

FIG. 12.—Isopach map of net sandstone in Hygiene zone of Pierre Shale.

because it is an area of little exploratory activity for gas and oil, sandstone units are at reasonable depth, more sandstone reservoirs are present, and two potential reservoirs (Lyons Sandstone and Dakota Group sandstones) which are oil and gas objectives in other parts of the basin are not explored actively. An aggregate thickness of more than 1,000 ft of porous sandstone is present.

In general the heavily populated strip close to the Front Range coincides closely with the basin axis. Most of the potential disposal reservoirs crop out in a discontinuous belt along the Front Range. The boundary between the uplift and basin here is a fault zone or monocline along which beds dip steeply eastward. Except in a few places, the band in which the reservoirs are at depths of less than 5,000 ft is very narrow. One exception is the southern end of the populous strip around Pueblo, where all the potential reservoirs are less than 5,000 ft deep. It is here that the relatively heavily populated area coincides with the best potential disposal area.

In the area between Denver and Cheyenne, there are several oil fields and some exploratory activity. The Jelm-Entrada sandstone is at depths of less than 5,000 ft only in a rather narrow band. Sandstone beds in the Hygiene zone of the Pierre Shale, generally at depths of less than 5,000 ft, appear to have the best potential as disposal reservoirs in this area.

BIBLIOGRAPHY

Bass, N. W., 1947, Structure contour map of the surface rocks of the Model anticline, Las Animas County, Colorado: U.S. Geol. Survey Oil and Gas Inv. Prelim. Map 68.
———— 1964, Oil and gas, *in* Mineral and Water Resources of Colorado: U.S. Govt. Printing Office, p. 45–67.
Berg, R. R., 1960, Cambrian and Ordovician history of Colorado, *in* Guide to the geology of Colorado: Rocky Mtn. Assoc. Geologists, p. 10–16.
———— 1962, Subsurface interpretation of Golden fault at Soda Lakes, Jefferson County, Colorado: Am. Assoc. Petroleum Geologists Bull., v. 46, p. 704–707.
Brainerd, A. E., and F. M. Van Tuyl, 1954, A resume of petroleum exploration and exploratory development in Colorado 1862–1954, *in* The oil and gas fields of Colorado: Rocky Mtn. Assoc. Geologists, p. 15–24.
Cobban, W. A., 1956, The Pierre Shale and older Cretaceous rocks in southeastern Colorado, *in* Guidebook to the geology of the Raton basin: Rocky Mtn. Assoc. Geologists, p. 25–27.

Cohee, G. V., chm., 1962, Tectonic map of the United States: U.S. Geol. Survey and Am. Assoc. Petroleum Geologists, 2 sheets, scale 1:2,500,000 (revision of 1944 map).
Curtis, B. F., 1963, Jurassic stratigraphic relationships in the northern Denver basin, *in* Geology of the northern Denver basin and adjacent uplifts: Rocky Mtn. Assoc. Geologists, p. 111–118.
Doeringsfeld, W. W., Jr., C. L. Amuedo, and J. B. Ivey, 1956, Structure contour map of the Raton basin, Colorado, *in* Guidebook to the geology of the Raton basin, Colorado: Rocky Mtn. Assoc. Geologists, map in pocket.
Dunn, H. L., 1959, Sandstones of the Pierre Formation in the Denver basin, *in* Symposium on Cretaceous rocks of Colorado and adjacent areas: Rocky Mtn. Assoc. Geologists, p. 132–136.
Edwards, J., Jr., 1963, Petrography of the basement rocks beneath the Denver basin in Colorado, *in* Geology of the northern Denver basin and adjacent uplifts: Rocky Mtn. Assoc. Geologists, p. 208–210.
Evans, D. M., 1966, The Denver area earthquakes and the Rocky Mountain Arsenal disposal well: Mountain Geologist, v. 3, no. 1, p. 23–36.
Harms, J. C., 1964, Structural history of the southern Front Range: Mountain Geologist, v. 1, p. 93–102.
Haun, J. D., 1963, Stratigraphy of Dakota Group and relationship to petroleum occurrence, northern Denver basin, *in* Geology of the northern Denver basin and adjacent uplifts: Rocky Mtn. Assoc. Geologists, p. 119–134.
———— and R. J. Weimer, 1960, Cretaceous stratigraphy of Colorado, *in* Guide to the geology of Colorado: Rocky Mtn. Assoc. Geologists, p. 58–65.
Hubert, J. F., 1960, Petrology of the Fountain and Lyons Formations, Front Range, Colorado: Colorado School Mines Quart., v. 55, 242 p.
Koopman, F. C., J. H. Irwin, and E. D. Jenkins, 1962, Use of inflatable packers in multiple testing of water wells: U.S. Geol. Survey Prof. Paper 450-B, p. 108–109.
MacKenzie, D. B., 1963, Dakota Group on west flank of Denver basin, *in* Geology of the northern Denver basin and adjacent uplifts: Rocky Mtn. Assoc. Geologists, p. 135–148.
Maher, J. C., 1953, Paleozoic history of southeastern Colorado: Am. Assoc. Petroleum Geologists Bull., v. 37, p. 2475–2489.
———— 1954, Lithofacies and suggested depositional environment of Lyons sandstone and Lykins formation in southeastern Colorado: Am. Assoc. Petroleum Geologists Bull., v. 38, p. 2233–2239.
Mallory, W. W., 1958, Pennsylvanian coarse arkosic redbeds and associated mountains in Colorado, *in* Symposium on Pennsylvanian rocks of Colorado and adjacent areas: Rocky Mtn. Assoc. Geologists, p. 17–20.
Martin, C. A., 1965, Denver basin: Am. Assoc. Petroleum Geologists Bull., v. 49, p. 1908–1925.
McConaghy, J. A., *et al.*, 1964, Hydrogeologic data of the Denver basin, Colorado: Colorado Water Conserv. Board, Basic Data Rept. 15, 224 p.
McCoy, A. W., III, 1953, Tectonic history of Denver basin: Am. Assoc. Petroleum Geologists Bull., v. 37, p. 1873–1893.
McKee, E. D., ed., 1957, Colorado measured sections, a symposium: Rocky Mtn. Assoc. Geologists, 70 p.

——— et al., 1956, Paleotectonic maps of the Jurassic System: U.S. Geol. Survey Misc. Geol. Inv. Map I-175.

——— et al., 1959, Paleotectonic maps of the Triassic System: U.S. Geol. Survey Misc. Geol. Inv. Map I-300.

Mechem, O. T., and J. H. Garrett, 1963, Deep injection disposal well for liquid toxic waste: Am. Soc. Civil Engineers Proc., Jour. Construction Div., p. 111–121.

Murray, H. F., 1957, Stratigraphic traps in Denver basin: Am. Assoc. Petroleum Geologists Bull., v. 41, p. 839–847.

Mygdal, K. A., 1963, Adena—largest field in Denver basin, in Geology of the northern Denver basin and adjacent uplifts: Rocky Mtn. Assoc. Geologists, p. 222–225.

Nolte, C. J., 1963, Potential stratigraphic accumulation of oil and gas in the Upper Cretaceous of the Denver basin, in Geology of the northern Denver basin and adjacent uplifts: Rocky Mtn. Assoc. Geologists, p. 156–161.

Odell, J. W., and D. L. Coffin, 1964, Water resources, in Mineral and water resources of Colorado: U.S. Govt. Printing Office, p. 233–283.

Oriel, S. S., and M. R. Mudge, 1956, Problems of lower Mesozoic stratigraphy in southeastern Colorado, in Guidebook to the geology of the Raton basin, Colorado: Rocky Mtn. Assoc. Geologists, p. 19–24.

Rold, J. W., 1961, The oil and gas potential of the lower and middle Paleozoic rocks of southeast Colorado, in Symposium on lower and middle Paleozoic rocks of Colorado: Rocky Mtn. Assoc. Geologists, p. 147–151.

Rothrock, D. P., 1960, Devonian and Mississippian Systems in Colorado, in Guide to the geology of Colorado: Rocky Mtn. Assoc. Geologists, p. 17–22.

Russell, W. L., 1961, Reservoir water resistivities and possible hydrodynamic flow in Denver basin: Am.

Assoc. Petroleum Geologists Bull., v. 45, p. 1925–1940.

Scopel, L. J., 1964, Pressure injection disposal well, Rocky Mountain Arsenal, Denver, Colorado: Mountain Geologist, v. 1, p. 35–42.

Scott, G. R., 1962, Geology of the Littleton quadrangle, Jefferson, Douglas, and Arapahoe Counties, Colorado: U.S. Geol. Survey Bull. 1121-L, 53 p.

——— and W. A. Cobban, 1959, So-called Hygiene group of northeastern Colorado, in Symposium on Cretaceous rocks of Colorado and adjacent areas: Rocky Mtn. Assoc. Geologists, p. 124–131.

Shaw, G. L., 1956, Subsurface stratigraphy of the Permian-Pennsylvanian beds, Raton basin, Colorado, in Guidebook to the geology of the Raton basin: Rocky Mtn. Assoc. Geologists, p. 14–18.

Smith, J. H., 1964, Geology of the sedimentary rocks of the Morrison quadrangle, Colorado: U.S. Geol. Survey Misc. Geol. Inv. Map I-428.

Tapp, S. C., 1961, Mississippian rocks of eastern Colorado, in Symposium on lower and middle Paleozoic rocks of Colorado: Rocky Mtn. Assoc. Geologists, p. 53–57.

Taylor, J. R., 1958, Pennsylvanian stratigraphy and history of northern Denver basin, in Symposium on Pennsylvanian rocks of Colorado and adjacent areas: Rocky Mtn. Assoc. Geologists, p. 64–68.

Thompson, W. O., 1949, Lyons Sandstone of Colorado Front Range: Am. Assoc. Petroleum Geologists Bull., v. 33, p. 52–71.

Waage, K. M., 1955, Dakota group in northern Front Range foothills, Colorado: U.S. Geol. Survey Prof. Paper 274-B.

——— 1961, Stratigraphy and refractory clayrocks of the Dakota Group along the northern Front Range, Colorado: U.S. Geol. Survey Bull. 1102.

Wilson, J. M., 1958, Stratigraphy and geologic history of the Pennsylvanian sediments of southeastern Colorado, in Symposium on Pennsylvanian rocks of Colorado and adjacent areas: Rocky Mtn. Assoc. Geologists, p. 69–73.

SEDIMENTARY HISTORY AND ECONOMIC GEOLOGY
OF SAN JUAN BASIN, NEW MEXICO AND COLORADO[1]

JAMES A. PETERSON,[2] ALLAN J. LOLEIT,[3] CHARLES W. SPENCER,[4] AND RICHARD A. ULLRICH[3]

Missoula, Montana 59801, and Farmington, New Mexico 87401

ABSTRACT

The San Juan basin contains up to 15,000 ft of sedimentary rocks ranging in age from Cambrian to Recent. Beginning with the Cambrian transgression, at least 10 major events in the sedimentary history of the basin area can be recognized. The earliest development of the area as a sedimentary basin or trough apparently took place in Pennsylvanian time, and the basin was maintained, with changing rates of subsidence and filling, through the remainder of geologic time. During the early Paleozoic, sedimentation was dominated by marine transgressions across the northwestern flank of the regional Transcontinental arch. The late Paleozoic history was strongly influenced by tectonism related to development of the Ancestral Rocky Mountains uplifts and associated downwarping. Dominantly cyclic marine carbonate deposition during the early phases of this event preceded the infilling of the trough with coarse clastics. The early Mesozoic is characterized by fluvial and eolian environments, interrupted periodically by thin marine transgressive deposits of nearshore redbeds. The final Mesozoic event was the widespread Late Cretaceous marine transgression which deposited a thick cyclic sequence of marine gray shale and sandstone, with interbedded coal. Final withdrawal of marine waters in Late Cretaceous time was associated with the rise of major uplifts on the northern and eastern sides of the basin and infilling of the basin area with stream, lacustrine, and paludal deposits during early Tertiary time. Late Tertiary regional uplift and resulting volcanism were accompanied by a regional dissection of the area by stream systems that evolved into the present drainage pattern of superposed streams. The sedimentary history is directly related to the occurrence of economic deposits in the basin. Major reserves of petroleum are in Cretaceous and Pennsylvanian rocks, coal in Cretaceous, and uranium in Jurassic and Cretaceous.

Much of the San Juan basin is considered potentially suitable for waste disposal, contingent upon such factors as depth, volume of waste, petroleum and mining activities, present and future groundwater needs, and other industrial and cultural considerations. The Chaco slope probably is the most favorable area for waste disposal.

INTRODUCTION

The San Juan basin occupies the southernmost part of the Colorado Plateau physiographic province. The topographic expression of the area is related in large part to moderate dissection of the flat Tertiary and uppermost Cretaceous sandstone and shale beds covering most of the basin. Broad plateaus and mesas, intervening steep-sided canyons, and dry arroyos dominate the area. Surface elevation ranges from 5,000 ft near Shiprock to more than 8,000 ft in the mountainous areas on the northern, eastern, and southern sides of the basin.

Except for the irrigated valleys and adjacent slopes, most of the land is government- or Indian-controlled. In the Chaco slope area, for ex-

[1] Manuscript received, June 23, 1965. Reprinted, with revisions, from Am. Assoc. Petroleum Geologists Bull., v. 49, no. 11, p. 2076-2119 (1965).

This report was prepared largely from the work done by a committee of the Four Corners Geological Society, organized in 1960 to expedite the work of the AAPG Research Committee's Subcommittee on Atomic Waste Disposal. The San Juan Basin Committee was composed of the following individuals with varying terms of service: Allan J. Loleit, El Paso Natural Gas Company; Charles W. Spencer, Texaco Inc.; James A. Peterson, chairman, Shell Oil Company; John W. Parker and Richard F. Spencer, Pan American Petroleum Corporation; and Harold H. Brown, consultant. Richard A. Ullrich, El Paso Natural Gas Company, contributed to the report and presented the San Juan basin paper before the Association at Durango, Colorado, September 29, 1964.

The writers gratefully acknowledge the suggestions and critical review of the manuscript by Frank E. Kottlowski and Reuben J. Ross. The committee's work was aided by the cooperation and interest of many local geologists in addition to the committee members. Supplementary data on drill-stem tests, water analyses, and core analyses were supplied by several oil companies actively exploring the basin. Drafting and other expenses in connection with preparation of the report were subsidized in part by the United States Atomic Energy Commission.

[2] University of Montana.

[3] El Paso Natural Gas Company.

[4] Texaco, Inc.

ample, land ownership is approximately as follows: Indian, 50 per cent; railroad, 25 per cent; public domain, 15 per cent; state, 5 per cent; and private, 5 per cent.

Other than farming and ranching, the main industry currently is exploration for and production of oil and gas. Much of the central basin is occupied by the huge Blanco-Dakota gas field (Fig. 6). The intensive drilling and exploratory activity that prevailed during the 1950's has leveled to a slower but steady pace.

REGIONAL GEOLOGIC SETTING

The San Juan basin is one of three prominent structural basins in the Four Corners area of Utah, Colorado, Arizona, and New Mexico. The basin is slightly elongate north-south, about 150 mi in length, and 100 mi in width (Figs. 1, 2). Older rocks are well exposed in many places on the surrounding uplifts (Fig. 2). In the basin is as much as 15,000 ft of sedimentary rocks representing a wide variety of environmental and depositional types.

The basin is bounded on the north by the San Juan–La Plata Mountains, on the east by the Archuleta-Nacimiento uplifts, on the south by the Zuni uplift, and on the west and northwest by the Four Corners platform (Fig. 1). The deepest part of the basin occupies an arcuate belt close to and paralleling its northern and northeastern boundary (Fig. 5). The southern part of the basin is generally called the Chaco slope (Fig. 2), a broad structural shelf sloping gently northeastward into the main confines of the basin. Along the other basin borders, uppermost Cretaceous beds dip steeply into the basin along rather narrow hogback belts adjacent to the enclosing uplifts.

The interior structure of the basin is not complicated by subsidiary folding in the younger beds; in fact, the overall contour of the basin slope is remarkably gentle (Fig. 4). Joint patterns of generally random lineament have been mapped through most of the basin. A thorough summary of the basin structure and structural history is presented by Kelley (1957).

Tertiary intrusive rocks are not present in most of the basin. However, in the northeastern corner a north-south-aligned dike swarm occupies an area of about 400 sq mi, and in the Cabezon area in the extreme southeastern part of the basin, an area of 500–600 sq mi contains numerous Tertiary volcanic necks, plugs, dikes, and associated basaltic lava flows.

The earliest development of the basin seems to have occurred during Pennsylvanian time when the area was an elongate northwest-southeast marine sedimentary trough, bounded on the southwest by the ancient Zuni uplift and on the east and north by the Nacimiento–San Luis uplifts (Fig. 9). This general basin shape was maintained through most of the late Paleozoic and Mesozoic Eras. The present shape of the basin is essentially the result of intense Laramide (Late Cretaceous–Tertiary) folding.

ECONOMIC GEOLOGY

The San Juan basin contains large resources of petroleum, coal, uranium, and groundwater. These deposits have been exploited since the early part of the 20th century, but intensive development did not take place until after World War II.

PETROLEUM

The first wildcat well in New Mexico, a dry hole, was drilled in 1907 near Farmington in the northwestern part of the San Juan basin. According to Gregory (1917), the first indication of oil was found in 1911 in a well drilled for water in the Seven Lakes area (Fig. 6) in the southern part of the basin. This well stimulated considerable drilling activity, but although six of the wells had shows of oil or gas in the Mesaverde, none could be produced commercially; by 1913 the field essentially was abandoned.

The next important discovery was in 1921, when gas was produced from Farmington sandstone in a well drilled near Aztec. This well supplied Aztec with gas for several years, but no immediate attempt was made to exploit the discovery because of a lack of market.

Oil and gas were found in the Dakota Sandstone in 1922 at the Hogback and Ute Dome fields (Fig. 6) and in 1925 at Barker Creek. Gas also was found in the Pennsylvanian carbonate section at Rattlesnake. Production of oil was stimulated by local refinery construction and the available

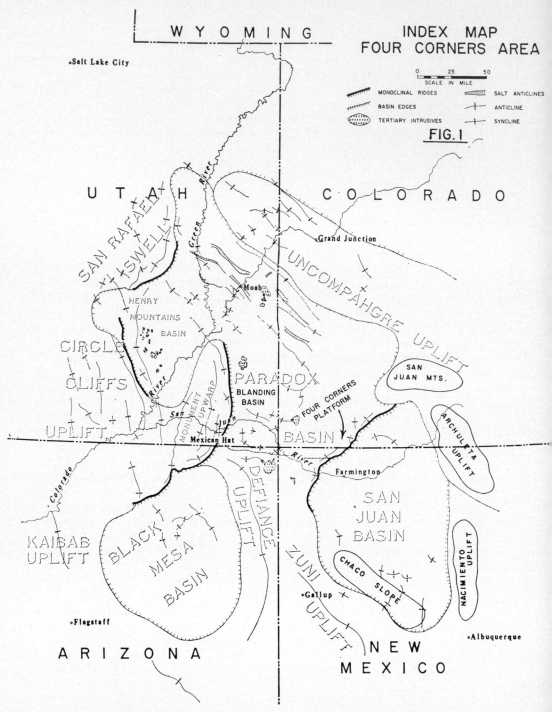

FIG. 1.—Regional index map of Four Corners area showing major uplifts and basins with superimposed minor features.

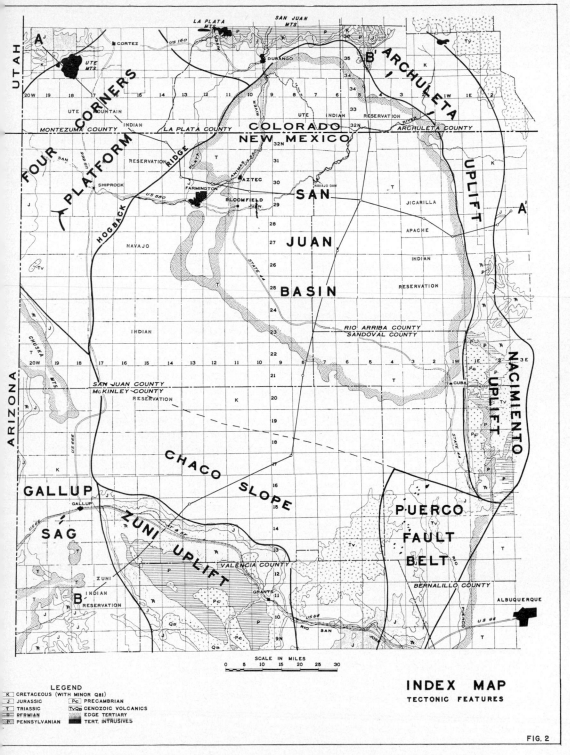

FIG. 2

INDEX MAP
TECTONIC FEATURES

SCALE IN MILES
0 5 10 15 20 25 30

Fig. 2.—Index and geologic outcrop map of San Juan basin with major tectonic features. Positions of cross sections A-A' (Fig. 7) and B-B' (Fig. 8) are shown.

limited transportation facilities, but development of gas reserves was severely curtailed by lack of market until after World War II. A development program began in 1946, but extensive exploration of the Blanco gas field did not begin until 1951, when a gas pipeline to California was built by El Paso Natural Gas Company. Meanwhile other significant discoveries had been made, including gas in the Pennsylvanian at Barker Creek in 1945, minor oil in the Mississippian at Table Mesa in 1951, and oil and gas in the Pennsylvanian at Hogback in 1952. In 1953, noncommercial oil was found in the Entrada Sandstone at the Media field. Development continued rapidly during the 1950's, especially after the Pacific Northwest pipeline was completed in 1955. The San Juan basin area (including the Four Corners platform) now contains 43 oil and 47 gas fields with total cumulative production to January 1, 1964, of approximately 94 million bbl of oil and 3 trillion cu ft of gas. Some of these fields are one-well fields, possible field extensions, or marginal producers. Most of the Cretaceous fields are grouped together as the "Blanco Mesaverde-Basin Dakota" on Figure 6.

On January 1, 1964, there were 8,264 producing wells in the San Juan basin, of which 1,926 were oil wells and 6,338 gas wells, distributed as follows (in descending stratigraphic order).

Producing formation	Oil	Gas
Cretaceous		
Torrejon-Puerco	0	6
Farmington sandstone	6	9
Fruitland Formation	0	49
Pictured Cliffs Sandstone	0	2,797
(incl. Fruitland in Colorado)		
Lewis Shale	0	1
Chacra sandstone	0	41
Mesaverde Group	51	2,301
Gallup Sandstone (incl. Tocito)	1,696	5
Mancos Shale	67	0
Greenhorn Limestone	1	1
Dakota Sandstone	95	1,102
Pennsylvanian		
Paradox Formation	10	23
Total	1,926	6,338

MINING

Mining operations in the San Juan basin mainly have been for coal and uranium. A small open-pit operation now mines gypsum from the Jurassic Todilto Limestone near San Ysidro in the southern part of the basin. Local sand and gravel-pit operations are scattered about the basin for community and highway use.

Coal.—The Cretaceous System of the San Juan basin contains large reserves of coal, mostly sub-bituminous, but some of bituminous quality. Despite the large size of these coal deposits, mining until recently has been confined to small local operations because of low demand. A major coal-stripping project began in 1962 about 15 mi west-southwest of Farmington to supply the Four Corners Power Plant, a large steam electricity generating plant operated by the Arizona Power and Light Company. This plant now is using about 4,200 tons per day of coal from the basal Fruitland Formation (Fig. 3). Additional interest in utilization of the readily accessible strip-coal deposits suggests continued expansion of this activity in the future.

Estimates of coal reserves differ somewhat according to the date and author quoted. Figures given in 1948 listed about 54 billion short tons of original coal reserves in the New Mexico part of the basin. Current estimates based on additional studies since 1948 may be 60 billion tons or more of reserves with less than 3,000 ft of overburden. In the Colorado part of the basin, estimates are listed as 9.646 billion tons (Yingst, 1960). Thus the total for the entire basin is about 70 billion tons.

The largest coal reserves are in the Fruitland and Menefee Formations of the uppermost Cretaceous in the northern part of the basin (Fig. 3). In the southern part of the basin, the Dilco and Gibson Coal Members of the Crevasse Canyon Formation and the Fruitland Formation contain the most important deposits. Minor coal beds also are found in the Dakota, Gallup, and Cliff House Sandstones. Some of them are used locally for domestic needs.

Uranium.—Major deposits of uranium ore have been developed during the past 10 years in the Grants uranium district on the Chaco slope along the southern border of the San Juan basin (Fig. 2). These ores are processed by six operating mills with a total rated capacity of 10,500 tons per day. Total reserves are estimated by the Atomic Energy Commission at 55 billion tons or 63 percent of the U.S. total.

The rise of the uranium mining industry in the Grants uranium district closely parallels that of the oil and gas industry in the northern part of the basin. Both industries underwent their greatest growth in the early 1950's and now are developing at a relatively steady pace.

The major uranium deposits of the Grants area are in the Jurassic and Upper Cretaceous beds of the mineral belt. The Todilto Limestone (lower limestone unit) and the Morrison Formation (sandstones and conglomerates of the Westwater Canyon Sandstone and Brushy Basin Shale Members) (Fig. 3) contain more than 95 percent of the reserves (Hilpert, 1963).

WATER SUPPLY

Most of the San Juan basin is drained by the tributary system of the San Juan River, which flows from northeast to west across the northwestern corner of the basin and into Utah, where it joins the Colorado River (Fig. 1). In general, most of the tributaries entering the main channel from the north are permanent streams draining the San Juan and LaPlata Mountains. Those entering from the south are intermittent streams draining the relatively flat semi-arid central part of the basin. The area southeast of the Continental Divide is drained by the Rio Puerco and Rio San Jose, which are tributaries of the Rio Grande.

In the central part of the basin, Tertiary sandstones and Quaternary gravels and sands make up the aquifers supplying water for cattle and local domestic use. The Cretaceous sandstones—especially the Dakota, Gallup, and Mesaverde sandstones—are also important sources of well water on the periphery of the basin. In the southern part of the basin, major supplies of water for communities in the San Jose Valley along the northeastern border of the Zuni uplift are recovered from the Permian sandstones and the San Andres Limestone.

STRATIGRAPHIC SUMMARY

This report is not intended to be a complete and detailed geologic discussion of the San Juan basin. The reader is referred to other publications for details on correlation problems, evidence for age designations, faunal data, history of terminol-

ogy, regional correlations, and reviews of previous work.

PRECAMBRIAN

Several wells have been drilled to the Precambrian in the San Juan basin (Fig. 5). These rocks also are exposed in the mountains on the northern, eastern, and southern sides of the basin. A general discussion of the lithologic and mineralogic character, age relations, and distribution of rock types of the Precambrian is given by Fitzsimmons (1963).

The Precambrian basement complex of the basin is mainly quartzite, granite, and mica schist. The few deep wells penetrating the Precambrian have encountered granite more commonly in the southern part of the basin, quartzite in the central part, and other types of metamorphic rocks in the northern part. However, no consistent patterns of distribution for these rock types can be established yet. The largest area of Precambrian exposure is in the San Juan Mountains on the northern border of the basin. Here the rocks include a thick section of metamorphosed sediments, mostly schist, gneiss, greenstone, and quartzite. Several granitic intrusions are also present. No carbonate rocks have been found in the metamorphosed sediments on the northwestern side of the San Juan uplift.

CAMBRIAN

Known Cambrian rocks are present only in the northern part of the San Juan basin, where there is as much as 150 ft of Upper Cambrian Ignacio sandstone and quartzite. The interval thins markedly southward and is absent in the southern half of the basin. Where present, the Cambrian section is not generally porous except for the quartzites which may be fractured in some parts of the basin.

Drilling depths to Cambrian-Precambrian rocks range from 4,500 to 8,500 ft on the Chaco slope and Four Corners platform to 12,000 to 15,000 ft in the deeper part of the basin (Fig. 5).

ORDOVICIAN-SILURIAN

Rocks of Ordovician and Silurian ages have not been recognized within the San Juan basin. In the

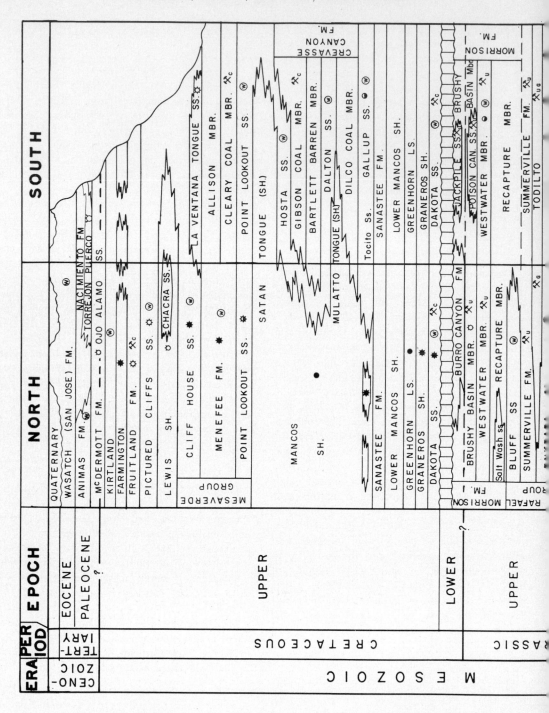

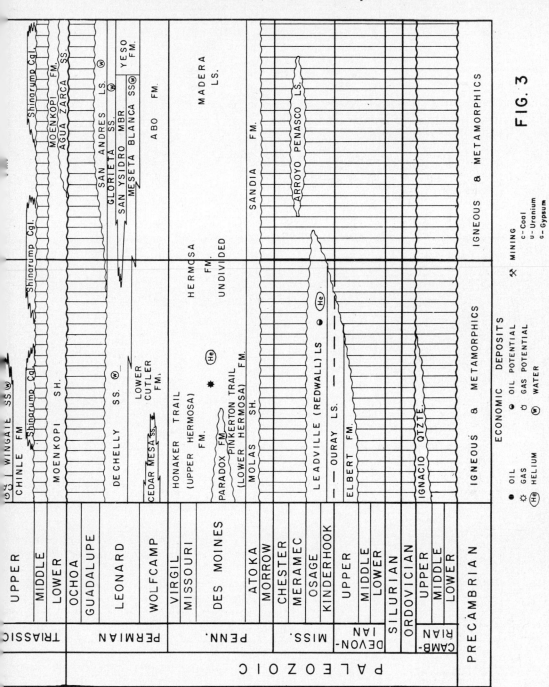

FIG. 3.—Stratigraphic correlation chart of San Juan basin showing economic deposits of current interest. In the Morrison Formation, the "Westwater Member" should be "Westwater Canyon Sandstone Member."

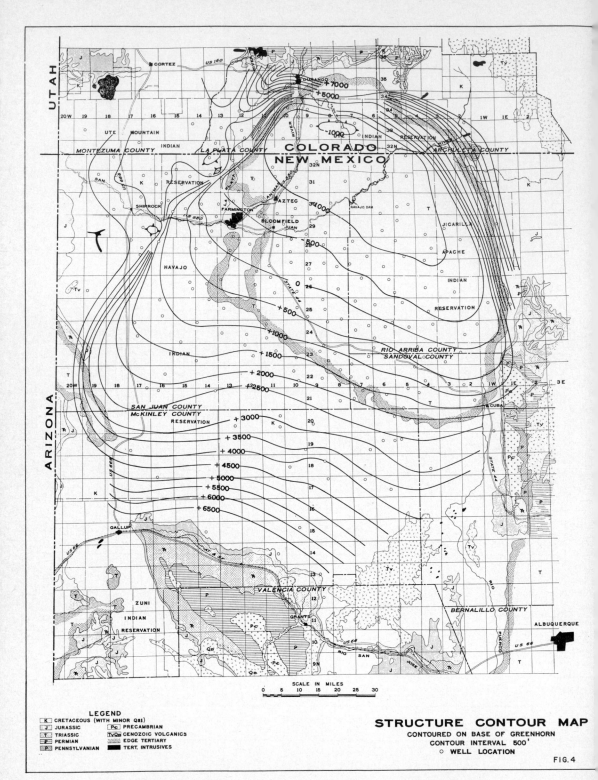

FIG. 4.—Structural contour map on base of Greenhorn Limestone marker.

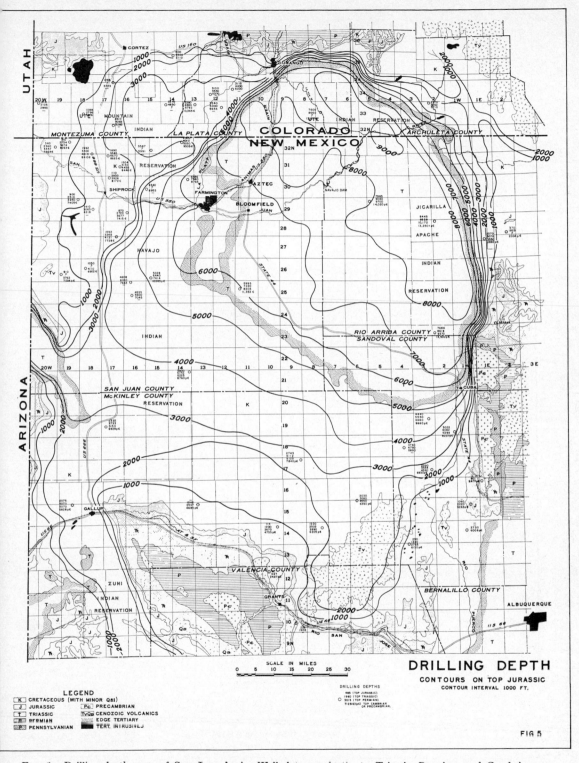

FIG. 5.—Drilling-depth map of San Juan basin. Well data on depths to Triassic, Permian, and Cambrian or Precambrian are also shown by figures on map.

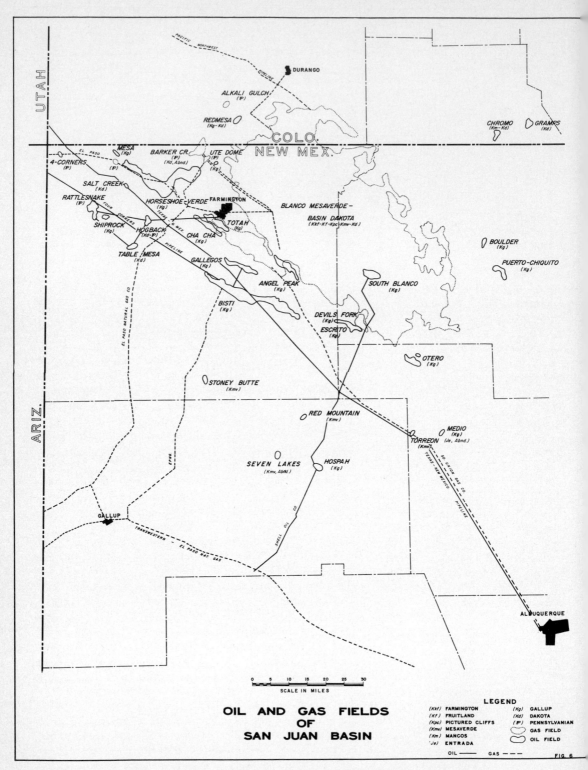

FIG. 6.—Oil and gas fields of San Juan basin.

northern part of the basin the Cambrian generally is overlain disconformably by Upper Devonian
or Mississippian rocks. In the central part of the
basin a thin Mississippian carbonate section overlies either the Cambrian or Precambrian. In the
southernmost part of the basin and on the major
uplifts, such as the Zuni and Nacimiento uplifts,
Lower Pennsylvanian clastics lie on Precambrian rocks (Figs. 7, 8).

DEVONIAN

The Devonian strata in the Four Corners area
are considered to be of Late Devonian age, although diagnostic fossil data are scarce. No rocks
of Early and Middle Devonian ages have been
recognized in the area. The Upper Devonian section is entirely marine and consists of sandy dolomite and some thin sandstone and green or red
shale beds. A basal sandstone unit, the McCrack-
en Sandstone Member of the Elbert Formation,
has discontinuous porosity, and, although the unit
is thin, it may be of interest for petroleum exploration.

The Devonian section is about 300 ft thick
on the Four Corners platform at the northwest
border of the basin; it thins southward and
pinches out across the north-central part of the
basin (Fig. 8).

MISSISSIPPIAN

A relatively thin carbonate section of Early
Mississippian age occurs in the northern part of
the basin. The unit contains as much as 50–75
ft of porous dolomite in the northwestern part
of the basin where the total section averages
150–200 ft in thickness. The porous dolomite,
the Leadville Limestone, generally yields large
quantities of salt water on drill-stem test, and several accumulations of carbon dioxide gas, some
with small percentages of helium, have been encountered. The porosity and permeability of the
dolomite section are high and relatively continuous. The most favorable reservoir development is
along the Four Corners platform, where the Mississippian is found at depths of 6,000–9,000 ft.

Mississippian carbonate strata (Parker and
Roberts, 1963) onlap the thin Upper Devonian section and thin toward the south and southeast
across the basin. This relationship results from the
influence of the Transcontinental arch, a broad,
early Paleozoic positive-trending feature extending
southwestward from the Canadian Shield across
central Colorado and north-central New Mexico.
This feature influenced the regional distribution
and onlap-offlap and sedimentary facies-pinchout
relationships of all the pre-Pennsylvanian sediments in the southern Rocky Mountains area.
The San Juan basin area occupied part of the
northwestern flank of this regional feature during
early Paleozoic time.

Mississippian rocks in the San Juan basin are
of Kinderhook-Osage age in the northern part of
the basin. Thin erosional remnants of Meramec
age lying on Precambrian rocks are found in the
southeastern part of the basin. Emergence of the
entire area occurred during Late Mississippian
time.

PENNSYLVANIAN

The basal Pennsylvanian is of Atoka or Atoka-
Morrow age, unconformably overlying Mississippian carbonates in the northern part of the basin
and resting on Precambrian or Mississippian
rocks in the southern part. The lowermost unit
(Molas Formation) is composed of red shale,
siltstone, and some sandstone, representing the
development of a soil surface during the Late
Mississippian emergence of the area and subsequent reworking by Early Pennsylvanian seas.
The redbeds grade upward into interbedded marine limestone, shale, and minor sandstone of the
Hermosa or Madera Formation.

The Early Pennsylvanian of the San Juan
basin reflects the beginning of a major change in
the paleotectonic-sedimentary history of the
southern Rocky Mountains area associated with
the breakup of the Transcontinental-arch trend.
Strong northwest-southeast uplift associated with
the early beginnings of the Ancestral Rockies occurred during this time. Related downwarping
caused the development of an elongate sedimentary trough along the southwestern flank of the
Uncompahgre–San Juan–Nacimiento uplifts. The
San Juan basin area occupied a part of this regional trough during Pennsylvanian and later
Paleozoic time. A broad belt of Pennsylvanian
shelf carbonates developed along the gentle
southwestern flank of this trough during Pennsyl-

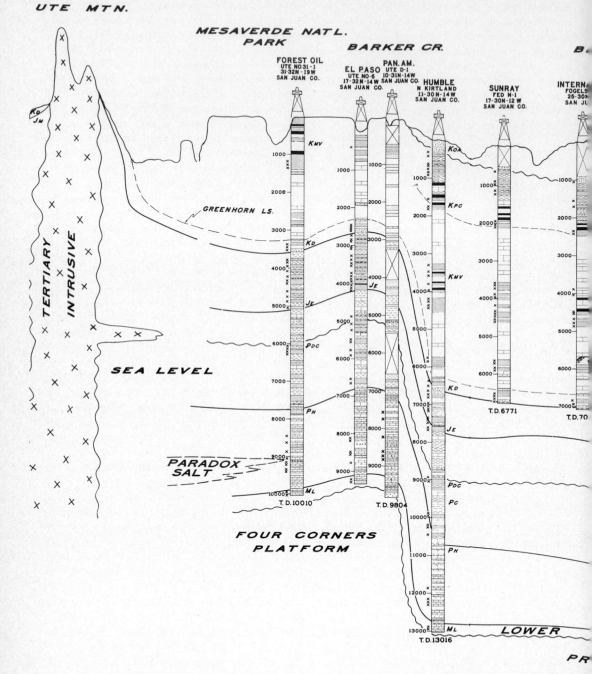

COLO. N. MEX.

W

UTE MTN.

MESAVERDE NATL. PARK

BARKER CR.

B

FOREST OIL
UTE NO31-1
31-32N-19W
SAN JUAN CO.

EL PASO
UTE NO-6
17-32N-14W
SAN JUAN CO.

PAN. AM.
UTE D-1
10-31N-14W
SAN JUAN CO.

HUMBLE
N KIRTLAND
11-30N-14W
SAN JUAN CO.

SUNRAY
FED N-1
17-30N-12 W
SAN JUAN CO.

INTERNA
FOGELS
25-30N
SAN JU

GREENHORN LS.

SEA LEVEL

TERTIARY INTRUSIVE

K_O
J_M

PARADOX SALT

FOUR CORNERS PLATFORM

K_{MV}

K_O

J_E

P_{DC}

P_H

M_L

T.D.10010

K_O

J_E

P_H

M_L

T.D.9804

K_{OA}

K_{PC}

K_{MV}

K_O

J_E

P_{DC}

P_C

P_H

M_L

T.D.13016

T.D.6771

T.D.70

LOWER

PR

FIG. 7.—West-east regional cross section A-A'. D

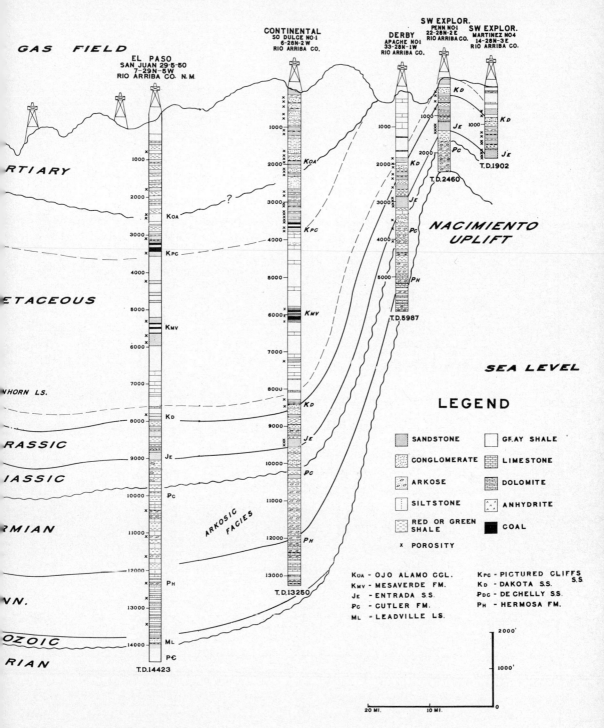

level. Figure 2 shows location of section.

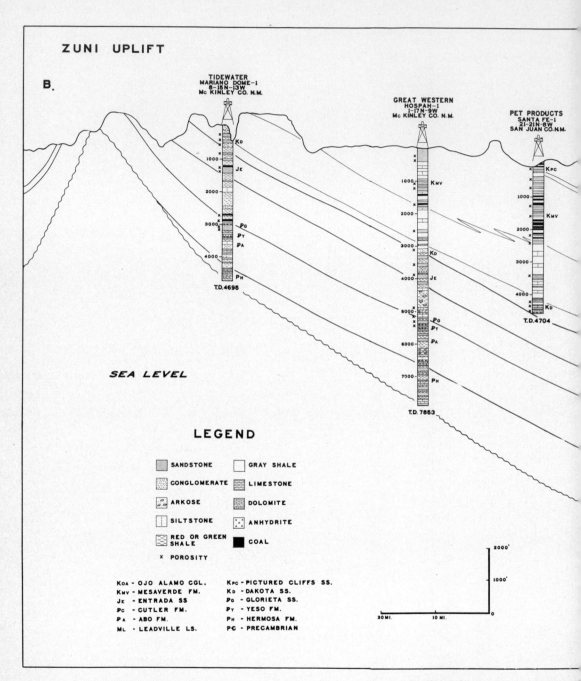

FIG. 8.—South-north regional cross section *B*

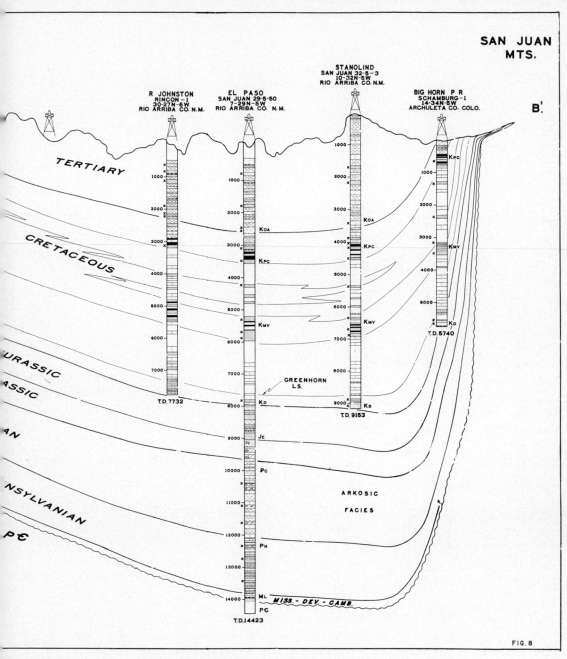

FIG. 8

um is sea level. Figure 2 shows location of section.

vanian time. The major carbonate buildup occurred on the southwestern shelf of the Paradox
basin, where most of the production from the
Pennsylvanian is located, but the belt also continued along the southwestern flank of the San
Juan basin and perhaps extended even farther
south. The Four Corners platform apparently underwent minor growth as a southwest-northeast
positive-trending feature during Pennsylvanian
time, causing shallow-water conditions and shelf-
carbonate development to extend northeastward
along the platform. At the same time a relatively
thick belt of deltaic sediments was deposited
along the northeastern border of the trough (Fig.

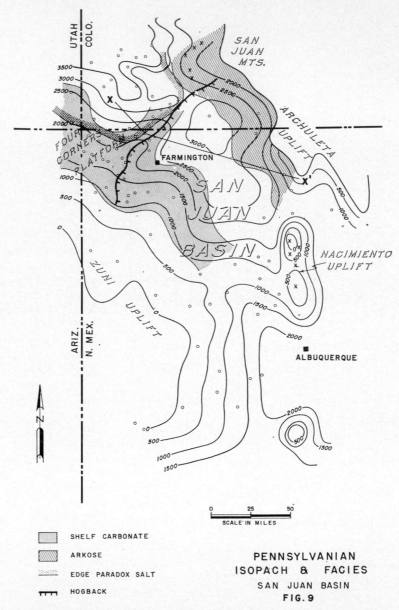

FIG. 9.—Regional isopach map of Pennsylvanian System in Four Corners area.

9). The combination of the southwest-northeast projection of shelf-carbonate buildup on the one side and the rapid accumulation of deltaic deposits on the other caused the Paradox basin to be cut off effectively from the main seaway at the southeast. This situation resulted in deposition of the Paradox-basin evaporites north of the Four Corners platform more or less as a sedimentary accident.

No evaporites have been found in the Pennsylvanian of the San Juan basin although the widely scattered well control in the deeper parts of the basin does not preclude their presence in minor amounts. The central-basin Pennsylvanian sediments as known are predominantly dark-gray to black shale, and argillaceous to silty, rather dense carbonates. Toward the east these beds grade into a belt of predominantly alluvial and nearshore marine clastic sediments derived from the highland bordering the eastern side of the basin (Figs. 9, 10).

Pennsylvanian carbonate mounds are important gas and oil reservoirs along the Four Corners platform on the northwestern side of the basin. The belt of shelf carbonates on the southwestern flank of the basin extends south of the Four Corners platform but, although a moderate amount of exploratory drilling of these beds has taken place, lack of porosity has prevented success to date.

Several authors have described thoroughly the Pennsylvanian history and sedimentation of the Four Corners area, including Wengerd and Strickland (1954), Wengerd and Matheny (1958), Peterson (1959), Fetzner (1960), and Wengerd (1962).

PERMIAN

Accelerated growth of the positive elements (San Juan Mountains-Archuleta uplift, Nacimiento uplift) along the eastern side of the basin trough occurred during Late Pennsylvanian and Permian time. The resulting increase of clastic influx from the east effectively caused almost complete regression of marine conditions from the area. In the central part of the basin the Permian section is characterized by red shale, siltstone, and sandstone grading upward into coarser clastics. These beds grade laterally into a largely

arkosic section near the uplift areas on the east and into much cleaner and well-sorted sandstone with interbedded red shale and siltstone at the southwest (Figs. 14–16).

Upper Permian sediments apparently are not present in the basin although lack of faunal data prevents an accurate age determination of the uppermost Permian beds in the arkosic section on the eastern and northern sides of the basin.

The Permian-Pennsylvanian contact is conformable throughout the San Juan basin, as far as can be determined. The boundary is characterized by an upward transition from Pennsylvanian limestones with interbedded red shale, siltstone, and sandstone to a general absence or scarcity of limestone within the redbeds of the Lower Permian Abo Formation. The age relations are based on very limited faunal data, mostly projected from outside the basin, but no physical evidence of significant unconformity is present in the Permian-Pennsylvanian transitional beds.

The gross Permian section is dominated by redbeds overlain by clean porous sandstone in the southern and western parts of the basin. Along the northeastern and northern sides of the basin, arkosic sandstone of moderate to poor porosity and redbeds are the dominant rock types. A thin carbonate and sandstone unit, the San Andres Limestone, occurs at the top of the Permian in the southernmost part of the basin, and a thin evaporitic section, the Yeso evaporites, is present a little lower in the section in the same area (Figs. 15, 16). Thickness of the total Permian section ranges from more than 2,000 ft in the southeastern and central parts of the basin to less than 1,500 ft on the northeastern and southwestern sides of the basin (Fig. 11).

The entire Permian sandstone section and associated redbeds, evaporites, and carbonates crop out in a continuous belt surrounding the Precambrian core of the Zuni uplift (Fig. 2). For a further discussion of Permian stratigraphy, the reader is referred to papers by Bass (1944), Northrup and Wood (1946), Beaumont and Read (1950), Read et al. (1951), McKee (1951a), and Baars (1962).

Abo Formation

The Abo is a sequence of interbedded continental and nearshore marine red shale and silt-

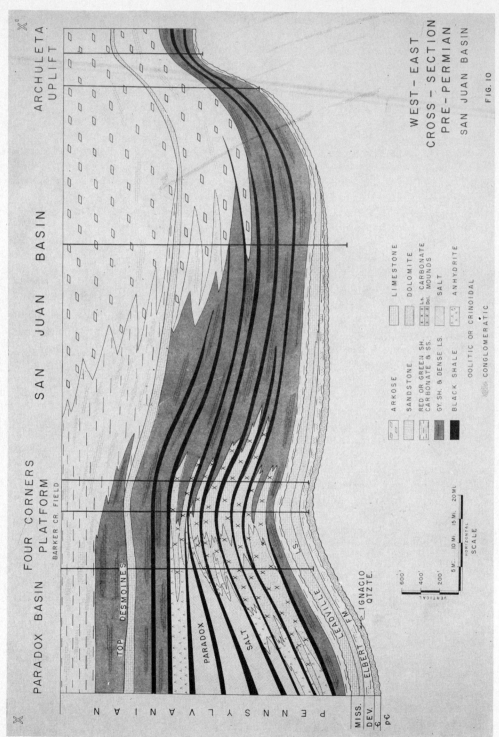

FIG. 10.—West-east cross section, pre-Permian.

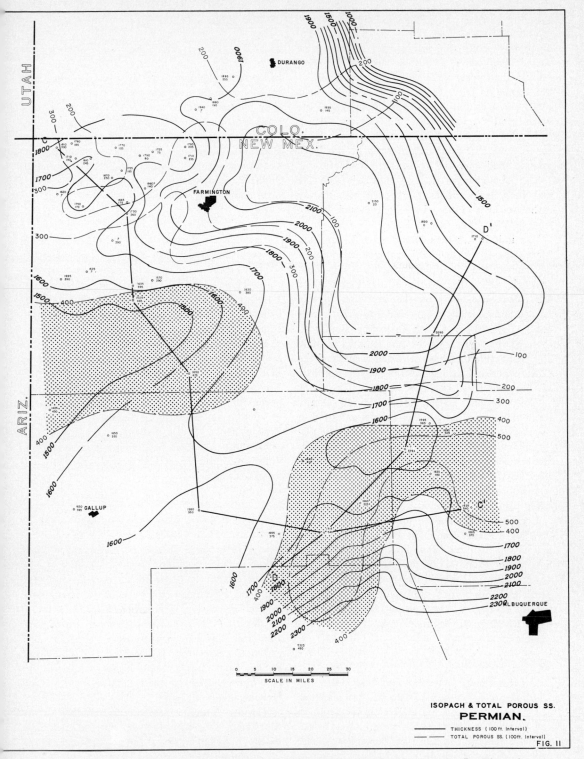

Fig. 11.—Isopach and total porous sandstone map of Permian System, San Juan basin. Location of cross sections C-C′ (Fig. 15) and D-D′ (Fig. 16) are shown.

stone with many thin interbedded sandstones or arkosic sandstones. Limestone nodules are common in the thicker shale units. The upper part of the formation tends to contain more and cleaner sandstone beds and along the southern side of the basin grades upward into the Meseta Blanca Sandstone Member of the Yeso Formation. Along the eastern and northeastern sides of the basin arkosic sandstone and redbeds predominate.

The Abo changes facies southward from the San Juan basin and is interbedded with marine carbonate beds (Hueco Limestone) which locally contain Wolfcamp fusulinids.

The unit is less than 200 ft thick in the Zuni Mountains outcrop and thickens gradually northward across the Chaco slope where it is 500–1,000 ft thick (Fig. 16). North of the Chaco slope the clean sandstones of the overlying Meseta Blanca and Glorieta change facies to arkosic redbeds of the upper Cutler Formation similar to those of the Abo. Thus the Abo loses its identity as a distinctive unit a short distance north of the Chaco slope and throughout the northeastern half of the basin (Fig. 14).

The sandstones of the Abo are varied, usually containing some feldspar, but are generally red in color and tend to be cemented with clay and calcareous material. However, many of the sandstone members show good self-potential development on the electric log and in some places show visual porosity in the drill cuttings. They are generally discontinuous in nature and presumably are isolated sandstone bodies, probably fluvial or lacustrine in origin. The main source for the clastic material in these sandstone beds was probably the San Juan Mountain–Archuleta uplift area of southwestern Colorado and north-central New Mexico. Total porous sandstone content of the unit is greatest in the southeastern part of the basin where it reaches more than 200 ft in total thickness.

Meseta Blanca-Glorieta Sandstones

The two major Permian sandstone units, the Glorieta Sandstone and Meseta Blanca Sandstone Member of the Yeso, are thickest in the southern and southeastern parts of the basin (Figs. 12–16). These units are composed of dune, beach, and bar sandstones which developed along the northwestern shores of the regional evaporite basin

that covered western Texas and southeastern New Mexico during most of Permian time. In most places the sandstones are highly porous, and in the outcrop area along the Zuni Mountains they contain potable water, especially the Glorieta Sandstone. As far as can be determined from the available control, the Glorieta and Meseta Blanca maintain generally good continuity as widespread, porous, blanket sandstone bodies, and in the San Juan basin subsurface are best developed along the Chaco slope (Figs. 12-16).

San Ysidro Evaporites

The Meseta Blanca and Glorieta sandstones are separated by the San Ysidro redbed-evaporite sequence over most of the southern part of the basin. Here the San Ysidro Member of the Yeso Formation is composed of 100–200 ft of interbedded anhydrite (or gypsum), red shale and siltstone, sandstone, and some dolomite. The evaporite and shale beds make an impermeable layer separating the widespread porous sandstone units of the Meseta Blanca from those of the Glorieta. The sandstone beds of the San Ysidro locally are porous and permeable and contain potable water in some localities on the northeastern flank of the Zuni uplift.

Like the Abo, the San Ysidro becomes more arkosic northward where it merges with the Cutler arkosic facies.

San Andres Limestone

The San Andres Limestone occupies the uppermost part of the Permian section in the southern part of the basin. It consists largely of marine dolomite and limestone and interbedded clean porous quartz sandstone in the outcrop areas of the Zuni Mountains. In the adjacent subsurface of the Chaco slope the carbonates thin abruptly northward (Fig. 13). The carbonates are of marine origin and generally are porous, although they are not everywhere permeable. The sandstone ranges from fine grained, highly calcareous or dolomitic, and impermeable to clean, porous, permeable, and well sorted.

The San Andres is an important aquifer in and near the outcrop belt along the northeastern flank of the Zuni uplift where the water-bearing beds are mainly limestone.

Drilling depths to the Permian range from

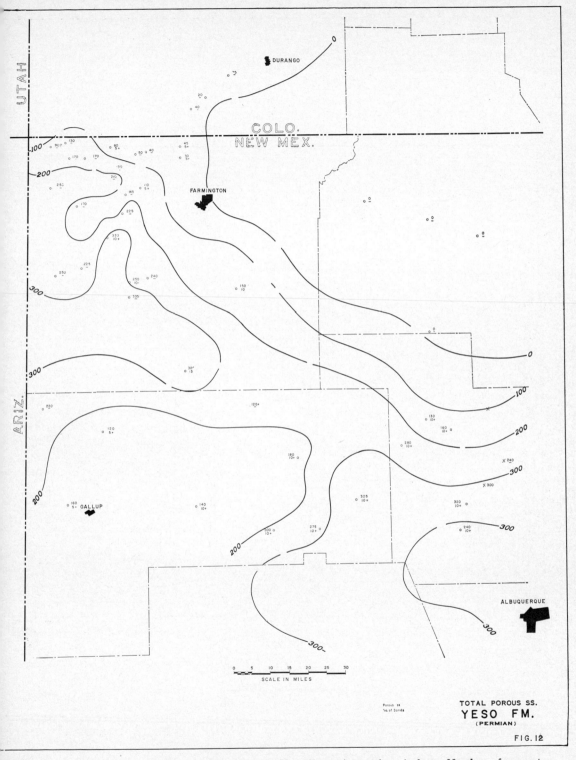

FIG. 12.—Total porous sandstone thickness map of Yeso Formation and equivalents. Number of separate sandstone beds within unit is also shown.

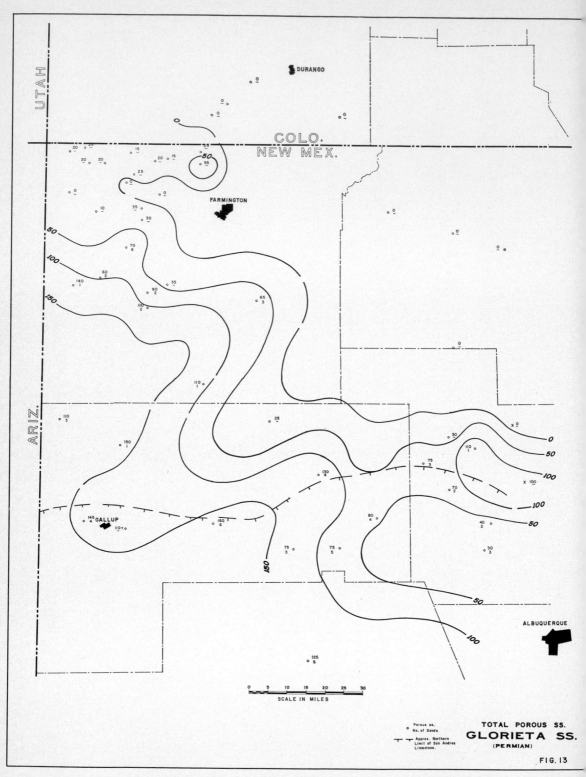

FIG. 13.—Total porous sandstone thickness map of Glorieta Sandstone and equivalents. Number of separate sandstone beds within unit is also shown. Note northern limit of San Andres Limestone unit which overlies Glorieta.

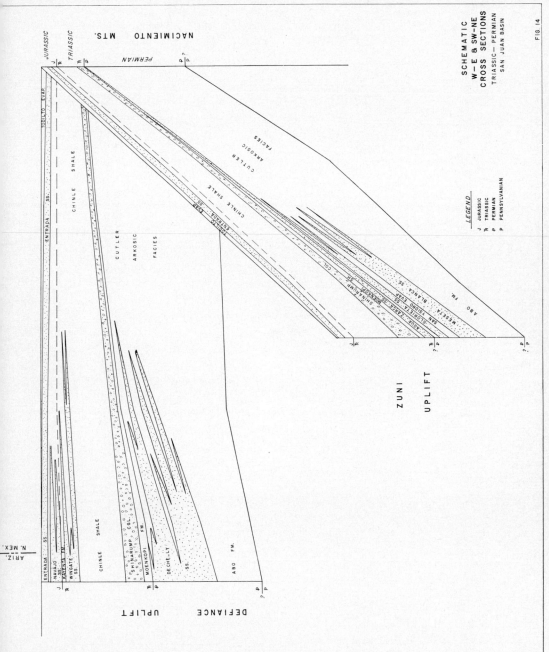

Fig. 14.—Schematic fence diagram showing regional relations between Triassic and Permian stratigraphic units in Defiance, Zuni, and Nacimiento uplift areas.

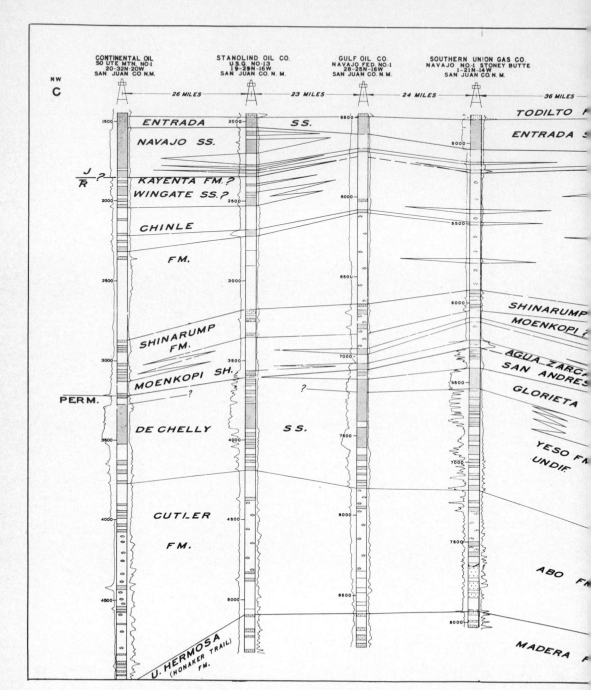

FIG. 15.—Northwest-southeast cross section *C-C'* of Triassic-Per▸

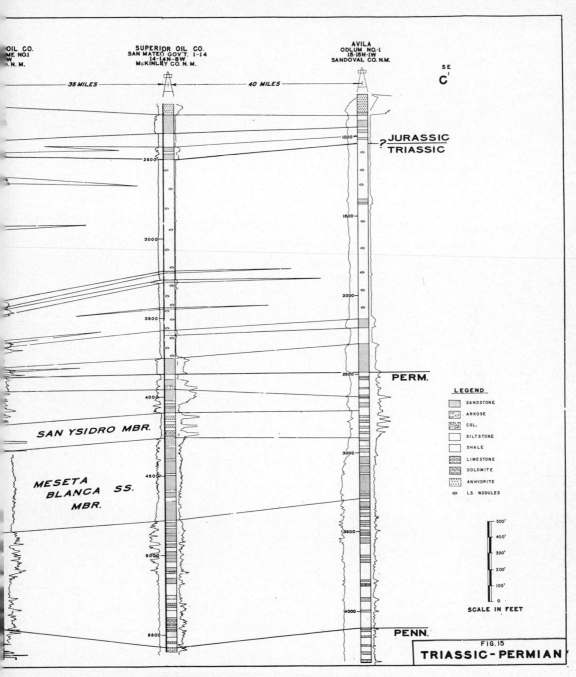

FIG. 15
TRIASSIC-PERMIAN

Juan basin. Position of cross section is shown on Figures 11 and 17.

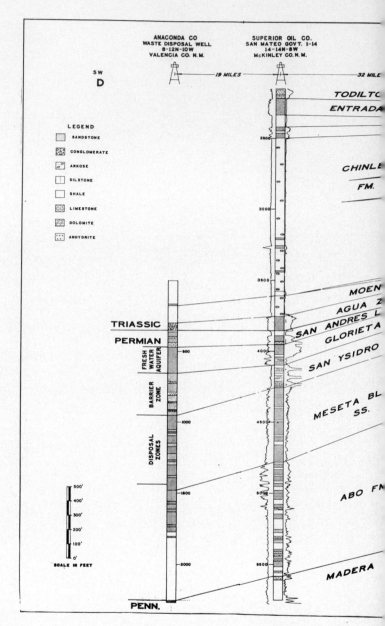

FIG. 16.—Southwest-northeast cross section *D-D'* of Triassic-Per~

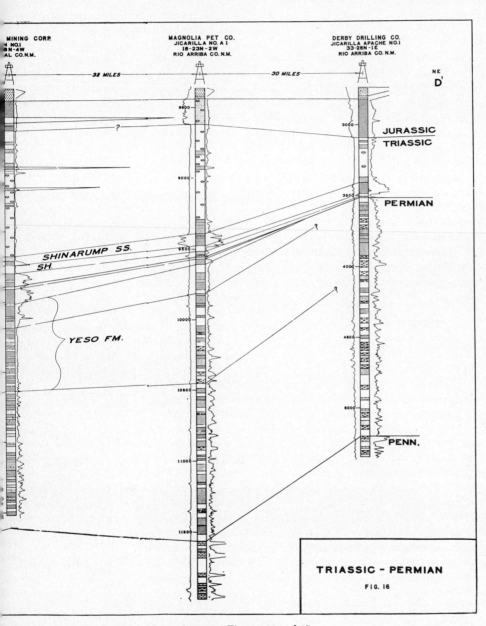

TRIASSIC - PERMIAN

FIG. 16

uan basin. Position of cross section is shown on Figures 11 and 17.

2,000–6,000 ft on the Chaco slope and Four Corners platform to 8,000–11,000 ft in the central San Juan basin.

Porosity and Permeability

Measurements of subsurface porosity and permeability of the Meseta Blanca, Glorieta, and San Andres are lacking because no cores are known to have been taken in these beds. However, these sandstones show good porosity in drill cuttings and have good electric-log porosity character. The Glorieta and San Andres aquifers produce large amounts of water in the Grants-Bluewater area on the northern flank of the Zuni uplift, indicating good porosity-permeability characteristics in the general outcrop area of these beds. The Meseta Blanca and Glorieta should have high porosity and permeability in the subsurface. The porous carbonate and sandstone beds of the San Andres extend into the subsurface only a short distance north of the outcrop belt.

TRIASSIC

The deposition of red shale, siltstone, and sandstone that began in Late Pennsylvanian time continued through the Triassic. The basal Triassic deposits (Moenkopi Formation) reflect a brief return of marine conditions to the Rocky Mountain shelf following regression during Late Permian time. The Middle Triassic apparently is not present and the Upper Triassic Chinle Formation consists entirely of continental deposits of red and varicolored shale, siltstone, sandstone, and conglomerate, and some argillaceous limestone.

The total Triassic thins progressively across the basin, ranging from more than 1,500 ft in the southern and western parts to less than 750 ft in the northern and northeastern parts near the San Juan–Archuleta uplifts (Fig. 17).

The Triassic subdivisions (Chinle, Shinarump, and Moenkopi) that are widely used on the Colorado Plateau cannot be defined adequately throughout much of the San Juan basin. These names generally are used in the subsurface in the northwestern part of the basin on the Four Corners platform and the terminology can be applied over much of the western and southern parts of the basin. However, because definition of the Chinle and Moenkopi depends on recognition of the erratic Shinarump unit, a consistent usage of these subdivisions has not been attained. The Shinarump progressively truncates the older Triassic beds toward the northeastern edge of the basin where it probably lies unconformably on the Permian Cutler Formation (Figs. 14, 16).

In the northwestern and western parts of the basin the Wingate-Navajo continental sandstone facies is present as the eastward projection of the regional belt of Upper Triassic–Jurassic dune sandstones that extends from central and eastern Arizona as far north as western Wyoming. The Wingate Sandstone currently is considered to be of Late Triassic age and, together with part of the Navajo Sandstone, probably grades laterally eastward into the upper part of what is called the Chinle Formation in the San Juan basin (Figs. 14–16). The exact age relations of these units are difficult to define, particularly in view of the generally nondiagnostic quality of the sparse fossil remains in these beds. The Triassic-Jurassic boundary is drawn questionably as shown on Figures 14–16, largely on the basis of regional electric-log and lithologic subsurface correlations.

Coarser clastic debris probably was derived from several source terranes, including the San Juan uplift in southwestern Colorado, the Archuleta-Nacimiento uplifts in north-central New Mexico, the Central Arizona uplift, and perhaps another uplift in west-central New Mexico. Other more local and smaller areas of uplift also may have contributed material. The sandstone and conglomerate probably were deposited by numerous intermittent stream systems, many probably with internal drainage. These genetic factors resulted in highly irregular and discontinuous sandstone-body geometry and highly varied degrees of sorting, cementation, grain size, and texture in the sandstone.

Although most of the Triassic sandstones cannot be mapped regionally because of their highly discontinuous nature, two main units, the Agua Zarca and Shinarump, can be defined throughout much of the basin. The relative distribution and extent of sandstone development in these units are shown on Figures 18 and 19. Further discussion of the Triassic section can be found in pa-

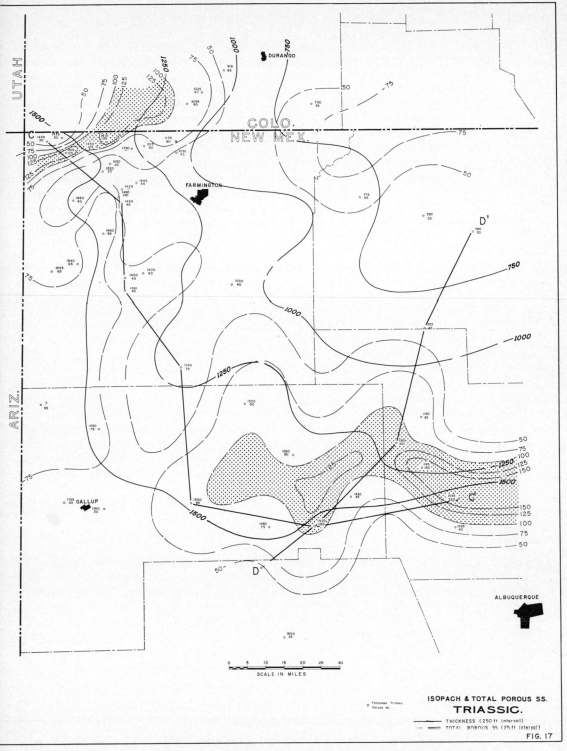

FIG. 17.—Isopach and total porous sandstone map of Triassic System, San Juan basin. Location of cross sections C-C′ (Fig. 15) and D-D′ (Fig. 16) is shown.

pers by McKee (1951b, 1954), Harshbarger *et al.* (1957), Momper (1957), and Stewart *et al.* (1959).

Agua Zarca Sandstone Member

The Agua Zarca Sandstone Member of the Moenkopi Formation is best developed in the southern and southeastern parts of the basin where it reaches a thickness of more than 100 ft (Fig. 18). Where thicker, the sandstone generally is clean, having well-sorted grains and many characteristics of the underlying Permian sandstones from which it may have been derived at least in part. The Agua Zarca characteristically has high porosity and permeability.

The age and correlation of the Agua Zarca sandstone have been disputed. Many workers have considered the unit to be the basal part of the Chinle and therefore to correlate generally with the Shinarump Member of the Chinle. Correlation studies made for this report indicate that the Lower Triassic Moenkopi Formation can be traced from southeastern Utah to the southern San Juan basin and that the Agua Zarca correlates with the basal part of the Moenkopi (Fig. 15). This analysis agrees with the interpretation of Momper (1957).

Moenkopi Formation

The Moenkopi Formation is a sequence of red to red-brown shale, siltstone, minor sandstone (other than the thick Agua Zarca sandstone), and rare shaly limestone. These strata are predominantly well bedded and probably represent a mixture of nearshore marine and nonmarine environments, including stream, floodplain, lacustrine, playa, mudflat, deltaic, and lagoonal deposition. The Moenkopi is 200–300 ft thick in the southwestern and western parts of the basin but thins toward the northeast, probably because of truncation by the overlying Shinarump conglomerate (Figs. 14, 16).

Shinarump (Conglomerate) Member

The Shinarump Member of the Chinle Formation is gray or tan conglomerate, sandstone, and siltstone with interbedded green or green-gray mudstone. The interval grades upward into the overlying varicolored Chinle shales, but the basal contact of the lower sandstones and conglomerates usually is rather sharp and in many places is associated with channel cuts in the underlying Moenkopi redbeds.

The Shinarump conglomerate and sandstone commonly are very poorly sorted and in many localities contain a large percentage of matrix clay material. Pebbles and granules in these beds include quartzite, chert, quartz, shale, and carbonate fragments ranging from well rounded to more commonly angular. Where the sandstone and conglomerate units locally contain good self-potential development on the electric log, porosity commonly is reported on sample logs.

Chinle Formation

The Chinle Formation is widespread throughout the San Juan basin, ranging in thickness from 800–1,000 ft in the western and southwestern part of the basin to less than 300 ft in the northern and northeastern part. The interval consists of varicolored red, purple, green, gray, and yellow, bentonitic, soft mudstone and some beds of siltstone or sandstone (Figs. 15, 16). Conglomerates are rare, but some thin units have been reported on sample logs. Shaly limestone beds are present at many localities. Environmentally, the Chinle is considered to be entirely of nonmarine origin, probably a combination of floodplain, lacustrine, playa, alluvial, and volcanic-dust or ash-fall sedimentation.

The Triassic-Jurassic boundary probably is in the upper part of the Chinle shales throughout the basin. The Wingate Sandstone, Kayenta redbeds, and Navajo Sandstone, which make up the uppermost Triassic and lowermost Jurassic of Arizona, interfinger eastward with the upper part of the Chinle Formation. Hence, if the Triassic-Jurassic boundary is placed near the base of the Navajo Sandstone in Arizona, it should occur within the upper part of the Chinle in the San Juan basin (Fig. 15). These relations are shown schematically on Figure 14.

Wingate-Navajo Sandstones

The Wingate and Navajo Sandstones of Arizona and Utah are present along the western border of the San Juan basin, where they are massive, highly porous, and permeable beds of eolian

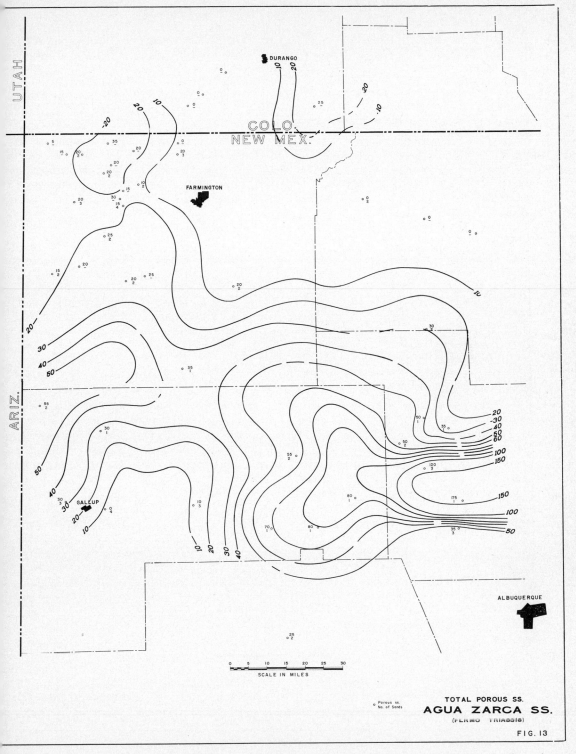

F_{IG}. 18.—Total porous sandstone thickness map of Agua Zarca sandstone and equivalents. Number of separate sandstone beds within unit is also shown.

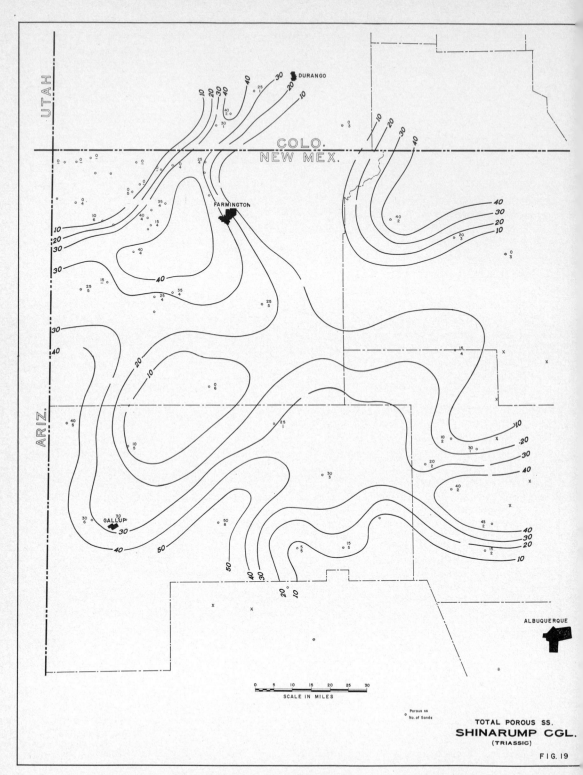

Fig. 19.—Total porous sandstone thickness map of Shinarump conglomerate. Number of separate sandstone beds within unit is also shown.

origin. Eastward these sandstones grade into the upper part of the Chinle, which in turn is overlain by the widespread Entrada Sandstone.

JURASSIC

The Jurassic System in the San Juan basin is a sequence of interstratified sandstone, siltstone, and shale, and minor amounts of carbonate and anhydrite or gypsum. The strata range in thickness from slightly less than 1,100 ft in the extreme southern part of the basin to slightly more than 1,500 ft in the west-central part, and to less than 1,000 ft near the northern edge. The interrelation of various Jurassic formations is shown on the stratigraphic chart (Fig. 3).

Studies by Silver (1948), Smith (1951), and Harshbarger et al. (1957) indicate that during Jurassic time a broad east-west-trending high, extending from central New Mexico to central Arizona, was present south of the area of study. Data compiled by McKee (1954) and others suggest that another low positive may have been present east and northeast of the basin. The lowermost Jurassic formations (Carmel, Navajo) of Utah and northeastern Arizona are not recognized in the main part of the basin where the Entrada Sandstone was deposited directly on the Triassic Wingate Sandstone or on the Chinle strata. The Entrada is a widespread sandstone and siltstone accumulation that in most of the basin area is overlain conformably by limestone and gypsum (anhydrite in subsurface) of the Todilto Limestone. Deposition of the Todilto beds was followed by accumulation of the red siltstone, shale, and sandstone of the Summerville Formation and its equivalents. The latter formation intertongues with and is overlain by the Bluff Sandstone and its equivalents, which comprise the uppermost strata in the San Rafael Group. The Morrison Formation overlies the San Rafael Group and is a varied sequence of interstratified sandstone, varicolored mudstone and shale, and minor conglomerate and fresh-water limestone. The Morrison in the San Juan basin area is divided into the Recapture Shale, Westwater Canyon Sandstone, and Brushy Basin Shale Members. It is overlain with only slight unconformity by Cretaceous sandstone, shale, and coaly beds.

The sandstone phase of the Entrada is primarily a porous and permeable blanket sandstone forming essentially one hydrologic unit. In contrast, sandstone beds within the Morrison Formation are characteristically discontinuous and enclosed within relatively impermeable claystone, mudstone, and shale.

Entrada Sandstone

The Entrada Sandstone of northwestern New Mexico is made up of two members, an upper sandy member underlain by a lower silty member. The upper sandy member is a relatively massive, reddish to orange and light-gray, friable, fine- to medium-grained sandstone of eolian and fluvial origin.

An average of 100–150 ft of total porous Entrada sandstone is present in the San Juan basin (Fig. 20). Porous sandstone thickness appears to decrease to less than 50 ft in the northeastern part of the basin. Published and unpublished measured-section data compiled by McKee and others (1956, Pl. 5) indicate the Entrada Sandstone to be slightly more than 200 ft thick where it crops out along the northern edge of the basin. The difference between indicated subsurface porous sandstone thickness and total Entrada Sandstone thickness in the outcrop here is attributed to a decrease toward the northeast in the amount of good porous sandstone within the overall Entrada interval. Porous Entrada sandstone on the Chaco-slope part of the San Juan basin ranges in thickness from about 200 ft to slightly less than 100 ft.

Morrison Formation

The Morrison outcrop has been much studied (Craig et al., 1955; Freeman and Hilpert, 1956; Harshbarger et al., 1957) but little is known of its character in the subsurface. In the San Juan basin it is primarily a fluviatile and lacustrine deposit characterized by lenticular sandstones enclosed in relatively impermeable claystone, mudstone, and shale. The thickness of individual sandstones changes very markedly even over a short distance. The total thickness of sandstone in the Morrison Formation, computed from subsurface data, ranges from less than 60 ft in the extreme southeastern and northeastern parts of the basin to 340 ft about 22 mi north of Gallup, New Mexico (Fig. 21).

In the northern part of the basin the sand-

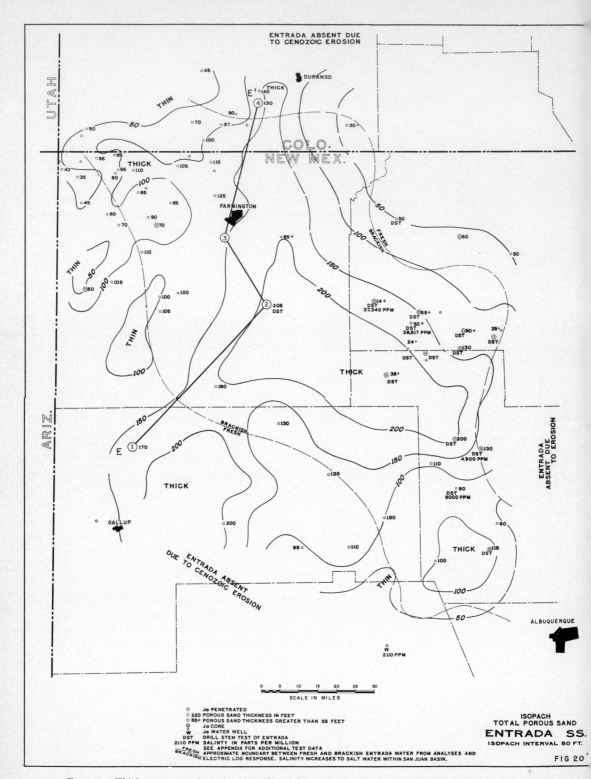

Fig. 20.—Thickness map of total porous Entrada sandstone. Note approximate boundary on Chaco slope between fresh-water (less than 5,000 ppm) and more saline-water areas. Position of cross section *E-E'* (Fig. 22) is shown.

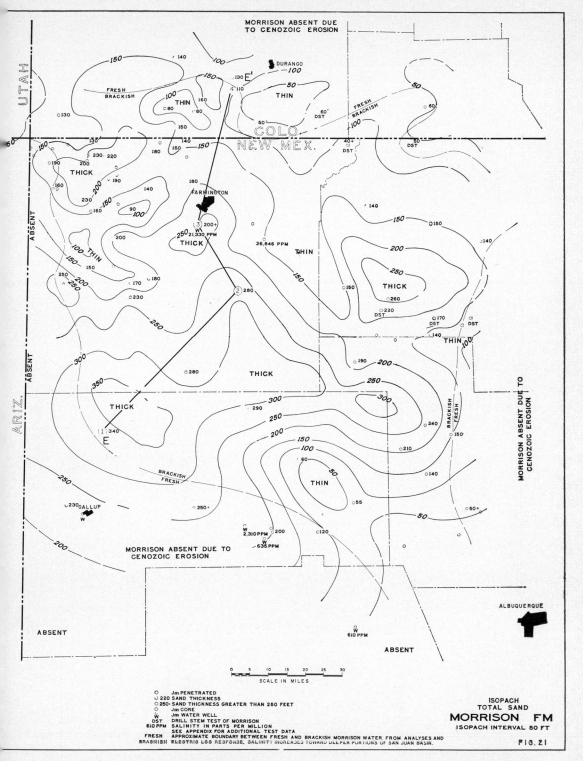

Fig. 21.—Total porous sandstone thickness map of Morrison Formation. Note approximate boundary on Chaco slope between fresh-water (less than 5,000 ppm) and more saline-water areas. Position of cross section E-E' (Fig. 22) is shown.

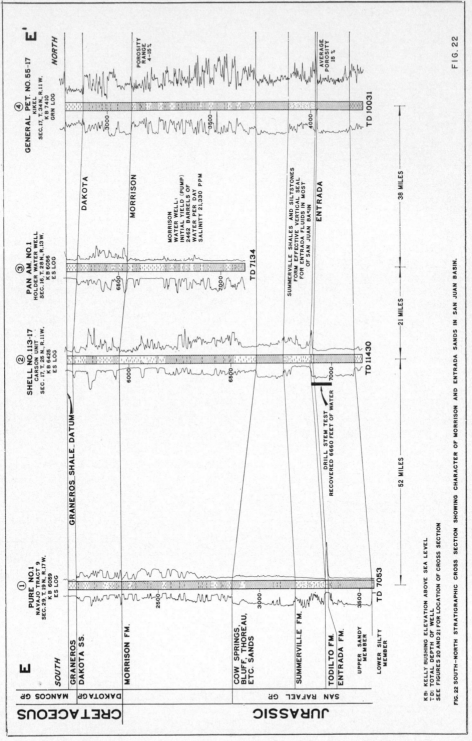

Fig. 22.—South-north stratigraphic cross section, Morrison-Entrada units. Position of cross section is shown on Figures 20 and 21.

stones are chiefly light green to gray and cream, fine to coarse grained, and locally slightly silicified. These sandstones are interbedded with green-gray, reddish, and brown claystone, mudstone, and shale. Intercalary siltstone and nodular limestone also are present. In the southern part of the basin, the Morrison sandstones are light gray to green-gray, white to pale orange and red-brown, and range in grain size from fine to very coarse; some conglomerate beds are present. Siliceous and calcareous cement is common. Some sandstone units are feldspathic.

The mineralogy of the Morrison sandstones is somewhat more varied than that of the Entrada. The porous beds have chiefly angular to rounded quartz grains. The feldspar content seems to increase in the southern and eastern parts of the basin. Some altered to partly altered volcanic-ash fragments have been noted. The sandstones are commonly cemented with carbonate and siliceous material which causes the strata to be fairly impermeable. Pyrite occurs in trace amounts.

CRETACEOUS

Cretaceous rocks in the San Juan basin consist mainly of interbedded marine sandstone and gray shale ranging in thickness from 4,000 to 5,250 ft. The thickness pattern is relatively uniform despite the abrupt facies changes across the basin (Fig. 23) and the recognized unconformity within the Gallup sequence.

A complete discussion of the complex intertonguing of the Cretaceous sandstone and shale is beyond the scope of this paper. The reader is referred to papers by Sears *et al.* (1941), Pike (1947), Budd (1952), Bozanic (1955), Burton (1955), Beaumont *et al.* (1956), Reese (1957), and Hollenshead and Pritchard (1961) for further discussion of the Cretaceous section.

LOWER CRETACEOUS

Rocks of Early Cretaceous age have not been positively identified within the San Juan basin. The upper part of the Morrison Formation is considered by many workers to be probably Early Cretaceous in age and probably equivalent to the Burro Canyon Formation of the Paradox basin.

UPPER CRETACEOUS
Dakota Sandstone

The Dakota Sandstone is the basal marine transgressive unit of the Upper Cretaceous. The unit is highly varied in character and consists of very fine- to coarse-grained sandstone, in places conglomeratic, and intervening dark-gray to black shale and coal lenses. Thicknesses range from 85 ft in the southern part of the basin near Gallup to 250 ft in the northern part in eastern La Plata County, Colorado; the average thickness is 200 ft. The formation is present throughout the San Juan basin in outcrop and in the subsurface (Fig. 24).

The Dakota lies unconformably on sandstone and shale of the Morrison Formation in most of the basin. Locally in the northern part of the basin, the Burro Canyon Formation of Early Cretaceous age is recognized underlying the Dakota. The Dakota is overlain by the marine sandstone and shale of the Graneros Shale.

The shales of the Dakota are dark gray to black, carbonaceous, and generally noncalcareous. The sandstones are fine grained to conglomeratic, quartzose, and contain minor feldspar; in many places they contain a high percentage of white clay matrix material. Most of the sand grains are angular to subangular and increase in sphericity toward the southwest (Burton, 1955).

The Dakota is one of the major oil- and gas-producing formations of the basin. Average characteristics of the Dakota reservoirs are summarized as follows: oil-producing thickness, 27 ft; water saturation, 25 percent; porosity, 11 percent; permeability, 14 md (Reneau and Harris, 1957). However, more recent studies of the gas-producing Dakota in the central part of the basin show an average producing thickness of 45 ft and porosity and permeability much less than those stated above. The Cretaceous section generally is fractured within the basin and fractures have been noted in all strata from the Dakota to the Lewis Shale.

Post-Dakota–Pre-Mesaverde

The post-Dakota, pre-Mesaverde part of the Cretaceous section is about 2,000 ft thick and comprises a complex series of intertonguing

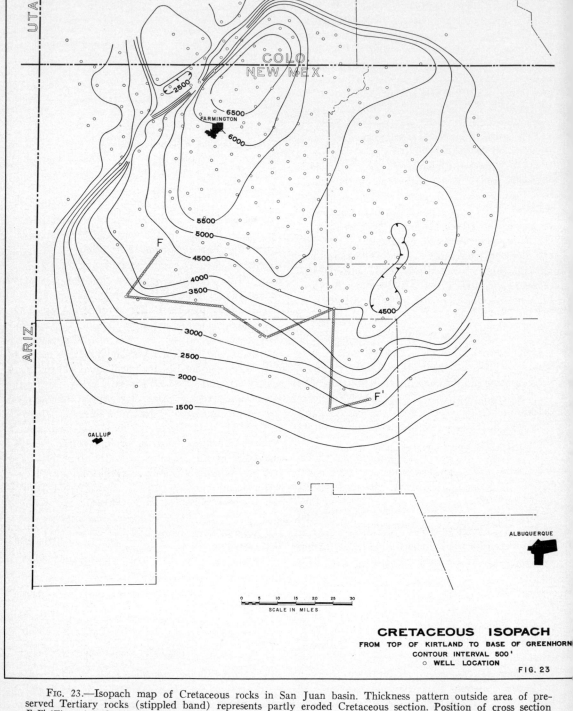

FIG. 23.—Isopach map of Cretaceous rocks in San Juan basin. Thickness pattern outside area of preserved Tertiary rocks (stippled band) represents partly eroded Cretaceous section. Position of cross section *F-F'* (Fig. 24) is shown.

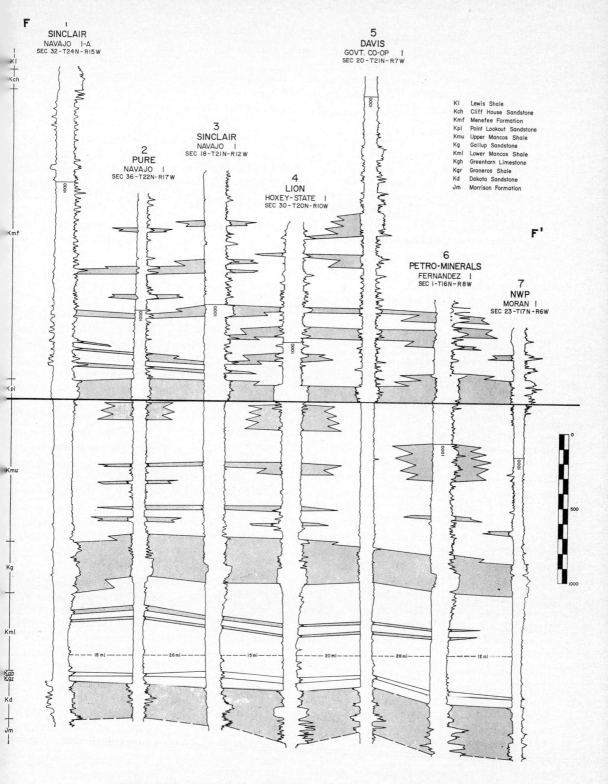

CRETACEOUS CROSS SECTION ACROSS CHACO SLOPE

Fig. 24.—Electric-log cross section of Cretaceous System, Chaco slope area. Datum is base of Point Lookout Sandstone. Position of cross section is shown on Figure 23.

sandstone, siltstone, shale, calcareous shale, and coaly to carbonaceous units laid down by repeated transgressions and regressions of the Cretaceous seas.

Graneros Shale.—The Graneros Shale is a dark-gray to black, silty, carbonaceous shale lying above the Dakota; it is considered by many workers, together with the Greenhorn Limestone, to be a part of the Mancos Shale. In parts of the basin the Graneros has a sandstone development which contains gas reserves.

Greenhorn Limestone.—The Greenhorn is a very argillaceous marine limestone, dark gray in the subsurface but weathering to a very light gray to white in outcrop. The base of the unit is defined easily on electric logs and is a persistent datum for the construction of contour maps (Fig. 24).

Gallup Sandstone.—The Gallup Sandstone is an important oil-producing unit that occurs 400–700 ft above the Dakota. It is also important as an aquifer in the southern part of the basin. The different producing intervals within the Gallup have wide ranges of permeability, porosity, and water and oil saturations. The averages are about 37 md permeability, 13.6 percent porosity, 30 percent water saturation, and 23.6 percent residual-oil saturation (Reneau and Harris, 1957).

Lenticular sandstone bodies are characteristic of the post-Dakota to pre-Mesaverde section (Fig. 24). Because of their nearshore marine origin, they are potentially capable of hydrocarbon production but are also of potential importance as aquifers, especially in the southern part of the basin.

The Gallup Sandstone formerly was placed in the basal part of the Mesaverde Group, particularly in the southern part of the basin. However, it now more commonly is excluded from the Mesaverde (Fig. 3) because it is not present at the type locality of the Mesaverde Group.

Mancos Shale.—The Mancos Shale in this summary is defined as the unit between the base of the Point Lookout Sandstone and the top of the Greenhorn Limestone. It is a medium- to dark-gray marine shale containing sandstone bodies deposited along an oscillating shoreline. Many of these sandstones are reservoirs or potential reservoirs for hydrocarbons. The Mancos makes up much of the surface exposure along the southern and western sides of the basin.

Mesaverde and Post-Mesaverde

The Mesaverde Group consists of, in ascending order, the Point Lookout Sandstone, the Menefee Formation (consisting of sandstone, shale, and coal beds), and the Cliff House Sandstone (Fig. 3).

Point Lookout Sandstone.—The Point Lookout Sandstone, a major gas producer in the basin, consists of very fine- to medium-grained, light- to medium-gray sandstones ranging in thickness from 140 ft to 250 ft. The sandstones usually contain a relatively high percent of clay and calcite cement. Permeability ranges up to 150 md, but the average is only 2.1 md; porosity averages 10 percent, and water saturation 34 percent (Reneau and Harris, 1957).

Menefee Formation.—The Menefee Formation thickens markedly toward the southwest from only 160 ft in the northeastern part of the basin to 3,500 ft in the Chuska Mountains on the southwestern edge of the basin. The unit is a minor gas and oil reservoir but is a major coal-producing unit. It is considered to have formed as coastal-swamp deposits along the oscillating Cretaceous shoreline and consists of lenticular sandstone, mudstone, carbonaceous shale, and many lenses of coal. The coal beds range considerably in thickness but many are of mineable size.

Cliff House Sandstone.—The Cliff House Sandstone averages about 100 ft in thickness and ranks second to the Point Lookout in gas production from the Mesaverde Group. The sandstones are medium gray, fine grained, well cemented with calcite and clay, and commonly laminated with light- to dark-gray carbonaceous shales. The average permeability is 0.54 md, the average porosity 10.3 percent, and average water saturation 28 percent. The quality of water in these beds is varied, usually becoming poorer with increasing depth.

Lewis Shale.—The Lewis Shale, above the Mesaverde, is a marine unit that characteristically intertongues with the underlying Cliff House and overlying Pictured Cliffs Sandstones. This marine shale grades entirely to sandstone southward but it attains a thickness of 2,000 ft or more on the eastern side of the basin.

One well in the northern part of the basin is producing gas from fractures in the Lewis Shale, and there may be other areas of potential fracture production.

Pictured Cliffs Sandstone.—The Pictured Cliffs Sandstone, one of the basin's major gas reservoirs, occurs above the Lewis marine shale and below a prominent basal coal interval of the Fruitland Formation (Fig. 3). The exact thickness of the Pictured Cliffs is difficult to measure on electric logs because of the intertonguing with the shales of the underlying Lewis. However, the gas-producing interval normally contains 10–70 ft of "pay" sandstone. This sandstone is grayish white, fine to medium grained, angular to subrounded, and cemented with bentonitic clays. The permeability averages 2.96 md; the porosity averages 18.1 percent; and water saturation averages 44 percent (Reneau and Harris, 1957).

Fruitland Formation.—The Fruitland is about 175 ft thick and consists of nearshore continental to marine sandstone, shale, and major deposits of coal. The sandstones produce gas in the northern and northeastern parts of the basin, and the unit is a major source of coal on the western side of the basin.

Kirtland Shale and the Farmington Sandstone Member.—The Kirtland is divided into an upper and a lower shale member separated by the Farmington Sandstone Member. The Kirtland is between 400 and 1,400 ft thick in the central part of the basin, and the Farmington sandstone ranges from 25 to 820 ft in thickness. The Kirtland is considered to be predominantly of fluviatile and perhaps lacustrine origin; however, some microfossils found in a shale in the Farmington Member indicate that it might be at least partly marine or lagoonal in origin. The sandstones of the Farmington contain much feldspar. Some gas and high-gravity oil are produced from the Farmington sandstone and also from a discontinuous sandstone in the upper Kirtland shale.

McDermott Formation.—The McDermott is an uppermost Cretaceous or basal Tertiary unit occurring locally above the Kirtland Shale. The unit is about 100 ft thick and consists of lenticular sandstone and conglomerate containing abundant water-laid volcanic debris. It has been identified only in the north-central part of the basin.

TERTIARY

"Ojo Alamo" Sandstone

A persistent unit of fluvial conglomerate and sandstone 50–100 ft thick lies above the Kirtland and can be traced in the subsurface through much of the basin. This unit is called the "Ojo Alamo" Sandstone by most workers, especially in the subsurface. However, the term "Ojo Alamo" appears to have been applied originally to beds within the Kirtland Shale. For this reason considerable confusion exists regarding the definition, age, and proper application of the term. The unit referred to here as "Ojo Alamo" lies directly below the Nacimiento beds and rests on top of the Kirtland Shale. It is considered to represent the stream deposits of the basal Tertiary, marking the beginning phase of the final basin infilling by debris from the San Juan and Archuleta uplifts as well as from the more widespread Cretaceous source area on the southwest.

The "Ojo Alamo" interfingers northward with the McDermott and overlying Animas Formations and is not recognizable in the northernmost part of the basin. A thorough discussion of the stratigraphy and nomenclatural problems of the "Ojo Alamo" is given by Baltz (1962).

Nacimiento-Animas Formations

The Nacimiento Formation consists of 500–1,500 ft of varicolored shale and arkosic sandstone and some conglomerate, and rare coal beds. The unit is entirely nonmarine, probably of fluviatile and lacustrine origin. Toward the north, the Nacimiento grades into an approximately contemporaneous facies referred to as the Animas Formation. The Animas facies in general is coarser than the Nacimiento, especially in the upper part, and contains much granitic and metamorphic as well as volcanic debris. These units indicate an increasing influx of clastic material from newly developing stream systems as the highland areas rose north and northeast of the basin in the San Juan Mountains area. Environmentally, the sediments probably are a mixture of stream-channel, floodplain, lacustrine, and swamp deposits. The beds contain vertebrates of Paleocene age.

In the southern part of the basin two faunal zones have been identified in the Nacimiento Formation, referred to as the "Torrejon-Puerco." Some gas is produced from the Torrejon-Puerco unit in the southeastern part of the basin.

San Jose (Wasatch) Formation

A sequence of variegated shale, sandstone, and some conglomerate unconformably overlies the Nacimiento-Animas Formations. These beds contain fossils of Eocene age and are as much as 2,000 ft thick where preservation is complete in the central part of the basin. The San Jose has been divided into several members by Baltz (1962), who describes thoroughly all the Tertiary units of the basin.

Igneous Rocks

Dikes and volcanic plugs of late Tertiary age are present in the southern and northeastern parts of the basin and on the Four Corners platform bordering the northwestern edge of the basin (Fig. 2).

QUATERNARY

Terrace gravels of Pleistocene age are common along the northern and eastern sides of the basin. These beds represent periodic episodes in the dissection of the basin area during fluctuating climates and runoff rates of the glacial epoch. Glaciation is especially pronounced in the San Juan Mountains north of the basin.

SUMMARY

At least 10 recognizable major events in the sedimentary history of the San Juan basin area can be listed.

1. *Cambrian transgression.*—Deposition of the relatively thin, widespread Ignacio Quartzite along the broad and gentle northwestern flank of the Transcontinental arch.

2. *Ordovician–Silurian–Early Devonian regression.*—No rocks of these ages have been recognized in the Four Corners area although no significant physical evidence of unconformity exists.

3. *Upper Devonian–Lower Mississippian transgression.*—Marine clastics and carbonates of Late Devonian age are overlain conformably by and overlapped by the marine fossiliferous limestone and dolomite of the Early Mississippian Leadville Limestone.

4. *Late Mississippian–Early Pennsylvanian regression.*—Solution effects and karst topography developed on the Mississippian carbonate surface as the result of regional uplift during this time.

5. *Pennsylvanian-Permian Ancestral Rockies tectonism and transgression.*—Strong uplift and associated downwarping of a northwest-southeast lineament formed a narrow mountainous belt (Uncompahgre-San Luis) with a rapidly subsiding parallel trough at the southwest, resulting in the earliest development of the San Juan basin.

6. *Triassic-Jurassic continental desert-alluvial environment with repeated marine incursion.*—Deposition of eolian sandstone over much of the southern Rocky Mountain area and intertonguing thin marine redbed, limestone, and gypsiferous deposits.

7. *Cretaceous transgression.*—Deposition of thick marine gray shale, sandstone, and coal deposits by the complex transgressive-regressive cycles of the Cretaceous seas.

8. *Late Cretaceous–Early Tertiary tectonic activity and basin filling.*—Final withdrawal of marine waters and deposition of the continental, extremely varied stream, lacustrine, and marsh beds of the Nacimiento, Animas, and San Jose Formations.

9. *Late Tertiary regional uplift with accompanying volcanism.*—During this time, dissection of the Colorado Plateau by the present-day stream systems probably began.

10. *Quaternary glaciation.*—Development of associated terrace gravels adjacent to the major mountainous areas.

POTENTIAL DISPOSAL RESERVOIRS

Many of the sandstone reservoirs suitable for waste disposal are eliminated from consideration because they are important as aquifers and/or as reservoirs for oil, gas, and helium. Also, mining of coal and other minerals from some strata precludes their consideration as waste-disposal reservoirs in certain areas.

If the oil- and gas-productive areas and the very deep part of the basin are excluded from consideration, the Chaco slope then is the most attractive area for subsurface disposal. It contains no major oil or gas fields and is not being explored actively for petroleum. There are several sandstone reservoirs at reasonably shallow depths which are potentially suitable for waste disposal. The area is sparsely populated and the climate is favorable for year-round operations. A major railroad and a cross-country highway serve the area.

Probably the most widespread sandstone of potential waste-disposal value is the Entrada. It is thickest in the southwest and central parts of the basin. The boundary between fresh and brackish water in the Entrada (Fig. 20) probably will be significant in determining the areas for waste disposal.

Other possible permeable reservoirs are the Mississippian dolomite (Leadville Limestone) in the northern part of the basin, the Triassic Agua Zarca Sandstone Member of the Moenkopi Formation in the south and southeast parts, and locally the Triassic Shinarump (Conglomerate) Member of the Chinle Formation. Sandstone units in the Morrison Formation might be suitable in some areas, but further study would be needed. Uranium is mined from several units in the Morrison.

The main aquifers in the basin are (1) Tertiary sandstones in the central part, (2) Cretaceous sandstones (Dakota, Gallup, Mesaverde) along the periphery, and (3) both the Permian sandstones and the San Andres Limestone in the southern part. Possibly some of the water-bearing sandstones (especially the Meseta Blanca in the Chaco slope area) are suitable for waste disposal in areas where they are not sources of potable water.

Some of the shale units in the Mancos Shale might serve for disposal of waste in slurry form into artificial fractures. However, units within the Mancos are sources of oil, water, and coal, and further study would be required for any particular area of interest.

The San Ysidro Member of the Yeso Formation offers the only possibility for storage of solid wastes in salt, although the salt facies actually occurs south of the San Juan basin proper.

In the event depleted petroleum reservoirs someday are proved suitable for waste disposal, the carbonate reservoirs of Pennsylvanian and Mississippian ages could provide large-volume waste-disposal facilities.

Before any disposal project is undertaken in the basin, a minimum of two or three holes should be drilled through the disposal units in the area of interest to thoroughly test the units for the necessary reservoir characteristics.

SELECTED REFERENCES

Allen, R. W., 1955, Stratigraphic gas development in the Blanco-Mesaverde pool, in Geology of parts of Paradox, Black Mesa and San Juan basins: Four Corners Geol. Soc., 1st Field Conf., p. 144–150.

Anderson, R. Y., and D. W. Kirkland, 1960, Origin, varves, and cycles of the Jurassic Todilto Formation, New Mexico: Am. Assoc. Petroleum Geologists Bull., v. 44, no. 1, p. 37–52.

Atwood, W. D., and K. Mathew, 1932, Physiography and Quaternary geology of the San Juan Mountains, Colorado: U.S. Geol. Survey Prof. Paper 166, 176 p.

Baars, D. L., 1962, Permian System of the Colorado Plateau: Am. Assoc. Petroleum Geologists Bull., v. 46, no. 2, p. 149–218.

Baltz, E. H., Jr., 1959, Stratigraphic relationships of Cretaceous and early Tertiary rocks of a part of northwestern San Juan basin: Univ. New Mexico, unpub. Master's thesis, 101 p.

———— 1962, Stratigraphy and geologic structure of uppermost Cretaceous and Tertiary rocks of the east-central part of the San Juan basin, New Mexico: Univ. New Mexico, unpub. Ph.D. thesis, 294 p.

Bass, N. W., 1944, Correlation of basal Permian and older rocks, southwest Colorado, northwest New Mexico, northeast Arizona, and southeast Utah (with text): U.S. Geol. Survey Oil and Gas Inv. Prelim. Chart 7.

Beaumont, E. C., and C. B. Read, 1950, Geologic history of the San Juan basin area, New Mexico and Colorado, in Guidebook of the San Juan basin, New Mexico and Colorado: New Mexico Geol. Soc., 1st Field Conf., p. 49–52.

———— C. H. Dane, and J. D. Sears, 1956, Revised nomenclature of Mesaverde Group in San Juan basin, New Mexico: Am. Assoc. Petroleum Geologists Bull., v. 40, no. 9, p. 2149–2162.

Bozanic, D., 1955, A brief discussion on the subsurface Cretaceous rocks of the San Juan basin, in Geology of parts of Paradox, Black Mesa and San Juan basins: Four Corners Geol. Soc., 1st Field Conf., p. 89–107.

Budd, H., 1952, Blanco field, San Juan basin, in Geological symposium of the Four Corners region: Four Corners Geol. Soc., p. 113–118.

Burton, G. C., 1955, Sedimentation and stratigraphy of the Dakota Formation in the San Juan basin, in Geology of parts of Paradox, Black Mesa and San Juan basins: Four Corners Geol. Soc., 1st Field Conf., p. 78–88.

Cooper, J. C., 1955, Cambrian, Devonian and Mississippian rocks of the Four Corners area (Colorado and Utah), *in* Geology of parts of Paradox, Black Mesa and San Juan basins: Four Corners Geol. Soc., 1st Field Conf., p. 59–65.

Craig, L. C., *et al.*, 1955, Stratigraphy of the Morrison and related formations, Colorado Plateau region: U.S. Geol. Survey Bull. 1009-E, p. 125–168.

Dane, C. H., 1946, Stratigraphic relations of Eocene, Paleocene and latest Cretaceous of eastern San Juan basin, New Mexico: U.S. Geol. Survey Prelim. Oil and Gas Inv. Chart 24.

Di Giambattista, C. D., 1952, Regional stratigraphy of Four Corners area, *in* Geological symposium of the Four Corners region: Four Corners Geol. Soc., p. 59.

Fetzner, R. W., 1960, Pennsylvanian paleotectonics of Colorado Plateau: Am. Assoc. Petroleum Geologists Bull., v. 44, no. 8, p. 1371–1413.

Fitzsimmons, J. P., 1963, Precambrian of the Four Corners area, *in* Shelf carbonates of the Paradox basin: Four Corners Geol. Soc., 4th Field Conf., p. 13–20.

—— A. K. Armstrong, and M. Gordon, Jr., 1956, Arroyo Peñasco Formation, Mississippian, north-central New Mexico: Am. Assoc. Petroleum Geologists Bull., v. 40, no. 8, p. 1935–1944.

Freeman, V. L., and L. S. Hilpert, 1956, Stratigraphy of the Morrison Formation in part of northwestern New Mexico: U.S. Geol. Survey Bull. 1030-J, p. 309–334.

Gregory, H. E., 1917, Geology of the Navajo country: a reconnaissance of parts of Arizona, New Mexico, and Utah: U.S. Geol. Survey Prof. Paper 93, 161 p.

Harshbarger, J. W., C. A. Repenning, and J. H. Irwin, 1957, Stratigraphy of the uppermost Triassic and the Jurassic rocks of the Navajo country: U.S. Geol. Survey Prof. Paper 291, 74 p.

Hilpert, L. S., 1963, Regional and local stratigraphy of uranium-bearing rocks, *in* Geology and technology of the Grants uranium region: New Mexico Bur. Mines and Min. Res. Mem. 15, p. 618.

Hollenshead, C. T., and R. L. Pritchard, 1961, Geometry of producing Mesaverde sandstones, San Juan basin, *in* Geometry of sandstone bodies: Tulsa, Oklahoma, Am. Assoc. Petroleum Geologists, p. 98–118.

Holmes, W. H., 1877, U.S. Geol. and Geog. Survey Ninth Ann. Rept. (for 1875).

Hoover, W. B., 1952, Regional structure of the Four Corners area, *in* Geological symposium of the Four Corners region: Four Corners Geol. Soc., p. 10–11.

Keller, W. D., 1962, Clay minerals in the Morrison Formation of the Colorado Plateau: U.S. Geol. Survey Bull. 1150, p. 90.

Kelley, V. C., 1957, Tectonics of the San Juan basin and surrounding areas, *in* Geology of southwestern San Juan basin: Four Corners Geol. Soc., 2d Field Conf., p. 44–52.

—— and N. J. Clinton, 1960, Fracture system and tectonic elements of the Colorado Plateau: Univ. New Mexico Pub. Geol., no. 6, p. 104.

Melton, F. A., 1925, The Ancestral Rocky Mountains of Colorado and New Mexico: Jour. Geology, v. 33, p. 84–89.

McKee, E. D., 1951a, Sedimentary basins of Arizona and adjoining areas: Geol. Soc. America Bull., v. 62, no. 5, p. 481–506.

—— 1951b, Triassic rocks of Arizona-New Mexico border area, *in* Guidebook of the south and west sides of the San Juan basin, New Mexico and Arizona: New Mexico Geol. Soc., 2d Field Conf., p. 85–92.

—— 1954, Stratigraphy and history of the Moenkopi Formation of Triassic age: Geol. Soc. America Mem. 61, 133 p.

—— *et al.*, 1956, Paleotectonic maps of the Jurassic System: U.S. Geol. Survey Misc. Geol. Inv. Map I-175.

Momper, J. A., 1957, Pre-Morrison stratigraphy of the southern and western San Juan basin, *in* Geology of southwestern San Juan basin: Four Corners Geol. Soc., 2d Field Conf., p. 85–94.

Northrup, S. A., and G. H. Wood, 1946, Geology of the Nacimiento Mountains, San Pedro Mountains and adjacent plateaus in parts of Sandoval and Rio Arriba Counties, New Mexico: U.S. Geol. Survey Prelim. Oil and Gas Inv. Map 57.

Parker, J. W., 1957, Nacimiento Mountains—history and relationship to the San Juan basin, *in* Geology of southwestern San Juan basin: Four Corners Geol. Soc., 2d Field Conf., p. 73–77.

—— and J. W. Roberts, 1963, Devonian and Mississippian stratigraphy of the central part of the Colorado Plateau, *in* Shelf carbonates of the Paradox basin: Four Corners Geol. Soc., 4th Field Conf., p. 31–60.

Peterson, J. A., 1959, Petroleum geology of the Four Corners area: New York, Fifth World Petroleum Cong. Proc., Sec. 1, Paper 27, p. 499–523.

Pike, W. S., Jr., 1947, Intertonguing marine and non-marine Upper Cretaceous deposits of New Mexico, Arizona, and southwestern Colorado: Geol. Soc. America Mem. 24, 103 p.

Read, C. B., *et al.*, 1951, Stratigraphy of the outcropping Permian rocks around the San Juan basin, *in* Guidebook of the south and west sides of the San Juan basin, New Mexico and Arizona: New Mexico Geol. Soc., 2d Field Conf., p. 80–84.

Reese, V. R., 1957, Cretaceous oil and gas horizons in the San Juan basin, Colorado and New Mexico, *in* Geology of southwestern San Juan basin: Four Corners Geol. Soc., 2d Field Conf., p. 36–39.

Reeside, J. B., Jr., 1924, Upper Cretaceous and Tertiary formations of the western part of the San Juan basin, Colorado and New Mexico: U.S. Geol. Survey Prof. Paper 134, p. 1–70.

Reneau, W. E., Jr., and J. D. Harris, Jr., 1957, Reservoir characteristics of Cretaceous sands of the San Juan basin, *in* Geology of southwestern San Juan basin: Four Corners Geol. Soc., 2d Field Conf., p. 40–43.

Romer, A. S., 1950, The Abo Formation and its vertebrate fauna: Soc. Vertebrate Paleontology, 4th Field Conf. Guidebook, p. 48–56.

Sears, J. D., C. B. Hunt, and T. A. Hendricks, 1941, Transgressive and regressive Cretaceous deposits in southern San Juan basin, New Mexico: U.S. Geol. Survey Prof. Paper 193-F, p. 110–121.

Silver, Caswell, 1948, Jurassic overlap in western New Mexico: Am. Assoc. Petroleum Geologists Bull., v. 32, no. 1, p. 68–81.

Simpson, G. G., 1948, The Eocene of the San Juan

basin, New Mexico: Am. Jour. Sci. v. 246, p. 257–282, p. 363–385.

———— 1950, Lower Tertiary formations and vertebrate fauna of the San Juan basin, *in* Guidebook of the San Juan basin, New Mexico and Colorado: New Mexico Geol. Soc., 1st Field Conf., p. 85–89.

Smith, C. T., 1951, Problems of Jurassic stratigraphy of the Colorado Plateau and adjoining regions, *in* Guidebook of the south and west sides of the San Juan basin: New Mexico Geol. Soc., 2d Field Conf., p. 99–102.

———— 1957, Geology of the Zuni Mountains, Valencia and McKinley Counties, New Mexico, *in* Geology of southwestern San Juan basin: Four Corners Geol. Soc., 2d Field Conf., p. 53–62.

Stewart, J. H., G. A. Williams, H. F. Albee, O. B. Raup, and R. A. Cadigan, 1959, Stratigraphy of Triassic and associated formations in part of the Colorado Plateau: U.S. Geol. Survey Bull. 1046-Q, p. 487–576.

Stokes, W. L., 1944, Morrison and related deposits in and adjacent to the Colorado Plateau: Geol. Soc. America Bull., v. 55, p. 951–992.

Strobell, J. D., Jr., 1956, Geology of the Carrizo Mountains area in northeastern Arizona and northwestern New Mexico: U.S. Geol. Survey Oil and Gas Inv. Map OM-160.

Umbach, P. H., 1952, Exploration and development in the San Juan, Paradox, and Black Mesa basins, *in* Geological symposium of the Four Corners region: Four Corners Geol. Soc., p. 22–26.

Ver Wiebe, W. A., 1930, Ancestral Rocky Mountains: Am. Assoc. Petroleum Geologists Bull., v. 14, p. 765–788.

Wengerd, S. A., 1962, Pennsylvanian sedimentation in Paradox basin, Four Corners region, *in* Pennsylvanian System in the United States: Tulsa, Oklahoma, Am. Assoc. Petroleum Geologists, p. 264–330.

———— and M. E. King, 1952, Geological bibliography of the Four Corners region, *in* Geological symposium of the Four Corners region: Four Corners Geol. Soc., p. 135–145.

———— and M. L. Matheny, 1958, Pennsylvanian System of Four Corners region: Am. Assoc. Petroleum Geologists Bull., v. 42, p. 2048–2106.

———— and J. W. Strickland, 1954, Pennsylvanian stratigraphy of Paradox salt basin, Four Corners region, Colorado and Utah: Am. Assoc. Petroleum Geologists Bull., v. 38, no. 10, p. 2157–2199.

Yingst, P. O., 1960, Coal resources of Colorado: Colorado School Mines Mineral Industries Bull., v. 3, no. 5, 8 p.

INDEX